Prefix and Suffix Names of Some Common

Class	Functional group	Prefix	Suffix
A. Indicated by suffix only			
Paraffins	—C—C—	. . . . . .	-ane
Olefins	—C=C—	. . . . . .	-ene
Acetylenes	—C≡C—	. . . . . .	-yne
B. Indicated by prefix or suffix			
Carboxylic acids	—COOH	Carboxy-	-oic acid
Aldehydes	—CHO	Carboxaldo-	-al
Sulfonic acids	—SO_2OH	Sulfo-	-sulfonic acid
Ketones	—C— (C=O)	Keto-	-one
Alcohols	—OH	Hydroxy-	-ol
Thiols	—SH	Mercapto-	-thiol
Amines	—NH_2	Amino-	-amine
Ethers	—O—	Alkoxy-	ether
Sulfides	—S—	Alkylmercapto-	sulfide
C. Indicated by prefix only			
Fluorinated molecules	—F	Fluoro-	. . . . . .
Chlorinated molecules	—Cl	Chloro-	. . . . . .
Brominated molecules	—Br	Bromo-	. . . . . .
Iodinated molecules	—I	Iodo-	. . . . . .
Alkylated molecules	—R	Alkyl-	. . . . . .
Nitrated molecules	—NO_2	Nitro-	. . . . . .

Dennis D. Yoder
1200 N. Indiana, Lot 22
Ch. 203   TWTh   1:30

E. CAMPAIGNE

Professor of Chemistry
Indiana University

Elementary

ORGANIC
CHEMISTRY

PRENTICE-HALL, INC.
Englewood Cliffs, N. J.   1962

PRENTICE-HALL CHEMISTRY SERIES
Kenneth S. Pitzer, Editor

Preface

This text is written for a one semester course in organic chemistry, and is based on the author's 20 years' experience in teaching a brief course in organic chemistry. The text is written for students who have one semester of general chemistry as a prerequisite. It is intended to serve students who wish a one-year survey of chemistry, and those who have biological applications as their main interest. The majors include home economics, pre-nursing, pre-dental, pre-optometry, agriculture, and education (Science Teaching). The course has also been taken at Indiana University by biology and geology majors who desire an introduction to organic chemistry.

In writing an elementary text, designed to present the fundamentals of a science for those who wish to use it for a basic understanding to be applied to other fields, it is important to be selective. It becomes necessary to define the broad areas, and then to illustrate them by special applications. The system of presenting organic chemistry in an integrated manner, combining aliphatic and aromatic chemistry, is best for this type of approach. The application of the old teaching maxim, "First tell them what you are going to tell them, then tell them, and finally tell them what you told them," can also be applied to a suitable outline of such an elementary course. The author has found that providing a complete survey of the nomenclature for all of the organic compounds to be discussed in the book provides an excellent way in which to "First tell them what you are going to tell them." In this way, the students are introduced to all classes of organic compounds, and it becomes much easier to discuss the transformations involved in syntheses and reactions of these compounds when the students already know the nomenclature of starting compounds and products. Following a careful study of Chapter 2, the student will find that, essentially, each of the later chapters is a review of something already mentioned.

With the exception of certain chapters covering topics of special interest, the remainder of the book is concerned with the discussion of hydrocarbons and their derivatives. In order to provide some relief from the systematic outline of this chemistry, the special chapters on Petroleum and Rubber (Chapter 6), and Fats, Waxes and Detergents (Chapter 12) are interspersed at appropriate places to provide suitable breaks at examination times.

Because of the necessary omission of a large body of the more complex information about organic chemistry that must be made in such an elementary survey, references to modern advanced texts are given at the end of each chapter. The intellectually curious student who wishes to learn more about a specific subject may do so in any library available to him which would contain these advanced textbooks. Study questions are included at the end of each chapter, and an effort has been made to pitch these questions at various levels of difficulty. It should be possible for the instructor to choose from among the study questions offered a suitable selection for the students of his class.

To "Tell them what you told them," a section entitled "New Terms and Concepts" at the beginning of each chapter provides a brief outline of the important ideas presented. It is hoped that the student will use these as a method of review. Any lack of understanding of the statements made in "New Terms and Concepts" should be remedied by reference to the chapter itself.

A special effort has been made in the drawings of the molecular models to present some concept of the three-dimensional structure of these molecules. The illustrations used here are not true ball and stick models, but rather artistic impressions. The author is greatly indebted to Mr. Harvey Frye, of the Graphic Arts Department at Indiana University, for assistance in developing these drawings, and to the Prentice-Hall staff artists for the final versions. I should like to express appreciation to my wife, Jean, for her forbearance and consideration during the long evenings of writing and correcting the manuscript in its various stages, and to thank the several secretaries, Eleanor, Alice, Karen, and Judy, who spent many difficult hours deciphering my hen-scratching and translating magnetic tapes on this material.

E. C.

Contents

ELEMENTARY ORGANIC CHEMISTRY

new terms & concepts

Organic chemistry is vital in life processes.
Organic substances were first isolated from living organisms,
leading to the "vitalistic theory."
A synthesis of urea by Wöhler helped overthrow this theory.
Atoms form several kinds of chemical bonds: electrovalent,
covalent, and coordinate covalent bonds.
Electronegativity of the atoms influences the kinds of bonds formed.
Covalent bonds are most important in carbon compounds.
By means of equivalent covalent bonds in a tetrahedral structure,
carbon forms chains and rings.
Compounds with the same numbers and kinds of atoms in different
arrangements are called isomers.
Carbon can combine with hydrogen, oxygen,
the halogens, sulfur, and nitrogen, to form many functional groups, these being: hydrocarbons,
alcohols, ethers, aldehydes, ketones, acids, amines, nitriles, and organic sulfur compounds.
When like atoms combine in different ways to form different functional groups they produce
functional isomers. The relation of radicals to homologous series is described.

1

Organic chemistry

Organic chemistry may be defined as the chemistry of the carbon compounds. However, this concise definition does not convey the importance of the field. Life itself is a series of organic reactions. The food we eat, the clothes we wear, the medicines we take, and the fuels, insecticides, dyes, and plastic products we use every day are all organic compounds. The human body is made up of many different kinds of organic compounds, and their reactions comprise the very essence of the life process. The response of the body in health and in disease ultimately depends on chemical reactions of organic compounds.

Organic substances are widely distributed in nature. Among the minerals we find petroleum and coal, both of which serve as crude sources for many pure organic compounds. From plants we obtain such substances as starch, alcohol, sugar, camphor, turpentine, and quinine. From the animal world come fats, leather, silk, and wool. However, by far the greatest source of organic compounds is the chemical laboratory. Most of the naturally occurring substances have been duplicated or improved in the laboratory, and many new substances that have no counterpart in nature, such as lead tetra-ethyl for improving motor fuels, and the silicone compounds used as high-temperature lubricants, have been developed by the synthetic organic chemist.

The foundations of organic chemistry were laid about the year 1800. However, many organic substances such as indigo, madder, soap, sugar, alcohol, and mineral oil were known to the ancients. Most of the eighteenth century chemists were interested in analyzing materials,

3

in the hope of finding new elements. The analysis of material from living sources seemed unprofitable, since they yielded only a few elements, chiefly carbon, hydrogen, oxygen, nitrogen, and sometimes sulfur and phosphorus, but very few others. Moreover, these substances were difficult to work with by the methods available. They were unstable, charring at low temperatures (250–300°C), and thus resembled the tissues of organs from whence they came. Hence the name "organic," meaning "from the organs," was applied to this class of compounds by Berzelius about 1807. At first it was assumed that only living organs could produce these substances, owing to the mysterious *vital force* of life. However, this *vitalistic theory* was invalidated by an experiment reported by Friedrich Wöhler about 1828. By heating the inorganic salt, ammonium cyanate, he prepared a compound called urea, a substance previously obtained only from urine, a product of the living organs.

1.01 $$NH_4{}^+OCN^- \longrightarrow H_2NCONH_2$$

ammonium   urea

cyanate

The discovery that organic compounds could be synthesized in the laboratory started a whole new school of chemistry, devoted to the study of the preparation and properties of new compounds, which has been so fruitful that today nearly a million compounds have been described, and hundreds of new ones are reported every month.

At first, the study of organic chemistry will seem entirely different from the chemistry studied so far. This difference arises from two important factors. One is the *nomenclature*—because of the many new words the student must learn, the study of organic chemistry may be compared to learning a new language. The second factor is that practically all organic reactions involve *covalent bonds*, formed by sharing pairs of electrons between atoms.

Kinds of chemical bonds

There are two important kinds of bonds which hold atoms together. These are called *electrovalent* bonds and *covalent* bonds. An *electrovalent* bond is formed when one atom loses its bonding electron to another atom to form ions. For example, when sodium (Na) reacts with chlorine (Cl_2) to form sodium chloride (NaCl), sodium, which has one

1.02 $$2\,Na + Cl_2 \longrightarrow 2\,Na^+Cl^-$$

valence electron in its outer shell, loses the electron to form sodium ion (Na^+). At the same time, the chlorine, with seven electrons in its outer valence shell, picks up one electron for each chlorine atom, thus forming the stable valence shell of eight electrons in the chlorine ion with a negative charge (Cl^-). In this manner, the ionic compound sodium chloride is formed. In the crystal state, the ions of sodium and chlorine are held together by attraction of their opposite charges. However, if sodium chloride is dissolved in water, the ions separate and are free to move about in the water solution. This can be demonstrated by showing the electrical conductance of the salt solution. Most of the reactions studied in inorganic chemistry have been reactions between ions. For example, when silver nitrate is mixed with sodium chloride in solution, there is an immediate precipitate of silver chloride. This is caused by the rapid reaction between silver ion and chloride ion.

1.03 $$Ag^+NO_3^- + Na^+Cl^- \longrightarrow AgCl + Na^+NO_3^-$$

These rapid reactions are generally characteristic of ionic compounds. They are caused to take place by the formation of a precipitate, an un-ionized substance, or by the formation of a gas.

A *covalent bond*, on the other hand, is formed by two atoms sharing a pair of electrons, each atom donating one bond to the shared pair. For example, the elements which exist as bi-atomic molecules are held together by covalent bonds. Hydrogen gas has the formula H_2, and the molecule of hydrogen is held together by a typical covalent bond, in which each hydrogen atom contributes one electron to form a bonding pair. In the same way, chlorine gas, which has the formula Cl_2, is formed by two atoms of chlorine, each of which contributes one of its seven bonding electrons to form a covalent pair.

$$H:H \qquad :\overset{..}{C}l:\overset{..}{C}l:$$

The two atoms of hydrogen are held at a certain distance apart, and the molecule of hydrogen has a definite size and shape (Figure 1.01). The same is true for the chlorine molecule (Figure 1.02) which has a similar shape, although the chlorine molecule is much larger.

Fig. 1.01

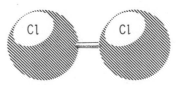

Fig. 1.02

It should be noted that the electrovalent bond was formed between atoms of widely different electronegativity, whereas the strongest covalent bonds are formed between atoms of similar negativity. The *electronegativity* of an atom is a measure of its attraction for electrons. The atoms on the upper right-hand side of the periodic table have the highest electronegativity and, therefore, the strongest attraction for electrons. Fluorine, for example, is the most electronegative of all the atoms and reacts by attracting electrons to itself very strongly. On the other hand, the atoms on the left-hand side of the periodic table are the least electronegative, cesium being the least electronegative atom of all. This means that cesium reacts most easily by losing its electron to some other atom, and usually forms electrovalent bonds. If the two atoms forming a bond are not widely different in electronegativity, neither atom will attract the electrons with sufficient force to form ions. Instead, the atoms share the electrons to form a covalent bond. If the atoms forming a covalent bond have identical electronegativity, as is the case in the hydrogen molecule, or in the chlorine molecule, then the bonding pair of electrons is held exactly equally between the two atoms. However, if the two atoms participating in a covalent bond have different electronegativity, then one of the atoms will attract the pair of electrons a little more strongly than the other, causing the pair of electrons to be displaced a little more toward the more electronegative atom. In this case, a *polar* covalent bond will be formed, in which one end of the bond is a little more positive than the other end, even though the molecule is not ionized. Such a polar covalent bond is found in hydrogen chloride (HCl), in which the chlorine which is more electronegative pulls the electron pair nearer and is the more negative end of the molecule (Figure 1.03). In water (H_2O), the oxygen is the more negative end of each of the two bonds formed with hydrogen (Figure 1.04). The greater the difference between the electronegativity of the two atoms involved in the bond, the greater the polarity of the bond. If the difference in the electronegativity between the two atoms is sufficiently large, the electron furnished by the atom of lower electronegativity will be transferred completely to the more electronegative

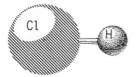

Fig. 1.03

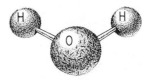

Fig. 1.04

atom, and an ionic bond, rather than a covalent bond, will result. It now becomes apparent that there is no sharp dividing line between the compounds in which the bonding is covalent, and those in which the bonding is ionic. Covalent bonds are usually formed between atoms whose electronegativity difference is less than 2, while electrovalent bonds are usually formed when the difference in the electronegativities is greater than 2. It is not surprising that carbon forms strong covalent bonds with the other elements listed in the right-hand column in Table 1.01.

*Covalent when dif. <2
Electrovalent when dif. >2*

Compounds containing covalent bonds do not react as rapidly as those containing ionic (electrovalent) bonds. This is because the covalent bond must be broken by collision with the reagent. For example, if silver nitrate is shaken with carbon tetrachloride (CCl_4), no reaction is observed. The mixture must be heated for a long time before the white precipitate of silver chloride can be observed. Organic reactions are usually reactions of covalent bonds, proceed at relatively slow rates, and are seldom 100 per cent complete.

Covalent bonds slower to react

It is possible to form a covalent bond between two atoms, in which one of the atoms has donated both of the electrons to the bonding pair. Such a special case is called *coordinate covalence*. An example of coordinate covalence may be found in the ammonium ion (NH_4^+). Ammonia (NH_3) is formed by ordinary covalent bonds between hydrogen and nitrogen.

$$1.04 \qquad \begin{matrix} H \\ H\!:\!\overset{..}{N}\!: \\ H \end{matrix} + H^+ \longrightarrow \left[\begin{matrix} H \\ H\!:\!\overset{..}{N}\!:\!H \\ H \end{matrix}\right]^+$$

The unshared pair of electrons on the nitrogen atom are now available for use in bond formation. For example, ammonia can now combine

TABLE 1.01   ELECTRONEGATIVITY VALUES OF SOME COMMON ELEMENTS

Element	Electronegativity	Element	Electronegativity
Cesium	0.7	Hydrogen	2.1
Potassium	0.8	Phosphorus	2.1
Sodium	0.9	Iodine	2.4
Barium	0.9	Carbon	2.5
Lithium	1.0	Sulfur	2.5
Calcium	1.0	Bromine	2.8
Magnesium	1.2	Nitrogen	3.0
Aluminum	1.5	Chlorine	3.0
Iron	1.6	Oxygen	3.5
Silicon	1.8	Fluorine	4.0

with a hydrogen ion to form the ammonium ion. Although ammonia is a neutral molecule, when it combines with a hydrogen ion it forms the ammonium ion with a unit positive charge. The formation of a coordinate covalent bond is possible only between an atom with an unshared pair of electrons in its valence shell and an atom or ion that needs a pair of electrons to complete the stable electronic configuration of an inert gas.

Reactions involving covalent bonds

When a covalent bond in a molecule is broken, the pair of electrons forming the bond may separate in several ways. The pair may split, one electron remaining with each part of the molecule to form radicals. This is called "homolytic" cleavage, and the radicals so

$$A:B \longrightarrow A\cdot + B\cdot$$

formed are very reactive. For example, when chlorine is radiated by light, it tends to be more reactive because some of the molecules break down into atoms by the homolytic process. The electron pair may re-

1.05 $:\ddot{C}l:\ddot{C}l: \longrightarrow 2:\ddot{C}l\cdot$

main with one part of the molecule (usually the more electronegative part) forming ions. This is called "heterolytic" cleavage, and is more

$$A:B \longrightarrow A^+ + B:^-$$

common with polar covalent bonds. For example, when hydrogen chloride is dissolved in water, the proton is transferred to the water molecule, leaving the chloride ion. Covalent bonds between carbon

1.06 $H:\ddot{O}: + H:\ddot{C}l: \longrightarrow \left[H:\ddot{O}:H\right]^+ + :\ddot{C}l:^-$
                   $\quad\ \ H \qquad\qquad\qquad\quad\ H$

atoms may break either homolytically or heterolytically, depending on the kind and conditions of reactions. Homolytic cleavage produces so-called "free" radicals, which are very reactive and have only a transient existence. Heterolytic cleavage produces both positive carbonium

$$R_3C:CR_3 \longrightarrow 2\,R_3C\cdot \qquad \text{homolytic}$$

carbon "free"
radical

$$R_3C:CR_3 \longrightarrow R_3C^+ + \left[:CR_3\right]^- \qquad \text{heterolytic}$$

carbonium   carbanion
ion

ions and negative carbanions. These are also extremely reactive species. The organic reactions described in the following chapters will involve these particles.

The special properties of carbon

Carbon occupies a unique position in the periodic table. Being in the fourth group of the second period, it has four valence electrons in its outer shell; and with only two inner electrons, it does not strongly attract or repel electrons. Therefore, it does not tend readily to lose or gain electrons to form electrovalent bonds, but shares its valence electrons with other atoms to form *four* covalent bonds, which are in a fixed position at the four corners of a tetrahedron, and have a definite length (Figure 1.05). Carbon is the strongest covalent bond former of all the elements. It can form stable compounds by sharing electrons with both electropositive elements such as hydrogen (Figure 1.06) and electronegative elements such as chlorine (Figure 1.07), or by sharing two pairs of electrons with oxygen, as in Figure 1.08.

Since the three-dimensional structures of the carbon compounds are difficult to visualize, they can be simplified to two-dimensional illustrations as seen below the figures.

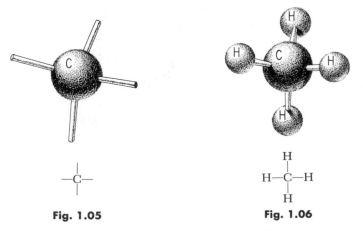

Fig. 1.05   Fig. 1.06

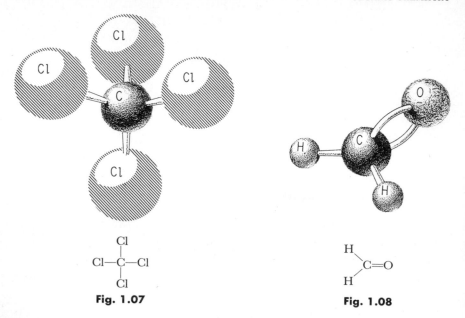

$$
\begin{array}{c}
\quad\quad\; Cl \\
\quad\quad\; | \\
Cl-C-Cl \\
\quad\quad\; | \\
\quad\quad\; Cl
\end{array}
\qquad\qquad
\begin{array}{c}
H \\
\;\;\diagdown \\
\quad\;\; C=O \\
\;\;\diagup \\
H
\end{array}
$$

Fig. 1.07   **Fig. 1.08**

Carbon not only forms covalent bonds with different atoms, but can also form covalent bonds with other carbon atoms, so that several carbon atoms can unite to form chains (Figure 1.09), branched chains (Figure 1.10), or rings (Figure 1.11). This remarkable ability of carbon

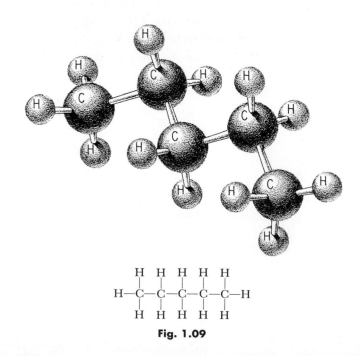

$$
\begin{array}{ccccc}
H & H & H & H & H \\
| & | & | & | & | \\
H-C-C-C-C-C-H \\
| & | & | & | & | \\
H & H & H & H & H
\end{array}
$$

Fig. 1.09

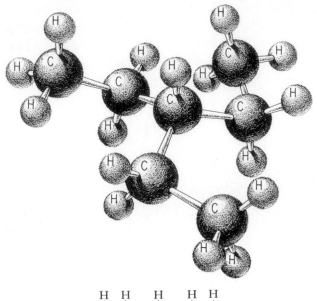

$$
\begin{array}{ccccc}
 & H & H & & H & H & H \\
 & | & | & & | & | & | \\
H-C-C- & C & -C-C-H \\
 & | & | & | & | & | \\
 & H & H & H-C-H & H & H \\
 & & & | & & \\
 & & H-C-H & & \\
 & & | & & \\
 & & H & &
\end{array}
$$

Fig. 1.10

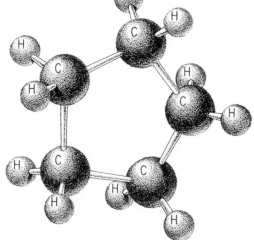

$$
\begin{array}{ccc}
 & H & H \\
 & | & | \\
H- & C & -H \\
 & | & \\
C & & C \\
| & & | \\
H & & H \\
H-C- & -C-H \\
| & & | \\
H & & H
\end{array}
$$

Fig. 1.11

to combine with itself as well as with other atoms in various ways permits the formation of many different compounds with the same molecular formula. For example, since carbon always has a valence of four, and hydrogen a valence of one, there are two ways in which four atoms of carbon and ten atoms of hydrogen may unite to form the compound C_4H_{10}:

$$CH_3-CH_2-CH_2-CH_3 \qquad\qquad CH_3-CH-CH_3$$
$$\qquad\qquad\qquad\qquad\qquad\qquad\qquad\quad |$$
$$\qquad\qquad\qquad\qquad\qquad\qquad\qquad CH_3$$

These two compounds, with the same molecular formula but different arrangements of the atoms, are called *isomers* of one another. The more carbon atoms there are in the formula, the greater the number of possible isomers. There are three isomers of the compound having the formula C_5H_{12}:

$$CH_3CH_2CH_2CH_2CH_3 \qquad CH_3CH_2CHCH_3 \qquad CH_3-\overset{\displaystyle CH_3}{\underset{\displaystyle CH_3}{\overset{|}{\underset{|}{C}}}}-CH_3$$

There are five isomers with the formula C_6H_{14} and nine isomers with the formula C_7H_{16} (the student should try drawing the structural formulas for all of these). The number of isomers increases rapidly with increasing numbers of carbon atoms, so that for C_8H_{18} there are 18, for $C_{10}H_{22}$ there are 75, etc. It should be pointed out that not all these different compounds are yet known, but they can exist.

Compounds of carbon with other elements

Organic chemistry deals chiefly with compounds containing carbon, hydrogen, oxygen, nitrogen, sulfur, and halogens. If one remembers that hydrogen and the halogens have a valence of *one,* oxygen and sulfur a valence of *two,* nitrogen a valence of *three,* and carbon *four,* and that in any stable compound all valences must be shared with other

$$H- \qquad\quad Cl- \qquad\quad -O- \qquad\quad -\overset{|}{N}- \qquad\quad -\overset{|}{\underset{|}{C}}-$$

atoms, it is possible to visualize nearly all the important classes of organic compounds by considering the ways in which these various atoms can combine with one another. Carbon, for example, not only shares bonds with other carbon atoms to form chains and rings as previously mentioned, but a carbon atom can share two or three bonds with another carbon atom to form double or triple bonds (Figures 1.12–1.14). By satisfying the other available bonds in these carbon structures with hydrogen atoms, we can illustrate examples of three important classes of simple compounds of hydrogen and carbon (hydrocarbons) (Figures 1.15–1.17). Those compounds which have single bonds between carbon atoms are saturated hydrocarbons, or *paraffins*. When double or triple bonds occur between carbon atoms the compounds are said to be *unsaturated*. Those containing carbon-to-carbon double bonds are *olefins* and those having triple bonds between carbon atoms

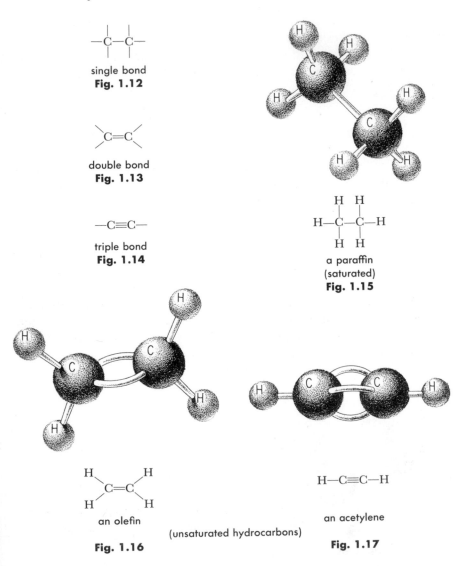

single bond
Fig. 1.12

double bond
Fig. 1.13

triple bond
Fig. 1.14

a paraffin
(saturated)
Fig. 1.15

an olefin

(unsaturated hydrocarbons)

Fig. 1.16

an acetylene

Fig. 1.17

are called *acetylenes* (the name comes from the first member of the series, C_2H_2).

Since halogen atoms have a valence of one, they can substitute for any of the hydrogen atoms in the above formulas, to form a new class of compounds, the halogenated hydrocarbons. Note that an even larger

$$\begin{array}{cc} & \text{H} \quad \text{H} \\ & | \quad | \\ \text{H}-&\text{C}-\text{C}-\text{Cl} \\ & | \quad | \\ & \text{H} \quad \text{H} \end{array} \qquad \begin{array}{cc} & \text{Cl} \quad \text{Cl} \\ & | \quad | \\ \text{Cl}-&\text{C}-\text{C}-\text{Cl} \\ & | \quad | \\ & \text{Cl} \quad \text{Cl} \end{array} \qquad \begin{array}{cc} & \text{Cl}-\text{C}=\text{C}-\text{Cl} \\ & | \quad | \\ & \text{H} \quad \text{Cl} \end{array}$$

chlorinated hydrocarbons

number of isomers exists among this class of compounds, since the *position* of the halogen atom on the carbon chain can vary. For example, there are two compounds with the formula C_3H_7Br, and two with the formula $C_2H_4Cl_2$. (Remember that carbon has a tetrahedral structure,

$$\begin{array}{cc} CH_3CH_2CH_2Br & CH_3CHCH_3 \\ C_3H_7Br & | \\ & Br \end{array} \qquad \begin{array}{cc} CH_3CHCl_2 & ClCH_2CH_2Cl \\ & C_2H_4Cl_2 \end{array}$$

and that molecules are three-dimensional.) The student should prove to himself, by three-dimensional drawings or the use of molecular models, that such formulas as

$$\begin{array}{cc} \text{H} \\ | \\ \text{H}-\text{C}-\text{Cl} \\ | \\ \text{Cl} \end{array} \quad \text{and} \quad \begin{array}{cc} \text{H} \\ | \\ \text{Cl}-\text{C}-\text{Cl} \\ | \\ \text{H} \end{array} \quad \text{do not depict different compounds.}$$

Oxygen atoms have two valences, which greatly increases the ways in which oxygen can form covalent bonds with carbon and hydrogen. Single bonds between carbon and oxygen occur in two classes of compounds, the *alcohols* (Figure 1.18) and the *ethers*. Note that the alcohols

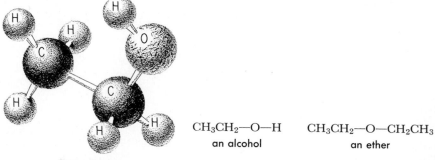

$$CH_3CH_2-O-H \qquad CH_3CH_2-O-CH_2CH_3$$
an alcohol   an ether

Fig. 1.18

are characterized by the presence of a monovalent —OH (*hydroxyl*) group and the ethers by the oxygen situated between two carbon atoms (C—O—C). Double bonds between oxygen and carbon occur in two classes of compounds, the *aldehydes* (Figure 1.19) and the *ketones* (Figure 1.20).

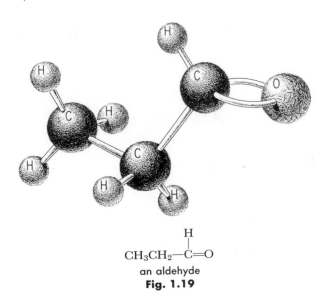

$$\overset{\displaystyle H}{\underset{\displaystyle}{CH_3CH_2-C}}=O$$

an aldehyde
Fig. 1.19

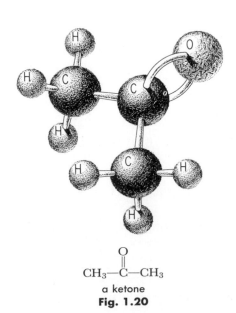

$$\overset{\displaystyle O}{\underset{\displaystyle}{CH_3-C-CH_3}}$$

a ketone
Fig. 1.20

The aldehydes are characterized by the group $-\overset{\overset{\text{H}}{|}}{\text{C}}=\text{O}$ (carbox-

aldehyde) and the ketones by the $-\overset{\overset{\text{O}}{||}}{\text{C}}-$ (carbonyl) group. Combinations of both the double-bonded and single-bonded oxygen atoms occur in the *carboxylic acids* (Figure 1.21), and in the *esters*. The car-

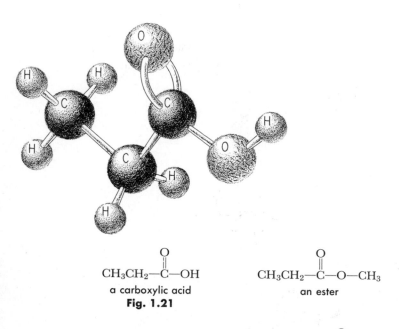

$$CH_3CH_2-\overset{\overset{\text{O}}{||}}{\text{C}}-OH \qquad\qquad CH_3CH_2-\overset{\overset{\text{O}}{||}}{\text{C}}-O-CH_3$$

a carboxylic acid   an ester

Fig. 1.21

boxylic acids contain the characteristic group $-\overset{\overset{\text{O}}{||}}{\text{C}}-OH$ (carboxyl group), and the ester $-\overset{\overset{\text{O}}{||}}{\text{C}}-O-C$ where the hydrogen of the carboxylic acid has been replaced by a carbon atom.

Nitrogen atoms are commonly trivalent, and can share one, two, or three bonds with one or more carbon atoms. When nitrogen shares single bonds with carbon atoms, a class of compounds called *amines* is formed. These compounds may be thought of as being derived from ammonia by replacing one or more of the hydrogen atoms by carbon atoms (Figures 1.22–1.25). Compounds containing carbon-to-nitrogen triple bonds are *nitriles*. Nitrogen in its highest oxidized state may have a valence of five, and a series of organic compounds exist which contain the characteristic nitro group ($-NO_2$) sharing a bond with carbon.

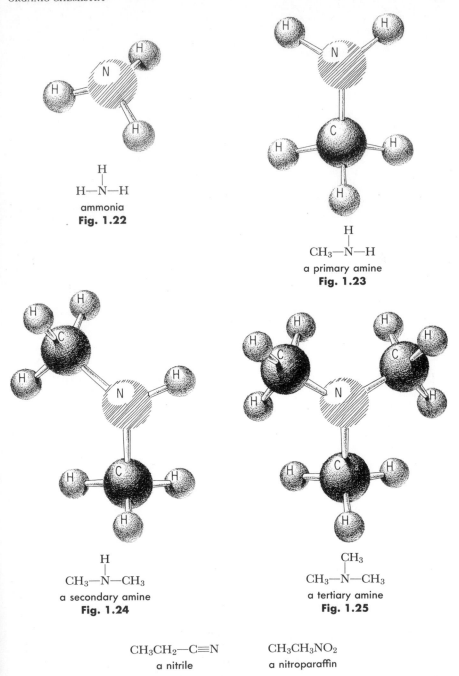

H
|
H—N—H
ammonia
Fig. 1.22

H
|
CH_3—N—H
a primary amine
Fig. 1.23

H
|
CH_3—N—CH_3
a secondary amine
Fig. 1.24

CH_3
|
CH_3—N—CH_3
a tertiary amine
Fig. 1.25

CH_3CH_2—C≡N
a nitrile

$CH_3CH_3NO_2$
a nitroparaffin

Sulfur, which is below oxygen on the periodic table, forms a series of organic sulfur compounds which are analogous in structure to the organic oxygen compounds. Thus we have *thiols* similar to alcohols, and *sulfides* similar to ethers. Sulfur, like nitrogen, can also occur in oxidized states, and a large series of organic compounds containing oxidized sulfur are known. The most important of these are the *sulfonic acids,* with the characteristic —SO_2OH group.

$$CH_3CH_2CH_2—S—H \qquad CH_3CH_2—S—CH_2CH_3 \qquad CH_3—SO_2OH$$

a thiol   a sulfide   a sulfonic acid

Homologous series and radicals

Examples have been given of compounds containing carbon and hydrogen; carbon, hydrogen, and halogens; carbon, hydrogen, and oxygen; carbon, hydrogen, and nitrogen; and carbon, hydrogen, and sulfur. The student should note that these represent the simplest kinds of combinations and illustrate the simple *functional groups* by which organic compounds are characterized and classified. These functional groups are responsible for the chief chemical (and physical) properties of the compounds, and the compounds are grouped together according to the similarity of their chemical behavior. For example, all amines are basic and are soluble in acids. We can then write the formulas of some simple primary amines which will have similar properties. Note that these all have the functional *amino* group (—NH_2) with the first

CH_3NH_2	a one-carbon primary amine
$CH_3CH_2NH_2$	a two-carbon primary amine
$CH_3CH_2CH_2NH_2$	a three-carbon primary amine
$CH_3(CH_2)_3NH_2$	a four-carbon primary amine
$CH_3(CH_2)_nNH_2$ or R—NH_2	general formula for continuous-chain primary amines

four differing from one another only by a —CH_2—. A series of organic compounds which differ by one —CH_2— unit (methylene group) each is called a *homologous series.* Individual members of a homologous series are called homologs. The symbol R (for radical) is merely a chemical shorthand symbol used in writing general formulas, and represents $CH_3(CH_2)_n$—, where $n = 0$ to infinity. We can designate any members of the homologous series of alcohols as R—OH, the ethers as R—O—R, the aldehydes as R—CHO, the ketones as R—CO—R, the carboxylic acids as R—COOH, the thiols as R—SH, the sulfides as R—S—R, and the sulfonic acids as R—SO_3H.

Many organic compounds contain more than one functional

group, and may exhibit the properties of all of the functions present, although these functions usually interact with one another to some extent to give each molecule special characteristics. *Polyfunctional* molecules are classified under the most dominant function. For example, $HOCH_2CH_2COOH$, which has both an alcohol and a carboxyl group, is regarded as a hydroxy acid because the acid properties are more predominant. In the same way $ClCH_2COCH_3$ is a chloro ketone, and NO_2CH_2CHO a nitro aldehyde.

Functional isomers

Several examples of *position* isomers have already been given. These differ from each other by the position of a functional group on the carbon chain, for example, the alcohols of formula

$$C_3H_7OH \qquad CH_3CH_2CH_2OH \quad and \quad CH_3CHOHCH_3$$

A second type of isomerism should be mentioned here, *functional isomerism*. This can exist where an atom having two or more valence bonds can combine with carbon in different ways to produce different functions. For example, the alcohol and the ether with structures CH_3CH_2OH and CH_3OCH_3 are isomers of the molecular formula C_2H_6O, and the aldehyde and ketone of structures CH_3CH_2CHO and CH_3COCH_3 are isomers of C_3H_6O. Some other types of isomerism will be described in later chapters.

Study Questions

1. How does our present definition of "organic chemistry" differ from the original meaning?

2. What unusual property of the carbon atom accounts for the large number of compounds it forms?

3. Which is the more negative end of the polar bond formed between carbon and hydrogen? Carbon and chlorine? Carbon and oxygen? Hydrogen and oxygen? Hydrogen and sulfur? Carbon and sulfur? Magnesium and carbon?

4. Write the formulas of two compounds having electrovalent bonds, and two compounds having covalent bonds.

5. Some molecules are made up of atoms bonded by all three kinds of bonds. Write the structural formula of such a molecule, and indicate which bonds are coordinate covalent and which covalent.

6. Draw structural formulas for CH_4, CH_3OH, CH_2O, CH_2O_2, and CO_2. How does each of these formulas differ from the others?

7. Show all of the ways in which 1 atom of oxygen, 2 atoms of carbon, and 6 atoms of hydrogen can combine to form compounds of the formula C_2H_6O.

8. There are four isomers having the formula C_4H_9Cl. Draw their structures.

9. Illustrate by a formula the structure of an alcohol, an amine, a nitrile, an aldehyde, a carboxylic acid, a hydrocarbon, and a ketone.

10. What is meant by "homologous series"? By "functional group"? By "position isomers"? By "unsaturated hydrocarbon"?

Advanced Reading References

Organic Chemistry, 3rd Ed., R. Q. Brewster and W. E. McEwen, Prentice-Hall, Inc., Englewood Cliffs, N. J., 1961, Chapter 1.

Chemistry of Organic Compounds, 2nd Ed., C. R. Noller, W. B. Saunders Co., Philadelphia, 1957, Chapter 1.

Organic Chemistry, 3rd Ed., L. F. Fieser and Mary Fieser, D. C. Heath and Co., Boston, 1957, Chapter 1.

new terms & concepts

Since it is impossible to memorize common or trivial names for thousands of known organic compounds, systematic names have been developed by the International Union of Chemistry.
The I.U.C. rules of nomenclature are based on the names of the alkanes and their related alkyl radicals.
Isomers of alkanes are named as substituted alkanes.
Unsaturated compounds are named as alkenes or alkynes.
The principal functions are named as suffixes, e.g., carboxylic acids, aldehydes, ketones, alcohols, thiols, amines.
Halogen, alkyl, and nitro groups are named by prefix only.
A choice of the simpler systematic name is permitted.

2

Naming organic compounds

It is apparent from the previous discussion that an enormous number of organic compounds are already known, new ones are prepared each day, and an infinite number can theoretically exist. It would be impossible to memorize individual names for all of these substances. In the early days of the science, only a few compounds were known, and each was given a trivial name which indicated its source, the name of the discoverer, or some special property, such as color, odor, flammability, etc. For example, the compound CH_3OH was called *wood alcohol*, since it was obtained by the destructive distillation of hard wood. *Acetum*, or vinegar, yielded *acetic acid* (CH_3COOH), and rancid butter gave *butyric acid* ($CH_3CH_2CH_2COOH$). *Alcool vini* (the most subtle of the wine), or alcohol (CH_3CH_2OH) from fermented fruit juice, when heated with sulfuric acid, formed a highly flammable substance, *ether* ($CH_3CH_2OCH_2CH_3$) (Greek, "to burn").

These names told little about the structure or functional groups present in the organic molecules. Since many new compounds were being synthesized after Wöhler's discovery, it soon became apparent that some systematic approach must be devised which would name new compounds in such a way as to be intelligible to all chemists. Attempts in this direction were begun as early as 1898, but a world-wide system was defined by agreement in the International Union of Chemistry and introduced about 1930. This system, known as the I.U.C. system, is under continuous study by committees of the International Union, so that new discoveries in the science can be systematically named. The I.U.C. system (1) names a compound according to its structural formula, (2) is understood by chemists in every country, and (3) provides rules which will permit even the most elementary student to name correctly any compound for which a structural formula can be written. In this system compounds are named as derivatives of the parent hydrocarbons, and it will be necessary for the student to memorize the names of at least the first ten members in the list of paraffins and the radicals derived from the paraffins (Table 2.01).

Inspection of Table 2.01 reveals two basic rules of the I.U.C. system:

1. *The names of the continuous-chain saturated paraffin hydrocarbons are derived from the Greek number corresponding to the number of carbon atoms present, followed by the suffix "-ane."* (The first four are exceptions to this rule since they are based on previously established names.)
2. *The name of the radical formed by removing one end-hydrogen is obtained by changing the ending "-ane" of the parent hydrocarbon to "-yl."*

It is now possible to name any paraffin hydrocarbon, whether continuous- or branched-chain. The names of the branched-chain compounds are formed by naming the branches as radicals attached to a longer continuous chain. For example, consider the isomers of hexane. The first structure has a chain of five carbon atoms, with a methyl group attached to the second carbon atom. It is therefore a methylpentane; the second structure also has a chain of five carbon

$$CH_3 \quad\quad\quad\quad\quad\quad\quad\quad\quad\quad\quad CH_3$$
$$\underset{1}{CH_3}-\underset{2}{CH}-\underset{3}{CH_2}-\underset{4}{CH_2}-\underset{5}{CH_3} \quad\quad \underset{1}{CH_3}-\underset{2}{CH_2}-\underset{3}{CH}-\underset{4}{CH_2}-\underset{5}{CH_3}$$
$$\text{2-methylpentane} \quad\quad\quad\quad\quad \text{3-methylpentane}$$

atoms, with a methyl group attached to the third carbon. The position of the methyl group must therefore be indicated by the number of the atom to which it is attached, hence the names, 2-methylpentane and 3-methylpentane. The third structure illustrates a chain of four carbon atoms, with methyl groups attached to the second and third. Two methyl groups, the one on the second and the one on the third carbon atom, are indicated by the name, 2,3-*di*methylbutane. Two methyl

$$CH_3 \quad CH_3 \quad\quad\quad\quad\quad\quad\quad CH_3$$
$$\underset{1}{CH_3}-\underset{2}{CH}-\underset{3}{CH}-\underset{4}{CH_3} \quad\quad \underset{1}{CH_3}-\underset{2}{C}-\underset{3}{CH_2}-\underset{4}{CH_3}$$
$$\quad\quad\quad\quad\quad\quad\quad\quad\quad\quad\quad CH_3$$
$$\text{2,3-dimethylbutane} \quad\quad \text{2,2-dimethylbutane}$$

TABLE 2.01 NAMES OF PARAFFINS AND DERIVED RADICALS

Compound	Name	Radical (R—)	Name
CH_4	Methane	CH_3—	Methyl
CH_3CH_3	Ethane	CH_3CH_2—	Ethyl
$CH_3CH_2CH_3$	Propane	$CH_3CH_2CH_2$—	Propyl
$CH_3(CH_2)_2CH_3$	Butane	$CH_3(CH_2)_3$—	Butyl
$CH_3(CH_2)_3CH_3$	Pentane	$CH_3(CH_2)_4$—	Pentyl
$CH_3(CH_2)_4CH_3$	Hexane	$CH_3(CH_2)_5$—	Hexyl
$CH_3(CH_2)_5CH_3$	Heptane	$CH_3(CH_2)_6$—	Heptyl
$CH_3(CH_2)_6CH_3$	Octane	$CH_3(CH_2)_7$—	Octyl
$CH_3(CH_2)_7CH_3$	Nonane	$CH_3(CH_2)_8$—	Nonyl
$CH_3(CH_2)_8CH_3$	Decane	$CH_3(CH_2)_9$—	Decyl
$CH_3(CH_2)_9CH_3$	Undecane	$CH_3(CH_2)_{10}$—	Undecyl
$CH_3(CH_2)_{10}CH_3$	Dodecane	$CH_3(CH_2)_{11}$—	Dodecyl
$CH_3(CH_2)_{11}CH_3$	Tridecane	$CH_3(CH_2)_{12}$—	Tridecyl
$CH_3(CH_2)_{12}CH_3$	Tetradecane	$CH_3(CH_2)_{13}$—	Tetradecyl
$CH_3(CH_2)_{13}CH_3$	Pentadecane	$CH_3(CH_2)_{14}$—	Pentadecyl
. . . . . .		. . . . . .	
$CH_3(CH_2)_{18}CH_3$	Eicosane	$CH_3(CH_2)_{19}$—	Eicosyl
$CH_3(CH_2)_{19}CH_3$	Heneicosane	$CH_3(CH_2)_{20}$—	Heneicosyl
$CH_3(CH_2)_{20}CH_3$	Docosane	$CH_3(CH_2)_{21}$—	Docosyl
. . . . . .		. . . . . .	
$CH_3(CH_2)_{28}CH_3$	Triacontane	$CH_3(CH_2)_{29}$—	Triacontyl
$CH_3(CH_2)_{29}CH_3$	Hentriacontane	$CH_3(CH_2)_{30}$—	Hentriacontyl
. . . . . .		. . . . . .	
$C_{40}H_{82}$	Tetracontane	$C_{40}H_{81}$—	Tetracontyl
$C_{50}H_{102}$	Pentacontane	$C_{50}H_{101}$—	Pentacontyl
etc.	etc.	etc.	etc.
C_nH_{2n+2}	Alkane	C_nH_{2n+1}—	Alkyl

groups, both on the second carbon of a four-carbon chain, are indicated by the name, 2,2-dimethylbutane, for the fourth structure.

3. *The longest continuous chain of carbon atoms is chosen as the root of the name, and the branches are indicated as prefixes. The positions of the branches are indicated by the lowest possible numbers.*

The student must remember that the molecules to be named are three-dimensional and the orientation of their structural pictures on a sheet of paper does not change the name. All of the following structures are the same, i.e. 2-methylpentane.

$$\overset{5}{C}H_3—\overset{4}{C}H_2—\overset{3}{C}H_2—\overset{2}{C}H—\overset{1}{C}H_3$$
$$|$$
$$CH_3$$

$$\overset{1}{C}H_3$$
$$|$$
$$\overset{2}{C}H—\overset{3}{C}H_2—\overset{4}{C}H_2$$
$$|$$
$$CH_3 \qquad \overset{5}{C}H_3$$

$$\overset{1}{C}H_3—\overset{2}{C}H—CH_3$$
$$|$$
$$\overset{3}{C}H_2$$
$$|$$
$$\overset{4}{C}H_2$$
$$|$$
$$\overset{5}{C}H_3$$

Other substituents, such as halogens and nitro groups, are also indicated by prefixes. In this way, even complicated hydrocarbon derivatives can be named without difficulty. The following examples illustrate the use of these rules.

$CH_3—CH_2—CH_2Cl$ 1-chloropropane

$CH_3—CH—CH_3$
$|$
NO_2 2-nitropropane

$CH_3—CH—CH—CH_2—CH—CH_2—CH_3$
$|$ $|$ $|$
CH_3 Br $CH_2—CH_3$ 2-methyl-5-ethyl-3-bromoheptane

$\qquad CH_3$
$\qquad |$
$CH_3—CH—C—CH—CH_3$
$\quad |\quad |\quad \backslash$
$\quad I\quad NO_2\ I$ 2,4-diiodo-3-nitro-3-methylpentane

$CH_3—CH_2—CH—CH_2—CH_2$
$\qquad\quad |\qquad\quad |$
$\qquad\quad CHCl\qquad CH_3$ 5-chloro-6-methyl-4,7-diethyldecane
$\quad |$
$CH_3\qquad CH—CH_3$
$|\qquad\quad |$
$CH_2—CH_2—CH—CH_2—CH_3$

Study these examples carefully to make sure the principles used in deriving these names are understood. Notice that the reverse reasoning can be easily applied, and structures written for compounds named systematically. Write the structures of the following compounds: 2-methylbutane, 1,2-dichloroethane, 3-ethyl-2,4-dinitrohexane.

Unsaturation is indicated in the carbon chain by changing the suffix. In the olefins, the double bond is indicated by changing the ending "-ane" to "-ene." Thus we have:

$CH_2=CH_2$ ethene

$CH_3CH=CHCH_3$ 2-butene

$CH_3CH_2C=CH_2$ 2-methyl-1-butene
$\quad\quad\quad |$
$\quad\quad\quad CH_3$

$$CH_2{=}CH{-}CH{=}CH_2 \qquad\qquad 1,3\text{-butadiene}$$

$$CH_2{=}CH{-}CH{=}CH{-}CH{=}CH_2 \qquad 1,3,5\text{-hexatriene}$$

$$CH_2{=}CH{-}\underset{NO_2}{CH}{-}CH{=}\underset{Cl}{C}{-}CH_3 \qquad \begin{array}{l}3\text{-nitro-5-chloro-}\\1,4\text{-hexadiene}\end{array}$$

The position of the double bond is indicated by the number of the lower of the two carbon atoms between which it lies. Two double bonds are indicated by the suffix *-diene*, three by *-triene*, etc. Notice that in the last example, the functions (double bonds) indicated by the suffix get the lowest numbers possible, regardless of the numbers which must be assigned to the prefixes. Similarly, in the acetylenes, the triple bond is indicated by changing the ending "*-ane*" to "*-yne*."

$HC{\equiv}CH$	ethyne	$CH{\equiv}C{-}C{\equiv}CH$	1,3-butadiyne
$CH_3C{\equiv}CCH_3$	2-butyne	$CH_2{=}CH{-}C{\equiv}CH$	1-butene-3-yne
$CH_3\underset{CH_3}{CH}C{\equiv}CH$	3-methylbutyne		

All combinations of unsaturations, such as triynes, enynes, dienediynes, etc. are possible. When both double and triple bonds are present, the double bond is given the lowest possible number.

4. *Unsaturation is indicated by changing the suffix ending of alkane to alkene for double bonds and alkyne for triple bonds. In numbering, the double bond takes precedence over the triple bond.*

Functional groups other than unsaturation may be indicated by either a prefix or a suffix. Derivatives are named in such a way that only the *principal* functional group and the unsaturations are named as suffixes. All other functional groups and substituents are indicated by prefixes. Table 2.02 lists some of the common functional groups, and their prefix and suffix names.

The following examples illustrate the use of the table in naming compounds.

CH_3CH_2COOH	propanoic acid
$CH_3CHOHCH_3$	2-propanol
$CH_3CHOHCOOH$	2-hydroxypropanoic acid
$CH_3CHSHCH_2NH_2$	1-amino-2-propanethiol

Note that in the first example the carboxy group is the principal function, and is named by adding the suffix *-oic acid* to the name of the

TABLE 2.02   PREFIX AND SUFFIX NAMES OF SOME COMMON FUNCTIONAL GROUPS

Class	Functional group	Prefix	Suffix
A. Indicated by suffix only			
Paraffins	$-\overset{\mid}{\underset{\mid}{C}}-\overset{\mid}{\underset{\mid}{C}}-$	. . . . . .	-ane
Olefins	$-\overset{\mid}{C}=\overset{\mid}{C}-$	. . . . . .	-ene
Acetylenes	$-C\equiv C-$	. . . . . .	-yne
B. Indicated by prefix or suffix			
Carboxylic acids	—COOH	Carboxy-	-oic acid
Aldehydes	—CHO	Carboxaldo-	-al
Sulfonic acids	$-SO_2OH$	Sulfo-	-sulfonic acid
Ketones	$-\overset{O}{\overset{\|}{C}}-$	Keto-	-one
Alcohols	—OH	Hydroxy-	-ol
Thiols	—SH	Mercapto-	-thiol
Amines	$-NH_2$	Amino-	-amine
Ethers	—O—	Alkoxy-	ether
Sulfides	—S—	Alkylmercapto-	sulfide
C. Indicated by prefix only			
Fluorinated molecules	—F	Fluoro-	. . . . . .
Chlorinated molecules	—Cl	Chloro-	. . . . . .
Brominated molecules	—Br	Bromo-	. . . . . .
Iodinated molecules	—I	Iodo-	. . . . . .
Alkylated molecules	—R	Alkyl-	. . . . . .
Nitrated molecules	$-NO_2$	Nitro-	. . . . . .

parent three-carbon compound propane. In the second example, the hydroxy group is the principal function, and it is named by adding the suffix -*ol* to the root word. The position of the hydroxy group must be numbered, but the carboxy group can occur only at the end of a carbon chain, and hence needs no number. In the third example, two functional groups are present, and a choice must be made as to which

is the *principal function* which will be named in the suffix. The rules do
not state which function is more important, and indeed any function
may be the most important for certain reactions or properties of the
molecule. Therefore the chemist has been allowed freedom of choice
in this matter. However, common usage has established the order
which appears in Table 2.02, and this will be the preferred choice
throughout this book. Since the carboxyl group occurs before the hydroxy group in the table, it is regarded as the principal function, and
the third example is named as a substituted propanoic acid. Similarly,
the fourth example is a substituted propanethiol.

When carboxyl and aldehyde groups are named as prefixes, their
carbon atoms are not counted as part of the chain. The following examples illustrate this:

$HCOCH_2CH_2COOH$

3-carboxaldopropanoic acid

$HOCOCH_2CH_2CHCH_2COOH$
$|$
$COOH$

3-carboxyhexanedioic acid

Unsaturations are not regarded as principal functions, although they
always are indicated by suffixes. Therefore, if another group is present
which can be named as a principal function, it will be indicated also
in the suffix, and given the lowest possible number.

$CH_2=CH-CH_2-CHO$
3-butenal

$CH_3-C\equiv C-\overset{O}{\overset{||}{C}}-CH_3$
3-pentyne-2-one

5. *The principal function is named as a suffix, all other functions except
unsaturation being indicated by prefixes.*

Some further examples which illustrate the naming rule so far given
should be checked by the student to make sure the principles are
understood.

1. $CH_2=CH-\overset{Cl}{\overset{|}{C}}=CH-CH_3$ 3-chloro-1,3-pentadiene

2. $CH_2=CH-\overset{Cl}{\overset{|}{C}}=CH-CH_2OH$ 3-chloro-2,4-pentadiene-1-ol

3. $HOOC-COOH$ ethanedioic acid

4. $HSCH_2CH_2OH$ 2-mercaptoethanol

5. $(CH_3CH_2)_2NH$ diethylamine

6. 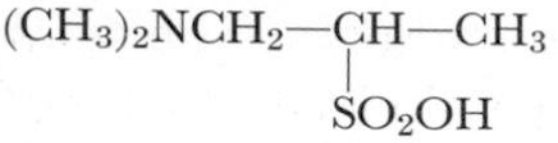 $(CH_3)_2NCH_2$—$\overset{\displaystyle |}{\underset{\displaystyle SO_2OH}{CH}}$—$CH_3$ 1-dimethylamino-2-propanesulfonic acid

7. CH_3CH_2—O—CH_2CH_3 ethyl ether

8. CH_3—O—CH_2CH_3 methoxyethane

9. $CH_3CH{=}CHCH{=}CHCH{=}CHCOOH$ 2,4,6-octatrienoic acid

When an organic molecule has several complicated substituents, it is sometimes simpler to name it as a derivative of the most highly substituted carbon chain, rather than the longest chain, as required by the third rule. For example, consider the following structure:

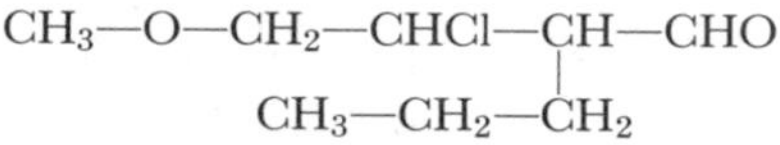

$$CH_3\text{—O—}CH_2\text{—CHCl—}\overset{\displaystyle |}{\underset{\displaystyle CH_3\text{—}CH_2\text{—}CH_2}{CH}}\text{—CHO}$$

By application of the first five rules, this compound should be named 2-(1-chloro-2-methoxyethyl)pentanal, but a simpler name is 2-propyl-3-chloro-4-methoxybutanal. In the same way, chains containing unsaturations are chosen for the root name in preference to longer saturated chains.

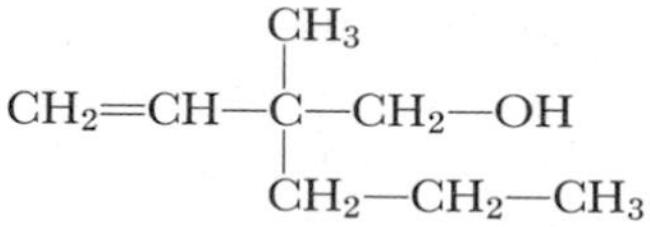

$$CH_2{=}CH\text{—}\overset{\displaystyle CH_3}{\underset{\displaystyle CH_2\text{—}CH_2\text{—}CH_3}{\overset{\displaystyle |}{\underset{\displaystyle |}{C}}}}\text{—}CH_2\text{—OH}$$

2-methyl-2-propyl-3-butene-1-ol
(not 2-methyl-2-ethenylpentanol)

6. *In complex compounds, the most highly substituted chain, rather than the longest, may be chosen as the root word, if a simpler name results.*

Six basic rules for naming organic compounds have been given. By application of these rules, the student may now find it possible to name systematically nearly any compound that will be found in this book. It should be noted, however, that many of the organic compounds which are most commonly studied have well-established trivial names by which they are known. It will be necessary to memorize these as they are described, since they are more generally used than the systematic names.

Study Questions

1. Write the correct I.U.C. names for the following:

CH_4, $CH_3(CH_2)_7CH_3$ $CH_3CHClCH{=}CH_2$ $CH_3CH(CH_3)CH_3$
$\qquad\qquad CH_3C{\equiv}CCH_3$ $CH_3CH{=}CHC{\equiv}CCH{=}CH_2$

2. What is meant by the terms principal function, unsaturation, function group, paraffin, I.U.C., halogenated hydrocarbon, continuous chain, alkyl radical, and structural formula? Illustrate each by an example.

3. Write structural formulas for 2-methylbutane, 2,2,4-trimethylpentane, 2-butene, 2,4-hexadiene, propyne, and 4-ethyl-2-heptane-5-yne.

4. What is the first rule to follow in naming a compound by the I.U.C. system?

5. Write the structural formulas for five isomers of C_6H_{14}, and name each by the I.U.C. system.

6. Name each of the following by the I.U.C. system:

   CH_3COOH $CH_3CHOHCH_3$ $CH_3CH_2CH_2CHO$
   $CH_3CH_2CH_2COCH_3$ CH_3NH_2.

7. Write structural formulas for the following: 3-chloro-1,3-pentadiene, propanedioic acid, 2-methoxybutanal, methyl ether, 1-amino-3-pentanone, 2-carboxy-1-propanol. Which one of the above compounds is incorrectly named? What is the correct name for this compound?

8. Write the structural formulas of the following compounds: acetic acid, wood alcohol, grain alcohol, butyric acid, acetone.

9. According to the rules of the I.U.C. system the following compound may be named in at least two ways. Write as many correct names for this compound as you can, and indicate which you think is best.

$$CH_3CH_2CH_2\underset{\underset{\displaystyle CH_3\overset{\|}{C}=O}{|}}{C}=\underset{\underset{\displaystyle Cl}{|}}{C}-C\equiv C-\underset{\underset{\displaystyle COOH}{|}}{CH}-CH_2CH_2CH_2SH$$

Advanced Reading References

"Definitive Rules for the Nomenclature of Organic Chemistry," *J. Am. Chem. Soc.* **82,** 5545–5575 (1960).

Organic Chemistry, G. B. Bachman, McGraw-Hill, New York, 1949, Chapter 3.

new terms & concepts

The simple compounds of carbon and hydrogen are used as fuels and
in chemical manufacture.
Their principal source is petroleum.
Paraffins are saturated and relatively unreactive.
They undergo substitution reactions.
For industry, isomerization and cracking are important reactions.
Preparation of pure paraffins can be accomplished by the Wurtz reaction or by
reduction of unsaturations, halogens, carbonyl groups, or the Grignard reagents.
Cycloparaffins commonly occur in natural plant and animal products.
They undergo substitution reactions and ring-opening reactions.
They can be formed by ring-closure reactions.

3

Saturated hydrocarbons: paraffins, cycloparaffins

Structurally, the simplest organic compounds are composed of carbon and hydrogen. Many compounds of this class occur in nature. For example, natural gas is about 75 per cent methane, CH_4. Petroleum is a rich source for most of the open-chain hydrocarbons. When petroleum is processed to make *gasoline,* large quantities of *olefins* are obtained. Coal produces *benzene* and other related *aromatic hydrocarbons* (see p. 73) which are obtained when the coal is coked. The chief use for these compounds is as fuel. The low-molecular-weight compounds are gases, and are used for heating purposes and for chemical manufacture. The higher-molecular-weight liquids are used as gasoline, diesel fuel, kerosene, and in oil-burning furnaces, while coal is an ancient fuel.

The saturated hydrocarbons which contain carbon-carbon single bonds are not very reactive, hence the name *paraffin,* meaning "poor affinity" (in Greek). The open-chain paraffins have the general formula C_nH_{2n+2}, which may be abbreviated RH, and are called *alkanes.*

THE PARAFFINS

Natural occurrence

Crude mineral oil, or petroleum, is a rich source of practically all members of this series. Oil-well gas contains *methane,* the simplest member, in highest concentration (75–100 per cent), but *ethane,* CH_3CH_3, *propane,* C_3H_8, and the *butanes,* C_4H_{10}, are also present. Methane is also present to some extent in coal gas (30–40 per cent) and in sewer gas (80 per cent) which is produced by bacterial decomposition of organic matter.

Physical properties

These substances in the pure state are odorless and colorless, and have the properties of general anesthetics, causing unconsciousness and, in higher concentrations, death. They are also very flammable, forming explosive mixtures with air. For these reasons, escaping gas is dangerous, and a warning substance possessing a strong odor, such as a mercaptan, is usually added to commercial fuel gas.

Pentane, C_5H_{12}, and *hexane,* C_6H_{14}, are low-boiling water-white liquids which are very flammable, and impure mixtures of these with other branched-chain relatives are called "petroleum ether." Gasoline is a mixture of higher-boiling paraffins. The waxy substance sold under the name "paraffin" is a mixture of high-molecular-weight paraffin hydrocarbons, low-melting but solid at room temperature, used to seal preserves and jellies and to make candles.

Table 3.01 lists the melting points and boiling points of the first ten alkanes (*italics*) and the isomers of butane, pentane, and hexane. Notice that the boiling points of the continuous-chain alkanes increase regularly with increasing molecular weight, but that branched-chain compounds are always lower-boiling than the corresponding continuous-chain compounds having the same number of carbon atoms. On the other hand, the melting points of compounds having symmetrical molecules are higher than the melting points of compounds whose molecules are less symmetrical. Compare, for example, the melting point of 2,2-dimethylpropane, which is very symmetrical in shape (Figure 3.01), with the melting points of its less symmetrical isomers, 2-methylbutane (Figure 3.02) and pentane (Figure 3.03).

The paraffins are insoluble in water, but soluble in most organic liquids. The paraffins are partially soluble in certain polar liquids, such as aniline or sulfur dioxide, but the solubility increases as these solvents are heated. The temperature at which a hydrocarbon becomes completely miscible with one of these solvents is called the Critical Solution Temperature (C.S.T.) and may be used to identify the hydrocarbon, since it is as characteristic as the melting point or boiling point.

TABLE 3.01   PHYSICAL PROPERTIES OF SOME PARAFFINS

Paraffin	M.P. °C	B.P. °C
Methane	−183	−161
Ethane	−172	−89
Propane	−188	−42
Butane	−138	0
2-Methylpropane	−159	−12
Pentane	−130	36
2-Methylbutane	−160	28
2,2-Dimethylpropane	−16	9
Hexane	−95	69
2-Methylpentane	−154	60
3-Methylpentane	−118	63
2,2-Dimethylbutane	−100	50
2,3-Dimethylbutane	−130.	58
Heptane	−91	98
Octane	−56	128
Nonane	−53	152
Decane	−30	172

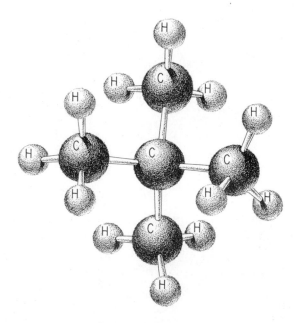

Fig. 3.01

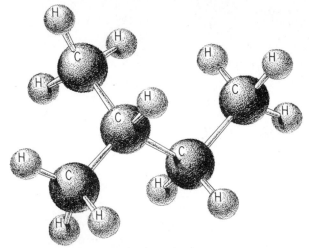

Fig. 3.02

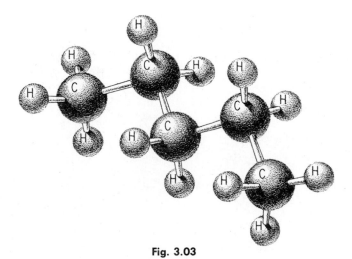

Fig. 3.03

Common names

The continuous-chain compounds are known by the I.U.C. names (see Chapter 2), but some of the lower branched-chain members are known by shorter trivial names. (The student should write out the I.U.C. name for each of the following compounds.)

$$CH_3-\underset{\underset{\displaystyle CH_3}{|}}{CH}-CH_3 \qquad CH_3-CH_2-\underset{\underset{\displaystyle CH_3}{|}}{CH}-CH_3 \qquad CH_3-\underset{\underset{\displaystyle CH_3}{\overset{\overset{\displaystyle CH_3}{|}}{C}}}{|}-CH_3$$

isobutane   isopentane   neopentane

$$CH_3-CH_2-CH_2-\overset{\overset{\displaystyle CH_3}{|}}{CH}-CH_3 \qquad CH_3-CH_2-\overset{\overset{\displaystyle CH_3}{|}}{\underset{\underset{\displaystyle CH_3}{|}}{C}}-CH_3 \qquad CH_3-\overset{\overset{\displaystyle CH_3}{|}}{CH}-\overset{\overset{\displaystyle CH_3}{|}}{CH}-CH_3$$

isohexane   neohexane   diisopropyl

Note how the systematic names reveal the structures, in contrast to the shorter trivial names.

Reactions of the paraffins

As stated previously, these compounds are relatively unreactive, and undergo only a few simple reactions which can be easily duplicated in the laboratory. Under special conditions they may be made to react to form certain products of industrial value.

1. *Oxidation.* The hydrocarbons burn with oxygen (air) to form carbon dioxide and water, with the liberation of large amounts of energy. This reaction is the basis of their value as fuels:

3.01 $$CH_4 + 2\,O_2 \longrightarrow CO_2 + 2\,H_2O + \text{energy}$$

Methane burns with a faintly luminescent blue flame which is hot and smokeless, and leaves a deposit of water on a cold surface. When the amount of oxygen is limited, however, a smoky yellow flame results owing to incandescent particles of unoxidized carbon; on a cold surface these leave a sooty deposit.

3.02 $$CH_4 + O_2 \longrightarrow C + 2\,H_2O$$

These reactions may be observed by simply varying the air supply to a Bunsen burner.

2. *Halogenation.* Paraffins react with chlorine or bromine in the presence of sunlight to replace one or more of the hydrogen atoms by halogen atoms, with the simultaneous formation of the hydrohalide. With a limited amount of halogen, the monohalide is formed.

3.03 $$CH_3CH_3 + Cl_2 \longrightarrow CH_3CH_2Cl + HCl$$

With excess halogen, all hydrogens may be replaced,

3.04 $$CH_3CH_3 + 6\,Cl_2 \longrightarrow Cl_3CCCl_3 + 6\,HCl$$

but an intermediate amount of halogen gives a mixture of products, i.e.:

3.05
$$CH_3CH_3 + 3\,Cl_2 \longrightarrow C_2H_5Cl + \underset{\text{2 isomers}}{C_2H_4Cl_2} +$$
$$\underset{\text{2 isomers}}{C_2H_3Cl_3} + \underset{\text{2 isomers}}{C_2H_2Cl_4} + C_2HCl_5 + C_2Cl_6 + HCl$$

The reaction does not take place in the absence of sunlight except at very high temperatures and, because of the formation of complicated products, is not very useful in the preparation of specific monohalo compounds. These can be prepared more readily by other methods. Paraffins react explosively with fluorine to form carbon, carbon tetra-fluoride (CF_4), and hydrogen fluoride. Iodine is not reactive enough to substitute for hydrogen atoms.

Reactions similar to the above, where hydrogen atoms are replaced by other atoms or functional groups, are called *"substitution reactions."* Halogenation may be schematically diagramed:

3.06 $R \dashv H + X \dashv X \xrightarrow{\text{sunlight}} R—X + H—X$ $X_2 = Cl_2$ or Br_2

The reaction is really more complex, however. The catalytic effect of sunlight shows that it is a *free radical chain* reaction. A *chain* reaction consists of three steps: the first is the reaction which starts a chain, usually catalyzed by heat, light, or decomposition of some unstable substance. This is the *initiating* reaction. The second step involves a series of reactions which constitute the chain, called the *propagating* reaction. Finally reactions may occur which stop the chains, and these are the *terminating* reactions. The sequence below illustrates the chain reactions involved in the chlorination of methane.

Initiating:

1. $Cl_2 \xrightarrow{\text{Sunlight}} 2\,Cl\cdot$

Propagating:

2a. $CH_4 + Cl\cdot \longrightarrow CH_3\cdot + HCl$

2b. $CH_3\cdot + Cl_2 \longrightarrow CH_3Cl + Cl\cdot$

2a. $CH_4 + Cl\cdot \longrightarrow CH_3\cdot + HCl$

2b. $CH_3\cdot + Cl_2 \longrightarrow CH_3Cl + Cl\cdot$

etcetera

Terminating:

3a. $CH_3\cdot + Cl\cdot \longrightarrow CH_3Cl$

3b. $Cl\cdot + Cl\cdot \longrightarrow Cl_2$

3c. $CH_3\cdot + CH_3\cdot \longrightarrow C_2H_6$

Notice that once a chain begins, the propagating step 2 may continue for a thousand or more times before one of the terminating reactions 3 occurs to interrupt the sequence.

3. *Nitration.* A mixture of methane and nitric acid vapor reacts at temperatures of 400° to 600° centigrade to form *nitromethane* and water. Under the same conditions, ethane produces both *nitroethane* and nitromethane. The reaction is, therefore, a complicated one,

3.07 $\qquad$ $CH_4 + HONO_2 \longrightarrow CH_3NO_2 + H_2O$

3.08 $\qquad$ $CH_3CH_3 + HONO_2 \longrightarrow CH_3CH_2NO_2 + CH_3NO_2 + H_2O$

but it is used industrially to produce some of the low-molecular-weight *nitroparaffins*.

4. *Isomerization.* The paraffins, under the influence of high temperatures and strong acid catalysts, such as sulfuric acid or anhydrous aluminum chloride, undergo rearrangement of their carbon-to-carbon bonds, so that one isomer may be changed to another. Since the branched-chain isomers have lower boiling points and burn slower than the continuous-chain isomers, they are of particular interest to motor-fuel manufacturers.

3.09 $\qquad$ $CH_3CH_2CH_2CH_3 \underset{}{\overset{AlCl_3}{\rightleftarrows}} \begin{matrix} CH_3 \\ | \\ CH_3-CH-CH_3 \end{matrix}$

5. *Cracking.* When paraffins are heated to high temperatures (400–500°C) in the absence of oxygen, they break down into smaller moleclues. Both carbon-hydrogen and carbon-carbon bonds are broken in this reaction, and hydrogen gas, lower-molecular-weight paraffins, and unsaturated hydrocarbons are produced. For example, when ethane is passed through a tube at 485°C, ethene and hydrogen are obtained.

3.10 $\qquad$ $CH_3CH_3 \xrightarrow{485°} CH_2{=}CH_2 + H_2$

The longer molecules decompose at slightly lower temperatures. Propane breaks down in two ways,

3.11 $\qquad$ $CH_3CH_2CH_3 \xrightarrow{460°} \begin{cases} CH_3CH{=}CH_2 + H_2 & 45\% \\ CH_2{=}CH_2 + CH_4 & 55\% \end{cases}$

either by loss of H_2 to form propene, or loss of methane to form ethene. The breakdown of butane is even more complex.

3.12 $\qquad$ $CH_3CH_2CH_2CH_3 \xrightarrow{435°} \begin{cases} CH_3CH_2CH{=}CH_2 + H_2 & 12\% \\ CH_3CH{=}CH_2 + CH_4 & 50\% \\ CH_2{=}CH_2 + CH_3CH_3 & 38\% \end{cases}$

Catalysts have been found which greatly promote this process at lower temperatures, and which favor the formation of certain products. This so-called "cracking" process is of great importance to the petroleum industry (Chapter 6).

Preparation of the paraffins

Although natural gas and petroleum are rich sources of the paraffins, the pure individual hydrocarbons, with the possible exceptions of methane and ethane, must be obtained by synthetic methods. There are two general methods which may be used to obtain pure paraffins.

1. *The Wurtz Reaction.* When an alkyl halide, such as iodoethane, is refluxed with an alkali metal, like sodium, the electropositive alkali metal reacts with the electronegative halogen, leaving organic radicals which are unstable and immediately react with themselves. Because

3.13
$$CH_3CH_2I + Na \longrightarrow [CH_3CH_2\cdot] + NaI$$
$$2[CH_3CH_2\cdot] \longrightarrow CH_3CH_2CH_2CH_3$$

of the great difference in boiling points between iodoethane (b.p. 72°C) and butane (b.p. 0°C), these may be easily separated to obtain pure butane. In the same way, other symmetrical paraffins may be readily obtained, according to the general equation:

3.14 $R{-}X + 2M + X{-}R \longrightarrow R{-}R + 2MX \qquad$ M = alkali metals, Na, Li, K, etc.
$\qquad\qquad\qquad\qquad\qquad\qquad\qquad\qquad\qquad$ X = halogens, Cl, Br, I

For example, we can prepare 2,3-dimethylbutane from 2-bromopropane:

$$CH_3{-}CH{-}Br + 2\,Li + Br{-}CH{-}CH_3 \longrightarrow$$

3.15 $\qquad\quad |\qquad\qquad\qquad\qquad |$
$\qquad\quad CH_3\qquad\qquad\qquad\qquad CH_3$

$$CH_3{-}CH{-}CH{-}CH_3 + 2\,LiBr$$
$$|\qquad |$$
$$CH_3\quad CH_3$$

2. *Reduction of Functional Groups.* Other functional groups, such as unsaturations, halogens, or carbonyl groups, may be reduced chemically or catalytically to form the paraffin hydrocarbons.

a) Olefins are reduced to paraffins by treating them with hydrogen gas at about 50 pounds per square inch pressure over finely divided platinum or nickel catalysts.

3.16 $\qquad\qquad CH_3{-}CH{=}CH_2 + H_2 \xrightarrow[\text{50 lb psi}]{\text{cat.}} CH_3{-}CH_2{-}CH_3$

3.17 $\qquad\qquad\qquad R_2C{=}CR_2 + H_2 \longrightarrow R_2CHCHR_2$

The difficulty with using this method as a source of pure paraffins is that pure olefins themselves must be available as starting materials. However, methods are known for preparing the pure olefins from other sources (Chapter 4).

b) The halogen atom in halogenated paraffins may be most conveniently replaced by hydrogen by a two-step process, involving first the formation of the organomagnesium compound, and second the treatment of this substance with acid. A halogenated hydrocarbon, such as bromoethane, reacts with magnesium, usually in the presence of *dry* ether, to form the organomagnesium halide.

3.18 $\qquad$ $CH_3CH_2Br + Mg \xrightarrow{C_2H_5OC_2H_5} CH_3CH_2MgBr$

Compounds of this type, i.e. organomagnesium halides, are called *Grignard reagents*, after Victor Grignard, the French chemist who described most of their properties. Grignard reagents are very reactive substances, and have many applications in the synthetic organic laboratory, so they will be referred to many times in these chapters. Very dry ether must be used in their preparation, since they react immediately with any acidic substance, such as water, to replace the magnesium by hydrogen.

3.19 $\qquad$ $CH_3CH_2MgBr + HOH \longrightarrow CH_3CH_3 + Mg(OH)Br$

We may then describe the reduction of halogenated hydrocarbons by the following:

3.20 $\qquad$ $RX + Mg \xrightarrow[\text{ether}]{\text{dry}} RMgX$

3.21 $\qquad$ $RMgX + H^+ \longrightarrow RH + Mg^{++} + X^-$

c) Carbonyl groups in aldehydes and ketones may be reduced directly to the methylene group

$$(-CO- + 2H_2 \longrightarrow -CH_2- + H_2O)$$

by chemical methods. For examples, hydrogen may be supplied to the carbonyl compound by the reaction of zinc with hydrochloric acid in the Clemmensen reduction. The reaction is not well understood, but the general equation may be written:

3.22 $\qquad$ $R_1COR_2 + 2H_2 \xrightarrow{Zn/H^+} R_1CH_2R_2 + H_2O$

Pure methane may be prepared in the laboratory by two special methods. Aluminum carbide is decomposed by water to give pure methane according to the equation:

3.23 $$Al_4C_3 + 12\,H_2O \longrightarrow 3\,CH_4 + 4\,Al(OH)_3$$

When the sodium salt of ethanoic acid (sodium acetate) is strongly heated with sodium hydroxide, it decomposes to form methane and sodium carbonate:

3.24 $$CH_3\!\!-\!\!\boxed{COONa + Na\!\!-\!\!O}\!\!-\!\!H \xrightarrow{\text{heat}} CH_4 + Na_2CO_3$$

This reaction unfortunately cannot be used for the preparation of higher homologs of methane in the pure state, since the decomposition is complex. For example, sodium propionate gives a mixture of ethane and ethene under these conditions.

THE CYCLOPARAFFINS

It can be seen from the following formulas

pentane   cyclopentane

that the molecule of pentane can easily be swung around so that the first carbon may be attached to the last carbon by a bond, without straining the other bonds in the chain. In this way a ring containing five methylene (CH_2) groups is obtained. Compounds of this type are known, and since chemically they resemble the paraffins, they are called *cycloparaffins*. In all rings containing five carbons or more, the bonds have the same tetrahedral angles as the paraffins, and therefore the compounds have exactly the same kinds of reactions as the paraffins. In the two compounds having smaller rings than five carbons, cyclobutane and cyclopropane, the angles of the bonds between the carbon atoms are obviously strained, being 90° in cyclobutane and 60°

cyclobutane   cyclopropane

in cyclopropane, whereas the normal bond angle between carbon atoms in the paraffins is 109°. This straining of the bond angles accounts for the unusual chemical reactivity of cyclobutane and cyclopropane. These compounds react as though they were unsaturated hydrocarbons.

Occurrence

Cycloparaffins and their derivatives are found widely distributed in nature. The five- and six-membered cycloparaffins occur commonly in petroleum in the *naphthene* fraction. Various combinations of three-membered, four-membered, five-membered, and six-membered rings occur in the *terpenes,* which are substances found in turpentine and other oils of the conifer. *Pinene* and *camphor* are among these sub-

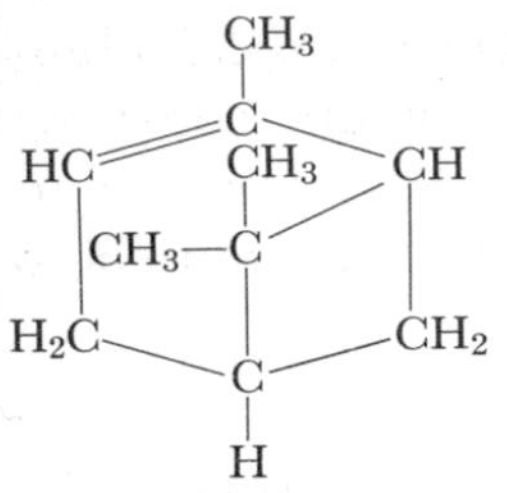

pinene

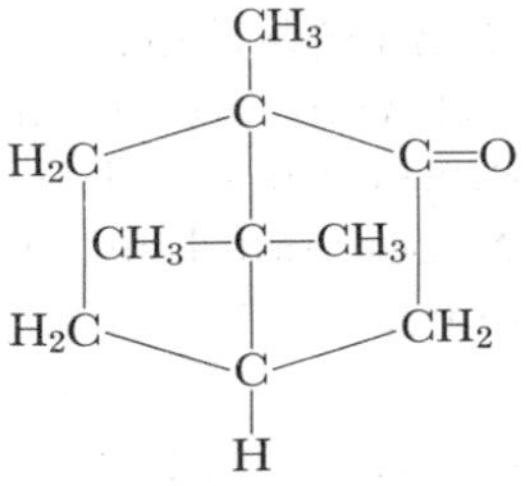

camphor

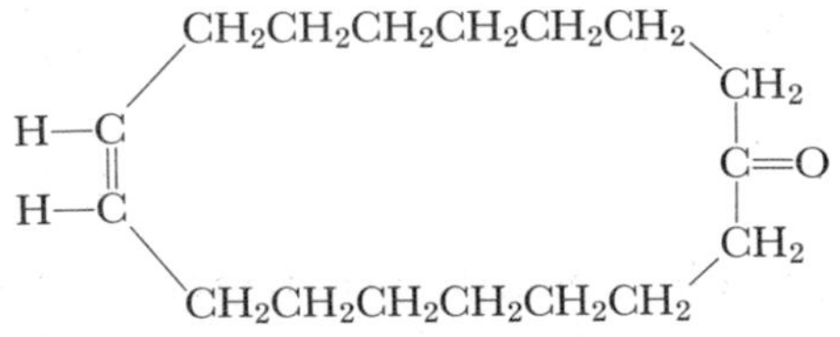

civetone

stances. Various combinations of five- and six-membered ring compounds are found in the *sterols* of the animal body. Rings containing up to 17 carbon atoms have been found in certain animal products, such as the perfume oils from the civet cat and musk ox.

Reactions of the cycloparaffins

Cycloparaffins react as do the paraffins when the ring has five or more carbon atoms and is unstrained. For example, cyclohexane reacts with bromine in the sunlight to form bromocyclohexane.

$$\textbf{3.25} \quad \underset{\text{CH}_2-\text{CH}_2}{\overset{\text{CH}_2-\text{CH}_2}{\text{H}_2\text{C}\diagup\diagdown\text{CH}_2}} + \text{Br}_2 \xrightarrow{\text{sun}} \underset{\text{CH}_2-\text{CH}_2}{\overset{\text{CH}_2-\text{CH}_2}{\text{H}_2\text{C}\diagup\diagdown\text{CHBr}}} + \text{HBr}$$

bromocyclohexane

It should be noted here that only one position isomer of the mono-bromocyclohexane is possible, since all of the hydrogens of cyclohexane are equivalent. Similarly, chlorination of cyclopentane, using a limited amount of chlorine in the sunlight, will produce chlorocyclopentane.

$$\textbf{3.26} \quad \underset{\text{H}_2\text{C}-\text{CH}_2}{\overset{\text{CH}_2}{\underset{|\qquad|}{\text{H}_2\text{C}\quad\text{CH}_2}}} + \text{Cl}_2 \xrightarrow{\text{sun}} \underset{\text{H}_2\text{C}-\text{CH}_2}{\overset{\text{CH}_2}{\underset{|\qquad|}{\text{H}_2\text{C}\quad\text{CHCl}}}}$$

chlorocyclopentane

However, as the strain increases in the ring, bonds between carbon atoms may be broken by various reagents. For example, if bromine is allowed to react with cyclobutane, two products may be formed. Ordinary substitution may occur to produce bromocyclobutane, or a carbon-to-carbon bond in the ring may be broken to produce 1,4-dibromobutane.

$$\textbf{3.27} \quad \underset{\text{CH}_2}{\overset{\text{CH}_2}{\text{H}_2\text{C}\diagup\diagdown\text{CHBr}}} \xleftarrow[\text{sunlight}]{\text{Br}_2} \underset{\text{CH}_2}{\overset{\text{CH}_2}{\text{H}_2\text{C}\diagup\diagdown\text{CH}_2}} \xrightarrow{\text{Br}_2} \text{BrCH}_2\text{CH}_2\text{CH}_2\text{CH}_2\text{Br}$$

$$\underset{\text{CH}_2}{\overset{\text{CH}_2}{\text{H}_2\text{C}\diagup\diagdown\text{CH}_2}} \xrightarrow[\text{cat.}]{\text{H}_2} \text{CH}_3\text{CH}_2\text{CH}_2\text{CH}_3$$

Cyclobutane may also be reduced with hydrogen over a catalyst to produce butane by breaking a carbon-to-carbon bond. Cyclopropane is even more reactive and with bromine will react easily to produce 1,3-dibromopropane. It is also easily reduced with hydrogen over a catalyst to produce propane. In each of these reactions the ring has opened.

$$\textbf{3.28} \quad \text{CH}_3\text{CH}_2\text{CH}_3 \xleftarrow[\text{cat.}]{\text{H}_2} \underset{\text{H}_2\text{C}-\text{CH}_2}{\overset{\text{CH}_2}{\diagup\diagdown}} \xrightarrow{\text{Br}_2} \text{BrCH}_2\text{CH}_2\text{CH}_2\text{Br}$$

Preparation of the cycloparaffins

Cyclohexane and its derivatives are most easily prepared by the direct reduction of benzene (see Chapter 5). The other cycloparaffins

are usually prepared by ring-closure methods. For example, the Wurtz synthesis may be used to close a ring. 1,5-dibromopentane may be reacted with sodium in dilute solution to produce cyclopentane.

3.29
$$H_2C \begin{array}{c} CH_2-CH_2-Br \\ \\ CH_2-CH_2-Br \end{array} + 2\,Na \longrightarrow H_2C \begin{array}{c} CH_2-CH_2 \\ \\ CH_2-CH_2 \end{array} + 2\,NaBr$$

Five- and six-membered rings are most readily formed in cyclization reactions. However, cyclopropane and cyclobutane may be prepared by similar ring closures, using dilute solutions. It has been found that zinc is a more effective metal in removing halogens to cause ring closures. For example, cyclopropane is most conveniently prepared by reaction of 1,3-dibromopropane with zinc.

3.30
$$H_2C \begin{array}{c} CH_2-Br \\ \\ CH_2-Br \end{array} + Zn \longrightarrow H_2C \begin{array}{c} CH_2 \\ | \\ CH_2 \end{array} + ZnBr_2$$

Other reactions which are suitable for forming carbon-to-carbon bonds can also be applied to ring closures. These will be described later.

Uses of the cycloparaffins

Since large-ring compounds occur in natural perfume oils, perfumers have been interested in the synthesis of compounds of this type. *Muskone* contains 15 members and *civetone* 17 members in the ring. Cyclopropane is a useful general anesthetic, although it is explosive when mixed with air. Cyclohexane and its derivatives have some use as industrial solvents, since they are readily available from benzene. Table 3.02 lists some of the melting points and boiling points of the

TABLE 3.02   PHYSICAL PROPERTIES OF SOME CYCLOPARAFFINS

Cycloparaffin	M.P. °C	B.P. °C
Cyclopropane	−127	−33
Cyclobutane	−50	15
Cyclopentane	−93	50
Cyclohexane	6	81
Cycloheptane	−12	120
Cyclooctane	15	155

lower-molecular-weight cycloparaffins. Notice the similarity in physical properties between the open-chain compounds (Table 3.01) and closed-chain compounds.

Study Questions

1. What is meant by a paraffin? a cycloparaffin? What is the most characteristic chemical reaction of these classes of compounds?

2. Write out the structural formulas of all of the isomeric heptanes, C_7H_{16}. Name each by the I.U.C. system.

3. Starting with methyl bromide, show by equations how methane, ethane, propane, and butane can be prepared.

4. Write structural formulas for: *a*) 2,2,4-trimethylpentane, *b*) 1-ethyl-2-methylcyclopropane, *c*) 2,6-dimethylheptane, *d*) 4-isopropyl-1-methylcyclohexane, *e*) 4-ethyl-2-methyl-5-propylnonane.

5. What two alkyl halides would you choose to prepare heptane by the Wurtz synthesis? Why?

6. Show how butane can be prepared in three different ways.

7. What are the principal commercial sources of the paraffin hydrocarbons?

8. Show by equations two methods for preparing pure methane in the laboratory.

9. Of the three isomers, octane, 2-methylheptane and 2,2,3,3-tetramethylbutane, which would have the higher boiling point? Which the higher melting point? Upon what principle do you base your answer?

10. Where do cycloparaffin derivatives occur in nature? Of what commercial use are they? What is the chief biological interest in these compounds?

11. What is the principal product formed when a limited amount of bromine reacts with each of the following in the presence of sunlight? Ethane, propane, cyclohexane, cyclopropane.

12. Show clearly your understanding of what is meant by *a*) the Wurtz synthesis, *b*) the Grignard reagent, *c*) the Clemmensen reduction, *d*) the "cracking" process.

13. A mixture of all the isomeric pentanes, obtained from petroleum, is chlorinated and distilled to produce a mixture of monochloro-

pentanes which is a useful commercial solvent. Write the structural formulas and I.U.C. names of all possible components of such a mixture.

Advanced Reading References

Organic Chemistry, 3rd Ed., R. Q. Brewster and W. E. McEwen, Prentice-Hall, Inc., Englewood Cliffs, N. J., 1961, Chapter 2.

Chemistry of Organic Compounds, 2nd Ed., C. R. Noller, W. B. Saunders Co., Philadelphia, 1957, Chapter 2.

Essential Principles of Organic Chemistry, James Cason, Prentice-Hall, Inc., Englewood Cliffs, N. J., 1956, Chapter 6.

Advanced Organic Chemistry, E. Earl Royals, Prentice-Hall, Inc., Englewood Cliffs, N. J., 1954, Chapters 2 and 3.

Organic Chemistry, 3rd Ed., L. F. Fieser and Mary Fieser, D. C. Heath and Co., Boston, 1957, Chapter 2.

new terms & concepts

Unsaturated molecules containing double or triple bonds exhibit
geometric isomerism, allowing for cis (on the same side) and trans (across) isomers.

Unsaturated groups react by addition.

The "oxo" process is a special example involving carbon monoxide.

When unsymmetrical reagents add to unsaturations, Markovnikov's rule indicates
the principal product.

The peroxide effect causes reversal of this rule.

Olefins are readily oxidized.

Baeyer's test is based on oxidation.

Ozonolysis cleaves the double bond.

The formation of addition polymers is an important industrial reaction of olefins.

Olefins may be prepared by petroleum cracking or by the elimination reaction.

Polyenes occur in nature.

Multiple double bonds are classified as cumulated, conjugated, or isolated.

Conjugated double bonds undergo 1,4-addition.

Isoprene is an important conjugated olefin found in nature.

Acetylenes react by addition or substitution.

Acetylene is an important raw material made inexpensively from coal or petroleum gas.

4

Unsaturated hydrocarbons: olefins, acetylenes

UNSATURATED HYDROCARBONS

Hydrocarbons containing one or more double or triple bonds are called unsaturated hydrocarbons. If but one double bond is present they are known as olefins, or alkenes. Because of the presence of the double bond, the olefins are more reactive than the paraffins, readily adding halogens to form the heavy, oily halogenated hydrocarbons, hence the name "olefin" meaning "oil-former." The I.U.C. class name "alkene" is more descriptive of the structure which is indicated by the general formula C_nH_{2n}. The acetylenic hydrocarbons, or alkynes, are characterized by the presence of the triple bond. Although the triple bond is more reactive than the double bond, compounds possessing it still resemble the olefins in many of their properties. The simple alkynes have the general formula C_nH_{2n-2}.

OLEFINS

Occurrence

The chief industrial source of olefins is the "cracking" of petroleum in the refining process (p. 89). Many complex olefins occur in nature. The terpenes, occurring in turpentine and other plant oils, contain cycloolefins, such as pinene (p. 43).

An important group of naturally occurring hydrocarbons containing the cyclohexene ring are the *carotenes,* which are yellow pigments present in carrots, apricots, sweet potatoes, squash, corn, and in leafy vegetables like spinach and broccoli. There are several of these substances, called *alpha, beta,* and *gamma* carotenes. These differ slightly in the position of certain double bonds, or in the number of cyclohexene rings which they contain. They are isomers of lycopene, $C_{40}H_{56}$, containing eight isoprene carbon skeletons (p. 96), and are important because they are converted in the body into Vitamin A.

β-carotene

Ethylene is a colorless gas of very faint odor, available compressed in metal cylinders. It has a low toxicity and produces deep anesthesia, and is frequently administered mixed with air or oxygen for minor surgical operations. Since mixtures of 3–34 per cent ethylene in air are explosive its use in operating rooms, like that of cyclopropane, is dangerous, especially in the presence of cauterizing instruments or electrical equipment which might spark. Ethylene aids the coloring processes and hastens the ripening of fruit, and is used for this purpose by commercial fruit shippers.

Common names

The name ethylene has been commonly used for ethene for many years, and the better-known lower members of the olefin series have similar common names, which although slightly longer are more euphonic. Compare the sound of the names in Table 4.01.

Physical properties

Olefins are quite similar in physical properties to the paraffins, boiling and melting only a few degrees different from their saturated analogs. In the pure state they are colorless, odorless, and tasteless. The melting points and boiling points of a few simple olefins are listed in Table 4.01. Notice that, as in the homologous series of paraffins (Table

TABLE 4.01   NAMES AND PHYSICAL PROPERTIES OF SOME SIMPLE OLEFINS

Formula	I.U.C. name	Common name	M.P. °C	B.P. °C
$CH_2{=}CH_2$	Ethene	Ethylene	−170	−104
$CH_2{=}CHCH_3$	Propene	Propylene	−185	−47
$CH_2{=}CHCH_2CH_3$	1-Butene	1-Butylene	−130	−5
$\underset{\displaystyle H}{\overset{\displaystyle H_3C}{{\diagdown}}}C{=}C\underset{\displaystyle H}{\overset{\displaystyle CH_3}{{\diagup}}}$	cis-2-Butene	cis-2-Butylene	−140	+4
$\underset{\displaystyle H}{\overset{\displaystyle H_3C}{{\diagdown}}}C{=}C\underset{\displaystyle CH_3}{\overset{\displaystyle H}{{\diagup}}}$	trans-2-Butene	trans-2-Butylene	−106	+1
$CH_2{=}C(CH_3)_2$	2-Methylpropene	Isobutylene	−141	−6
$CH_2{=}CHCH_2CH_2CH_3$	1-Pentene	Amylene	−138	+30
$CH_2{=}CHCH(CH_3)_2$	3-Methyl-1-butene	Isoamylene	−135	+25
$CH_2{=}CH(CH_2)_3CH_3$	1-Hexene	Hexylene	−98	+64
$CH_2{=}CH(CH_2)_4CH_3$	1-Heptene	Heptylene	−120	+95

3.01), the melting points of the homologs containing an odd number of carbon atoms are lower than would be expected (see Chapter 11). The branched-chain isomers generally boil lower than the corresponding continuous-chain isomers, as was the case with the paraffins.

Geometric Isomerism

Certain of the olefins exhibit another type of isomerism which is called *geometric isomerism* since it depends on the geometric arrangement of certain atoms and groups in the molecule. (In Table 4.01, two different compounds having the formula of 2-butene are listed.) These compounds have slightly different boiling points, and distinctly different melting points. If we make a three-dimensional model of 2-butene (see Figures 4.01 and 4.02) we see that there are two ways in which the methyl groups may be placed on the ethene structure and that, because of lack of free rotation at the double bond, the one model cannot be twisted to bring the methyl groups into the same position as they are in the other. They must therefore represent two structural isomers of 2-butene. They are known, and are called *cis* (on the same side) and *trans* (across) 2-butene. Because of their different structures, they have slightly different physical properties. The student should note that no geometric (or *cis-trans*) isomers of 1-butene or 2-methylpropene are

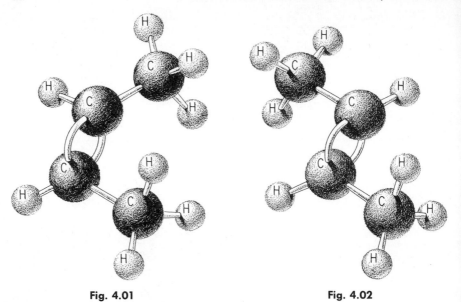

Fig. 4.01   Fig. 4.02

possible. Geometric isomers can only occur when each end of a double bond has two different substituents, that is:

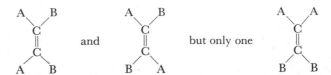

Geometric isomers are found in substituted cycloparaffins also. Free rotation is lacking in these ring compounds. Therefore two substituents on different carbon atoms may be at different distances from one another, depending on whether they are located in a *cis* or *trans* manner. For example, there are two 1,2-cyclopentanedicarboxylic acids, one melting at 139°C, the other at 161°C. The lower-melting is the *cis*-isomer (Figure 4.05(b)), and the higher-melting is *trans* (Figure 4.05(a)).

Rings having more than five atoms are no longer planar, but must assume a puckered shape. Cyclohexane may exist in two conformations, the so-called "chair" (Figure 4.03) or "boat" (Figure 4.04) forms. The chair form is the most stable, since all hydrogen atoms and carbon atoms are in the least hindered positions. In this structure the two carbon bonds not part of the ring are different. Those pointed up or down from the plane of the ring (parallel to the axis of the cycle) are called "axial" (Figure 4.03, "a") while those projecting out of the cycle

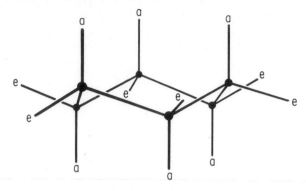

Fig. 4.03. "Chair."

Fig. 4.04. "Boat."

(at the equator of the cycle, so to speak) are called "equatorial" bonds (Figure 4.03, "e"). The geometry of substituted cyclohexanes is complex. Bulky groups, however, tend to assume equatorial positions which are least hindered. Therefore *trans*-1,4-cyclohexanedicarboxylic acid (Figure 4.06(a)) exists chiefly in the di-equatorial conformation, and is more stable and higher-melting than its *cis*-isomer. On the other hand, *cis*-1,3-cyclohexanedicarboxylic acid (Figure 4.06(b)), which also exists chiefly in the di-equatorial conformation, is more stable and higher-melting than its *trans*-isomer. The three-dimensional shape of molecules is important in understanding their properties. The field of "conformational analysis" has recently developed as chemists have found methods for determining the shape of molecules.

Reactions of the olefins

In the paraffins a substitution reaction involves breaking a carbon-hydrogen bond. This reaction takes place with difficulty and requires

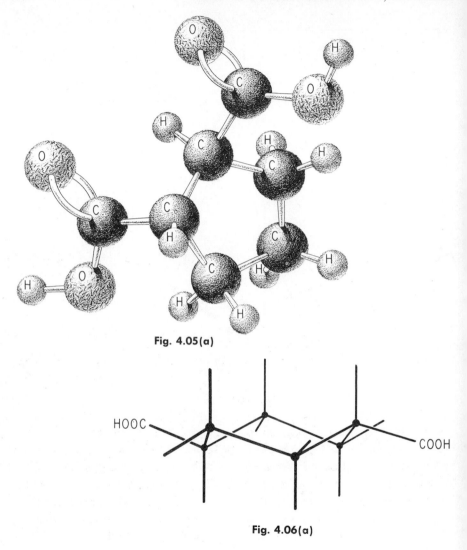

Fig. 4.05(a)

HOOC

COOH

Fig. 4.06(a)

high temperatures or activating light. The carbon-to-carbon double bond, on the other hand, is rather readily attacked by a number of reagents which simply add to it to form a new product, the sum of whose atoms is equal to those in the olefin plus the reagent.

$$-\overset{|}{C}=\overset{|}{C}- + A-B \longrightarrow -\overset{|}{\underset{A}{C}}-\overset{|}{\underset{B}{C}}-$$

Such reactions are called *addition reactions,* and are characteristic of unsaturated compounds.

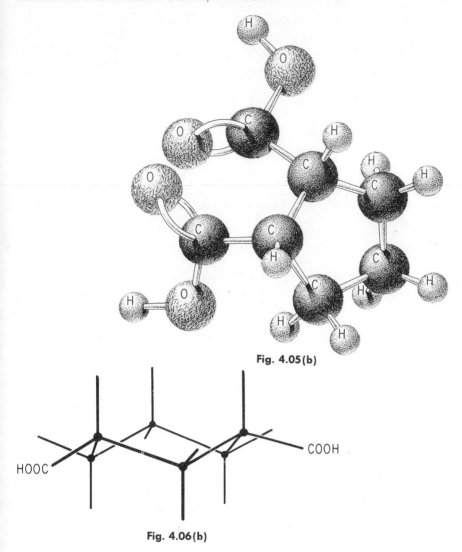

Fig. 4.05(b)

Fig. 4.06(b)

1. *Addition of Hydrogen.* In the presence of catalysts, hydrogen adds to the olefins to form the paraffins (see p. 40):

4.01 $R—CH=CH—R + H_2 \xrightarrow{\text{cat.}} R—CH_2—CH_2—R$

2. *Addition of Halogens.* Bromine adds rapidly to olefins. Ethylene, for example, forms 1,2-dibromoethane by this process.

4.02 $CH_2=CH_2 + Br_2 \longrightarrow BrCH_2CH_2Br$

The product, ethylene dibromide, may be added to leaded gasoline to prevent the accumulation of lead in the engine. Bromine solutions are rapidly decolorized by olefins, and this reaction may be used to test for the presence of the double bond. Chlorine also adds readily to the olefins, but iodine does not. Fluorine adds rapidly, but also reacts simultaneously by substitution, so that the products are very complex.

4.03 $R{-}CH{=}CH{-}R + X_2 \longrightarrow R{-}CHX{-}CHX{-}R$ X = Cl or Br

3. *Addition of the Hydrohalides.* Hydrogen chloride (the dry gas) adds readily to the double bond to form the monochloride.

4.04 $CH_3CH{=}CHCH_3 + HCl \longrightarrow CH_3CH_2CHClCH_3$

Hydrogen bromide adds even more readily, and hydrogen iodide most readily.

4.05 $CH_2{=}CH_2 + HI \longrightarrow CH_3CH_2I$

(This is the first good method presented for the introduction of an iodine atom into the organic molecule.) Hydrogen fluoride also adds in this way.

4.06 $R{-}CH{=}CH{-}R + HX \longrightarrow R{-}CH_2{-}CHX{-}R$

X = F, Cl, Br, or I

4. *Addition of Sulfuric Acid.* Olefins are soluble in concentrated sulfuric acid, reacting to form alkyl hydrogen sulfates. Ethylene, for example, forms ethyl hydrogen sulfate.

4.07 $CH_2{=}CH_2 + HOSO_2OH \longrightarrow CH_3CH_2OSO_2OH$

Note that the ethylene adds hydrogen to one end of the double bond and the hydrogen sulfate radical to the other, sulfuric acid adding as $H{-}OSO_2OH$. The alkyl hydrogen sulfates are chiefly valuable because the lower members of the series react rapidly with water to form alcohols.

4.08 $R{-}OSO_2OH + H_2O \longrightarrow R{-}OH + HOSO_2OH$

Thus, ethylene can be converted to ethanol by simply dissolving it in concentrated sulfuric acid, and then pouring the mixture into water.

4.09 $CH_2{=}CH_2 \xrightarrow{HOSO_2OH} CH_3CH_2OSO_2OH \xrightarrow{HOH} CH_3CH_2OH$

This reaction has proved very useful in the manufacture of alcohols from petroleum. The higher-molecular-weight alkyl hydrogen sulfates are not readily hydrolyzed in water, but form strong water-soluble acids whose salts are useful detergents (see p. 187).

5. *Addition of Hypochlorous Acid.* This acid has the formula H—O—Cl, but unlike sulfuric acid it adds to alkenes as if it were chlorine hydroxide, Cl—OH, with the bond between the chlorine and oxygen atoms being broken. With ethylene, the product is 2-chloro-

4.10 $$CH_2{=}CH_2 + HOCl \longrightarrow HOCH_2CH_2Cl$$

ethanol, or ethylene chlorohydrin, used in the manufacture of antifreeze solutions for car radiators.

6. *Addition of Sulfur Dichloride.* Sulfur dichloride, SCl_2, adds readily to olefins in two steps, first as Cl—SCl to form a chloroalkylsulfenyl chloride, which still has a reactive S—Cl bond. Further addition to more olefin can occur to yield a chloroalkyl sulfide. Ethylene reacts with sulfur dichloride to give *mustard gas,* a powerful lachrymator (tear gas) and vessicant (causes blisters).

4.11 $$CH_2{=}CH_2 + SCl_2 \longrightarrow ClCH_2CH_2SCl \xrightarrow{C_2H_4} ClCH_2CH_2{-}S{-}CH_2CH_2Cl$$

mustard gas

Markovnikov's Rule. In reactions 3, 4, 5, and 6, the addition reagent is unsymmetrical. The two parts of the reagent that add to either end of the double bond are different, and consist of a positive end and a negative end (Figure 4.07).

If the olefin to which these reagents add is also unsymmetrical, two isomers may be formed, i.e.,

+	−		
H	X	$CH_3CH{=}CH_2 + HBr \longrightarrow$	4.12
		$CH_3CH_2CH_2Br$ and/or $CH_3CHBrCH_3$	
H	OSO_2OH	$CH_3CH{=}CH_2 + HOSO_2OH \longrightarrow$	4.13
		$CH_3CH_2CH_2OSO_2OH + CH_3{-}\underset{\underset{OSO_2OH}{\mid}}{CH}{-}CH_3$	
Cl	OH	$CH_3CH{=}CH_2 + HOCl \longrightarrow$	4.14
		$CH_3CHClCH_2OH + CH_3CHOHCH_2Cl$	
ClS	Cl	$CH_3CH{=}CH_2 + SCl_2 \longrightarrow$	4.15
Fig. 4.07		$CH_3CH(SCl)CH_2Cl + CH_3CHClCH_2SCl$	

It is found in experiments that both isomers are formed in all cases, but the second always predominates. Thus, hydrogen bromide reacts with propylene to give a mixture of about 90 per cent 2-bromopropane and 10 per cent 1-bromopropane, while isobutylene reacts with concentrated sulfuric acid to give nearly 100 per cent of 2-methyl-2-propyl hydrogen sulfate.

4.16

$$CH_3-\underset{\underset{CH_3}{|}}{C}{=}CH_2 + HOSO_2OH \longrightarrow CH_3-\underset{\underset{CH_3}{|}}{\overset{\overset{CH_3}{|}}{C}}-OSO_2OH$$

A study of a large number of such reactions led the Russian scientist Markovnikov to propose an empirical rule by which it is possible to predict the main product of the reaction of unsymmetrical reagents. *When an unsymmetrical addition reagent adds to an unsymmetrical olefin, the most positive part of the reagent adds to the carbon of the double bond which has the most hydrogens.* For example, when hydrogen iodide adds to 2-methyl-1-butene, hydrogen, the positive part of the reagent, will add to carbon atom 1, which already has two hydrogens, while iodine, the negative end of the reagent, adds to carbon atom 2, which has no hydrogens, to form nearly pure 2-methyl-2-iodobutane.

4.17

$$CH_3CH_2\underset{\underset{CH_3}{|}}{C}{=}CH_2 + HI \longrightarrow CH_3CH_2-\underset{\underset{I}{|}}{\overset{\overset{CH_3}{|}}{C}}-CH_3 + CH_3CH_2\overset{\overset{CH_3}{|}}{C}H-CH_2I$$

more than 99%   less than 1%

In hypochlorous acid, chlorine, with an oxidation number $+1$, is the most positive part and this reagent will add to 1-butene to form as the chief product 1-chloro-2-butanol.

4.18 $CH_3CH_2CH{=}CH_2 + HOCl \longrightarrow CH_3CH_2CHOHCH_2Cl$

An unusual effect is observed when peroxides are used as catalysts in the addition of hydrogen bromide to unsymmetrical olefins. In this case the Markovnikov rule is just reversed, and propylene, for example, forms as the main product 1-bromopropane. This is known as the *peroxide effect.*

4.19 $CH_3-CH{=}CH_2 + HBr \xrightarrow{\ -O-O-\ } CH_3-CH_2-CH_2-Br$

Mechanism of addition to olefins

The carbon-carbon double bond is rich in electrons, since it is formed by two pairs of electrons, while an ordinary carbon-carbon bond (*sigma* bond) requires only one pair. The second pair of electrons (called the *pi*-bond pair) is available for reaction with electron-seeking (electrophilic) reagents. These may be positive ions or electron-poor reagents, which complete the octet by sharing the two electrons of the *pi*-bond. The electron-seeking reagent may be a neutral radical, which can complete its octet by sharing one electron of the *pi*-bond.

$$A^+ + \overset{\displaystyle}{C} \!:\! C \longrightarrow A-\overset{|}{\underset{|}{C}}-\overset{|}{\underset{|}{C}}{}^+ \qquad R\!\cdot + \overset{\displaystyle}{C} \!\cdot\!\cdot\! C \longrightarrow R-\overset{|}{\underset{|}{C}}-\overset{|}{\underset{|}{C}}\cdot$$

The addition of bromine to ethylene is ionic. Bromine is slightly ionized to very reactive electrophilic bromonium ions and bromide

4.20
$$:\!\overset{..}{\underset{..}{Br}}\!:\!\overset{..}{\underset{..}{Br}}\!: \rightleftharpoons \; :\!\overset{..}{\underset{..}{Br}}{}^+ + :\!\overset{..}{\underset{..}{Br}}\!:^-$$

ions. Bromonium ion attacks the *pi*-bond of ethylene, forming a complex which is partially stabilized by formation of a three-membered positively charged ring, the cyclic bromonium ion. Bromide ion can now attack the cyclic bromonium ion at the more electrophilic carbon atoms, producing 1,2-dibromoethane. Experiments have been carried

4.21
$$\begin{array}{c} H_2C \\ \overset{..}{\underset{..}{\shortparallel}} \\ H_2C \end{array} + :\!\overset{..}{\underset{..}{Br}}{}^+ \rightleftharpoons \left[\begin{array}{c} H_2C \\ | \;\;:\!\overset{..}{\underset{..}{Br}}\!: \\ H_2C \end{array} \right]^+ \rightleftharpoons \begin{array}{c} H_2C \\ | \; + \;\overset{..}{\underset{..}{Br}} \\ H_2C \end{array}$$

cyclic
bromonium ion

4.22
$$Br^- + \begin{array}{c} H_2C \\ | \; + \;\overset{..}{\underset{..}{Br}} \\ H_2C \end{array} \longrightarrow BrCH_2CH_2Br$$

out which confirm this suggested mechanism. For example, the second step involves attack on the cyclic bromonium ion by a negative ion. Therefore any negative ion should participate in the reaction. If the addition of bromine to ethylene is carried out in aqueous solution containing a high concentration of chloride ion, the products include dibromoethane, 1-bromo-2-chloroethane, and 2-bromoethanol. Since the solution contains three different negative groups (nucleophilic reagents)—bromide ion, chloride ion, or water—they may all attack cyclic bromonium ions, giving the different products.

4.23
$$:\!\overset{..}{\underset{..}{Cl}}\!:^- + \begin{array}{c} H_2C \\ | \; + \;Br \\ H_2C \end{array} \longrightarrow ClCH_2CH_2Br$$

4.24
$$H_2\overset{..}{O}: + \begin{array}{c} H_2C \\ | \; + \;Br \\ H_2C \end{array} \longrightarrow \left[H-\overset{+}{\underset{|}{O}}-CH_2CH_2Br \atop H \right] \longrightarrow HOCH_2CH_2Br + H^+$$

In the addition of hydrohalides, the proton forms a complex with the olefin, but because hydrogen has no extra electrons, the complex cannot form a ring, but instead is in equilibrium with two carbonium ions:

$$
4.25 \quad
\begin{array}{c} RCH \\ \parallel \\ H_2C \end{array} + HX \rightleftharpoons
\left[\begin{array}{c} RCH \\ \parallel \\ H_2C \end{array} \leftarrow H^+ \right] \rightleftharpoons
\left[\begin{array}{cc} RCH_2 & R\overset{+}{C}H \\ | & | \\ H_2C^+ & CH_3 \end{array} \right] + X^-
$$

The negatively charged halide ion can now attack either carbonium ion forming the alkyl halide. The major product will be produced from the most stable carbonium ion, which will exist in highest concentration in the equilibrium mixture. The nature of R— will affect the stability of the carbonium ions. Since alkyl groups are electron-releasing (+ inductive effect), each additional alkyl group attached to a carbonium ion stabilizes it. Therefore the order of stability of carbonium ions is III° > II° > I°.

$$
\begin{array}{c}
CH_3 \\ \downarrow \\
CH_3 \rightarrow \overset{+}{C} \\ \uparrow \\
CH_3
\end{array}
\quad > \quad
CH_3 \rightarrow \overset{+}{C}H \leftarrow CH_3
\quad > \quad
CH_3 \rightarrow CH_2^+
$$

$$\text{III°} \qquad\qquad \text{II°} \qquad\qquad \text{I°}$$

Notice that addition of hydrogen bromide to propylene involves equilibrium between a secondary propyl carbonium ion and a primary propyl carbonium ion. The major product arises from the former. This explains the Markovnikov rule.

$$
4.26 \quad
\begin{array}{c} CH_3 \rightarrow CH \\ \parallel \\ CH_2 \end{array} + HBr \longrightarrow
\left[\begin{array}{cc}
CH_3 \rightarrow \overset{+}{C}H & CH_3 \rightarrow CH_2 \\
\uparrow & \downarrow \\
CH_3 & CH_2^+
\end{array} \right]
$$

$$
\xrightarrow{\;Br^-\;} CH_3CHBrCH_3 + CH_3CH_2CH_2Br
$$

$$90\% \qquad\qquad 10\%$$

The peroxide effect is caused by a change in the mechanism of the addition of hydrogen bromide to unsymmetrical olefins. In this case, peroxides initiate a chain reaction (p. 38), and the controlling factor leading to predominantly primary bromide is the increased stability of secondary carbon free radicals.

Initiating:

$$1a. \quad ROOR \longrightarrow 2\,RO\cdot$$
$$1b. \quad RO\cdot + HBr \longrightarrow ROH + Br\cdot$$

Propagating:

2a. $CH_3CH{=}CH_2 + Br\cdot \longrightarrow CH_3\overset{\cdot}{C}HCH_2Br$

2b. $CH_3\overset{\cdot}{C}HCH_2Br + HBr \longrightarrow CH_3CH_2CH_2Br + Br\cdot$

etcetera

Other olefin reactions

7. *Addition of Carbon Monoxide and Hydrogen.* In the presence of certain cobalt catalysts, olefins add carbon monoxide and hydrogen at high pressure.

4.27 $CH_3(CH_2)_4CH{=}CH_2 + CO + H_2 \xrightarrow[\text{4000 psi}]{150^\circ C} CH_3(CH_2)_6CHO$

This reaction is of great industrial importance, since it provides a way of converting olefins from petroleum cracking into useful organic compounds, such as acids and alcohols. The reaction is known as the *oxo* reaction. The carbon monoxide-hydrogen gas mixture is readily available from coke and steam (the "water gas" reaction).

4.28 $C + H_2O \xrightarrow{1000^\circ C} CO + H_2$

8. *Oxidation.* The alkenes are flammable, burning in air with a slightly yellow flame to form carbon dioxide and water. With chemical oxidizing agents in aqueous solution they are initially converted to *glycols* (1,2-diols), but usually the glycols are further oxidized and the reaction becomes complex. However, this reaction has proved useful as a test for unsaturation. Cold dilute potassium permanganate solution oxidizes an olefin, and the permanganate is reduced to *manganese dioxide,* which can be seen in the solution as a brown precipitate.

4.29
$$3\,CH_2{=}CH_2 + 2\,KMnO_4 + 4\,H_2O \longrightarrow$$
$$3\,HOCH_2CH_2OH + \underline{2\,MnO_2} + 2\,KOH$$

This is known as *Baeyer's test* for unsaturation.

Ozonolysis is useful in determining the structure of olefins. An olefin will react with ozone in acetic acid solution to form an unstable *ozonide.* The ozonides are not usually isolated, since they may explode. Instead, they may be further oxidized with hydrogen peroxide to form acids or reduced with zinc to form aldehydes and/or ketones. For example, 2-butene could be converted into either ethanol or ethanoic acid in this way.

$$CH_3CH{=}CHCH_3 \xrightarrow[HOAc]{O_3}$$

4.30
$$\left[CH_3HC \underset{O-O}{\overset{O}{\diagup\diagdown}} CHCH_3 \right] \begin{array}{c} \xrightarrow[HOAc]{H_2O_2} 2\ CH_3COOH + H_2O \\[2ex] \xrightarrow[Zn/HOAc]{H_2} 2\ CH_3CHO + H_2O \end{array}$$

ozonide

An olefin having the formula C_6H_{12} may have 13 different possible structures. A chemist was given a pure sample of a low-boiling oil which decolorized a solution of bromine in carbon tetrachloride, gave a positive Baeyer's test, and had the formula C_6H_{12}. He ozonized the oil and reduced the ozonized solution with zinc dust. From the solution he isolated two compounds, propanal and propanone.

4.31
$$C_6H_{12} \xrightarrow[HOAc]{O_3} \xrightarrow[Zn/HOAc]{H_2} CH_3CH_2CHO + CH_3\overset{\overset{\displaystyle O}{\|}}{C}CH_3$$

From this he concluded that his original sample must have been 2-methyl-2-pentene. Can you follow his reasoning?

9. *Addition Polymerization.* When ethylene is treated with the proper catalysts, such as peroxides, it will add to itself by a chain reaction to form long chains of ethylene units. Sometimes there are as many as 800 ethylene units in a chain. This mixture of *polyethylene* (many ethylene) molecules is used in the manufacture of many useful plastic articles, such as nonbreakable glasses, transparent vegetable packages, "squeeze" bottles for drugs and cosmetics, and shower curtains (see Figure 4.08). This *addition polymerization* is characteristic of compounds possessing the double bond, and many olefins and substituted olefins can be polymerized to form useful *polymers* of different properties (Chapter 18).

4.32
$$x \quad R{-}CH{=}CH_2 \xrightarrow{\text{cat.}} (-CH{-}CH_2{-})x$$
$$\underset{R}{|}$$

polymer

Preparation of the olefins

The major industrial source of the olefins, such as ethylene, propylene, and the butylenes, is the "cracking" of petroleum (see p. 89) which yields a mixture of olefins and paraffins. In the laboratory, the

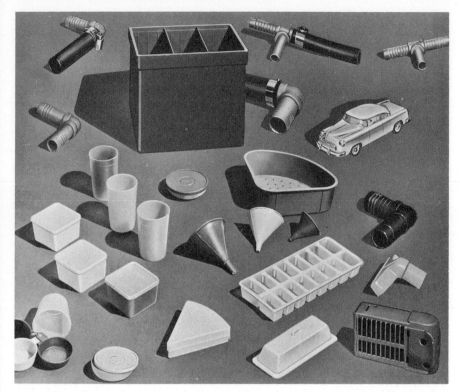

Fig. 4.08. A few examples of the many articles that can be molded from polyethylene. (Courtesy of Koppers Co., Inc.)

pure olefins are best prepared by the elimination reaction, i.e. removing from some other molecule the elements of water, halogen, or hydrohalide. This is accomplished by treating the compound with a reagent or conditions which will favor elimination of these small molecules.

1. *Dehydration of Alcohols.* When alcohols are heated to high temperatures in the presence of certain catalysts, such as alumina, or are treated with dehydrating agents, such as concentrated sulfuric acid, they lose the elements of water and form olefins.

4.33
$$H{-}\overset{\displaystyle H}{\underset{\boxed{H}}{C}}{-}\overset{\displaystyle H}{\underset{\boxed{OH}}{C}}{-}H \xrightarrow[350°]{Al_2O_3} CH_2{=}CH_2 + H_2O$$

4.34

$$CH_3-CH=CH-CH_3 + CH_2=CH-CH_2-CH_3$$
$$\quad\quad 80\% \quad\quad\quad\quad\quad\quad 20\%$$

Notice that in the second example, elimination may occur with hydrogen atoms on either carbon next to the hydroxylated carbon, but that the methylenic hydrogen is favored over the methyl hydrogen. In general, a correlary of the Markovnikov rule may be stated, "The more hydrogens attached to a carbon atom, the less easily is one lost." The order of ease of removal of hydrogen atoms is then:

$$\underset{\text{III}^\circ}{R-\underset{\underset{H}{|}}{\overset{\overset{R}{|}}{C}}-R} > \underset{\text{II}^\circ}{R-\underset{\underset{H}{|}}{CH}-R} > \underset{\text{I}^\circ}{R-\underset{\underset{H}{|}}{CH_2}}$$

2. *Loss of Hydrohalide.* In a very similar reaction, when organic halides are heated strongly or treated with strong bases, such as potassium hydroxide in alcohol solution, they lose the elements of the hydrohalide to form the olefin.

4.35

$$R-\underset{\underset{H}{|}}{CH}-\underset{\underset{Br}{|}}{CH_2} \xrightarrow{\text{alc.}}{\text{KOH}} R-CH=CH_2 + HBr$$
$$\qquad\qquad\qquad\qquad \hookrightarrow + KOH \longrightarrow KBr + H_2O$$

The hydrohalide is removed from the reaction by neutralization by the base. Iodine is more easily removed than bromine, which is more easily removed than chlorine. Like the hydrogens, a tertiary halogen is more easily removed than a secondary, which is more easily removed than a primary. Thus a III° iodine atom is much more easily removed than a I° chlorine atom. Indeed, tert-butyl iodide (2-methyl-2-iodopropane) forms isobutylene and hydrogen iodide by simply boiling in water.

4.36

$$CH_3-\underset{\underset{I}{|}}{\overset{\overset{CH_3}{|}}{C}}-CH_3 \xrightarrow{\text{boil}}{H_2O} CH_2=C(CH_3)_2 + HI$$

As with the alcohols, when elimination can occur in more than one way, a mixture of olefins will be formed.

3. *Elimination of Halogens.* When halogen atoms are present on adjacent carbons, they may be removed by heating the compound in the presence of powdered zinc. This reaction has the advantage of always locating the double bond in only one position without the formation of mixtures, but the vicinal dihalides are usually formed from the olefins, so that it is not a practical preparative method. Notice that all the above preparative methods are reversals of addition reactions of the olefins.

4.37 $CH_3—\underset{\underset{Br}{|}}{CH}—\underset{\underset{Br}{|}}{CH}—CH_3 + Zn \longrightarrow CH_3—CH=CH—CH_3 + ZnBr_2$

Polyenes

When more than one double bond is present in the same molecule, these bonds may have an influence on each other which changes their reactivity. This is especially true if the double bonds are close together. When both bonds are on the same carbon atom, we have a highly reactive unstable system of *cumulated* double bonds called *allenes*. On the other hand, when the double bonds are several carbon atoms apart, they react quite normally as individual double bonds, and are said to be *isolated.* The most interesting systems of double bonds are those which alternate with single bonds; these are said to be *conjugated,* and they undergo a special kind of addition.

$CH_2=C=CH_2$ $CH_2=CH—CH=CH_2$ $CH_2=CH—CH_2—CH_2—CH=CH_2$
cumulated   conjugated   isolated
allene   1,3-butadiene   biallyl

When 1,3-butadiene is allowed to react with less than half the amount of bromine required to saturate it, the principal product is found to be 1,4-dibromo-2-butene. The double bond has shifted into the middle of the molecule, with addition occurring at each end. This is called *1,4-addition,* and is characteristic of conjugated systems.

4.38 $CH_2=CH—CH=CH_2 + Br_2 \longrightarrow BrCH_2—CH=CH—CH_2Br$

This is easily explained in terms of the mechanism given (p. 58) for addition to olefins. Bromonium ion complexes with the conjugated diene to form a five-membered positively charged ionic ring. Attack by the negative bromide then leads to the 1,4-adduct.

4.39
$$\begin{array}{c} HC\!\!=\!\!CH_2 \\ \overset{\curvearrowleft}{} \\ HC\!\!=\!\!CH_2 \end{array} + :\overset{..}{\underset{..}{Br}}{}^+ \longleftrightarrow \left[\begin{array}{c} \quad\quad CH_2 \\ HC\diagup \quad\diagdown \\ \parallel \quad\quad + \quad Br \\ HC\diagdown \quad\diagup \\ \quad\quad CH_2 \end{array} \right] \overset{:\overset{..}{Br}:^-}{\longrightarrow} BrCH_2CH\!\!=\!\!CHCH_2Br$$

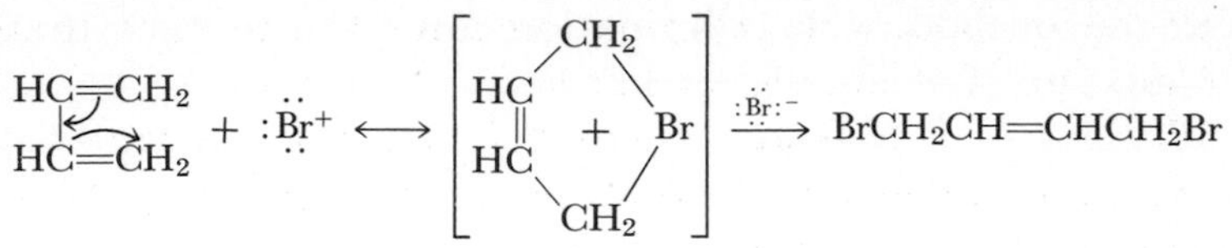

Hydrohalides also add 1,4- to conjugated systems. In this case the carbonium ion intermediate is stabilized by resonance. The chief product is the result of reaction of the attacking ion with the more reactive primary carbonium end of the resonating system.

4.40
$$\begin{array}{c} HC\!\!=\!\!CH_2 \\ | \\ HC\!\!=\!\!CH_2 \end{array} + H^+ \longrightarrow$$

$$\left[CH_3\!\!-\!\!\underset{+}{CH}\!\!-\!\!\overset{\frown}{CH}\!\!=\!\!CH_2 \longleftrightarrow CH_3\!\!-\!\!CH\!\!=\!\!\overset{\frown}{CH}\!\!-\!\!CH_2{}^+ \right]$$

$$\overset{X^-}{\longrightarrow} CH_3\underset{\underset{X}{|}}{C}H\!\!-\!\!CH\!\!=\!\!CH_2 + CH_3CH\!\!=\!\!CH\!\!-\!\!CH_2X$$

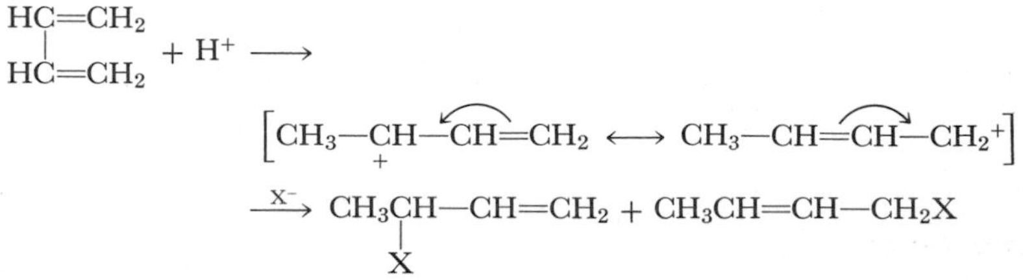

Conjugated olefins polymerize also by 1,4-addition, forming useful polymers having one double bond per monomer unit. An important

4.41 $n\,CH_2\!\!=\!\!CH\!\!-\!\!CH\!\!=\!\!CH_2 \longrightarrow (\!-\!CH_2\!\!-\!\!CH\!\!=\!\!CH\!\!-\!\!CH_2\!-\!)n$

monomer unit of this type which occurs widely distributed in nature is *isoprene* (2-methyl-1,3-butadiene). Isoprene occurs as a structural

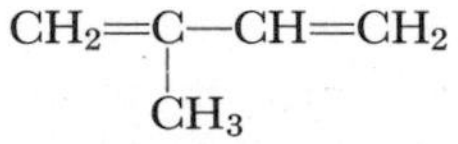

$$CH_2\!\!=\!\!\underset{\underset{CH_3}{|}}{C}\!\!-\!\!CH\!\!=\!\!CH_2$$

isoprene

unit in *rubber* (Chapter 6), turpentine oils, vitamins, hormones, plant coloring matter, etc. For example, *lycopene,* the red plant pigment of tomatoes, $C_{40}H_{56}$, is a polyene of the following structure:

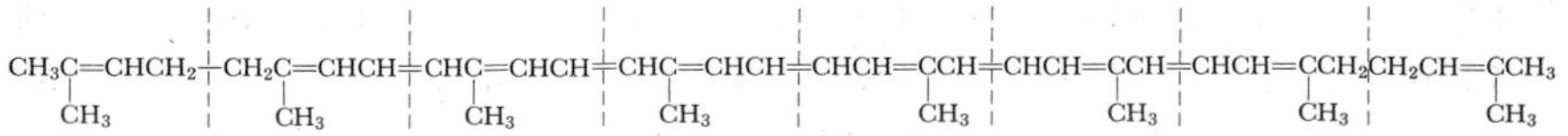

$$CH_3\underset{\underset{CH_3}{|}}{C}\!\!=\!\!CHCH_2\!\!+\!\!CH_2\underset{\underset{CH_3}{|}}{C}\!\!=\!\!CHCH\!\!+\!\!CH\underset{\underset{CH_3}{|}}{C}\!\!=\!\!CHCH\!\!+\!\!CH\underset{\underset{CH_3}{|}}{C}\!\!=\!\!CHCH\!\!+\!\!CHCH\!\!=\!\!\underset{\underset{CH_3}{|}}{C}CH\!\!+\!\!CHCH\!\!=\!\!\underset{\underset{CH_3}{|}}{C}CH\!\!+\!\!CHCH\!\!=\!\!\underset{\underset{CH_3}{|}}{C}CH_2CH_2CH\!\!=\!\!\underset{\underset{CH_3}{|}}{C}CH_3$$

lycopene

Notice that it contains eight isoprene carbon skeletons. The intense color is characteristic of the extensive conjugated bond system.

THE ALKYNES

Acetylene, C_2H_2, is the simplest member of this series and is also the most useful. It burns with oxygen to form an extremely hot flame (2600°C), and is used in oxyacetylene torches. Its many reactions make it an important raw material for manufacturing organic chemicals. The higher members are commonly named as derivatives of acetylene (Table 4.02).

TABLE 4.02   NAMES OF SOME SIMPLE ACETYLENES

$HC\equiv CH$	Ethyne	Acetylene
$CH_3-C\equiv CH$	Propyne	Methylacetylene
$CH_3CH_2-C\equiv CH$	1-Butyne	Ethylacetylene
$CH_3-C\equiv C-CH_3$	2-Butyne	Dimethylacetylene

Reactions of acetylene

Acetylene has two separate types of reactivity. The triple bond is unsaturated and undergoes addition reactions even more readily than the double bond. The hydrogen atoms of acetylene are acidic, and can be easily substituted.

1. *Addition Reactions.* Acetylene adds hydrogen in the presence of catalysts at low pressure to form first ethylene, and finally ethane. Similarly, a limited amount of bromine or chlorine adds to form first the trans-1,2-dihaloethene, but with excess halogen, acetylene is completely saturated to the 1,1,2,2-tetrahaloethane. The hydrohalides add to acetylene stepwise also, forming first the haloethenes, and in a second step the 1,1-dihaloethanes. These reactions are illustrated by the following equations:

4.42 $HC\equiv CH + H_2 \xrightarrow{cat.} CH_2=CH_2 \xrightarrow{H_2} CH_3-CH_3$

4.43 $HC\equiv CH + Br_2 \longrightarrow BrCH=CHBr \xrightarrow{Br_2} CHBr_2CHBr_2$

4.44 $HC\equiv CH + HI \longrightarrow CH_2=CHI \xrightarrow{HI} CH_3CHI_2$

Notice that Markovnikov's rule applies to the second step in the last example so that the product is the 1,1-diiodoethane. This rule applies also in addition of unsymmetrical reagents to the unsymmetrical acetylenes. For example, the reaction of hydrogen bromide with propyne produces 2-bromopropene:

4.45 $CH_3-C\equiv CH + HBr \longrightarrow CH_3-\underset{\underset{Br}{|}}{C}=CH_2$

Since the triple bond is more reactive than the double bond, when both are present in the same molecule the triple bond reacts first. This, as well as the Markovnikov rule, is illustrated by the addition of hydrogen chloride to *vinylacetylene* (1-butene-3-yne) to yield *chloroprene* (2-chloro-

1,3-butadiene), useful in the production of the *elastomer* (synthetic rubber) neoprene (Chapter 18).

4.46 $CH_2=CH-C\equiv CH + HCl \longrightarrow CH_2=CH-\underset{\underset{Cl}{|}}{C}=CH_2$

vinylacetylene   chloroprene

Vinylacetylene is formed by the condensation of two molecules of acetylene in the presence of a copper catalyst. The reaction is essentially addition of one molecule of acetylene as the unsymmetrical reagent $H-C\equiv CH$ to the unsaturated triple bond of another molecule of acetylene.

4.47 $HC\equiv CH + HC\equiv CH \xrightarrow[\text{NH}_4\text{Cl}]{\text{Cu}_2\text{Cl}_2} H_2C=CH-C\equiv CH$

Acetylene adds hydrogen cyanide, in the presence of a basic catalyst, to form acrylonitrile (cyanoethene):

4.48 $HC\equiv CH + HCN \xrightarrow{\text{cat.}} H_2C=CH-CN$

acrylonitrile

This substance is an important industrial raw material for the manufacture of polymers.

Acetylene adds water in the presence of mercuric ions in dilute sulfuric acid, to form *ethenol,* an unstable substance which immediately rearranges to *ethanal* (the equilibrium between enols and carbonyls is

4.49 $HC\equiv CH + H_2O \xrightarrow[\text{Hg}^{++}]{6\% \text{ H}_2\text{SO}_4} [CH_2=CHOH] \longrightarrow CH_3CHO$

discussed on page 141). *Ethanal* is an important industrial intermediate in the preparation of many useful chemicals (p. 150). Even arsenic trichloride may be added to acetylene in the presence of a catalyst to form chlorovinylarsenic dichloride, called *lewisite,* a potent systemic

4.50 $HC\equiv CH + AsCl_3 \xrightarrow{\text{AlCl}_3} ClCH=CHAsCl_2$

poison gas. Acetylene reduces dilute neutral potassium permanganate solutions, giving the characteristic brown precipitate of a positive *Baeyer's* test.

2. *Substitution Reactions.* Acetylene undergoes reactions not found in the olefin series, the replacement of the reactive acidic hydrogens attached to carbon carrying the triple bond. With active metals, salts are formed with the liberation of hydrogen. With heavy metal ions,

4.51 $2\,C_2H_2 + 2\,Na \longrightarrow H_2 + 2\,HC\!\equiv\!CNa$

like silver, copper, and mercury, acetylene produces insoluble salts
which precipitate from aqueous solution and are extremely explosive
when dry. This reaction serves as a test for the functional group
—C≡C—H, which will form a precipitate with silver or cuprous ions
in ammonia solution. This precipitate should never be allowed to dry
in a waste-jar, sink, or test tube. It can be destroyed by dissolving it
in nitric acid.

4.52 $C_2H_2 + Ag_2O \xrightarrow[\text{sol.}]{NH_4OH} Ag_2C_2 + H_2O$

4.53 $H\!-\!C\!\equiv\!C\!-\!CH_3 + Cu_2Cl_2 \xrightarrow[\text{sol.}]{NH_4OH} Cu_2(C\!\equiv\!C\!-\!CH_3)_2 + 2\,HCl$

The sodium acetylides are reactive organo-metallic compounds,
and, like the Grignard reagents, undergo many interesting reactions.
They are most conveniently prepared by the reaction of acetylene with
sodamide in liquid ammonia, and their reactions are usually brought

4.54 $HC\!\equiv\!CH + NaNH_2 \xrightarrow[NH_3]{\text{liq}} HC\!\equiv\!C\!-\!Na + NH_3$

about in the same vessel and solvent, without isolation of the acetylide.
For example, when iodoethane is added to the liquid ammonia solution of sodium acetylide, ethylacetylene (1-butyne) is formed.

4.55 $H\!-\!C\!\equiv\!C\!-\!Na + I\!-\!CH_2CH_3 \xrightarrow{NH_3} H\!-\!C\!\equiv\!C\!-\!CH_2\!-\!CH_3 + NaI$

This reaction provides a useful method for preparing various acetylene
homologs.

4.56 $CH_3\!-\!C\!\equiv\!C\!-\!H \xrightarrow[NH_3]{NaNH_2} CH_3\!-\!C\!\equiv\!C\!-\!Na \xrightarrow[NH_3]{CH_3CH_2Br}$

$$CH_3\!-\!C\!\equiv\!C\!-\!CH_2\!-\!CH_3$$
$$\text{2-pentyne}$$

Preparation of acetylenes

The most useful general method involves the use of sodium acetylide and its derivatives, described above. Acetylene itself is commercially available in compressed-gas cylinders, or may be prepared by
the decomposition of calcium carbide with water. The calcium carbide
is obtained by strongly heating a mixture of coke and limestone in an
electric oven.

4.57 $CaCO_3 \xrightarrow{\text{heat}} CaO + CO_2$
               limestone   lime

4.58 $CaO + 3 C \xrightarrow{3000°} CaC_2 + CO$

4.59 $CaC_2 + 2 H_2O \longrightarrow C_2H_2 + Ca(OH)_2$
            "carbide"

Acetylene may also be obtained commercially by the partial oxidation of methane with oxygen. Methane and oxygen are rapidly passed through an electric arc (contact time 0.01 second) at 1500°C and the products quenched in a water spray. In addition to acetylene, carbon monoxide and hydrogen are produced. These are valuable in the oxo process (p. 61) or in the synthesis of methanol (p. 120).

4.60 $4 CH_4 + 3 O_2 \longrightarrow 2 C_2H_2 + 6 H_2O$

4.61 $2 CH_4 + O_2 \longrightarrow 2 CO + 4 H_2$

Elimination reactions may be used to introduce the triple bond. For example, when 1,2-dibromopropane is treated with alcoholic potassium hydroxide, two molecules of hydrogen bromide are eliminated from each molecule of dihalide, forming propyne. Note how this provides a method for converting the double bond into the triple bond:

4.62 $CH_3-\overset{\boxed{H}}{\underset{\boxed{Br}}{C}}-\overset{\boxed{Br}}{\underset{\boxed{H}}{C}}-H + 2 KOH \longrightarrow CH_3-C{\equiv}C-H + 2 KBr + 2 H_2O$

4.63 $R-CH{=}CH-R \xrightarrow{Br_2} RCHBrCHBrR \xrightarrow[KOH]{alc.} R-C{\equiv}C-R$

Study Questions

1. Define what the organic chemist means by unsaturation, addition, substitution, olefin, alkyne.

2. Write structural formulas for all of the isomers having the formula C_4H_8, and name each by the I.U.C. system. (There are six!)

3. What is meant by geometric isomerism? How many isomers of 2-pentene are there? How many isomers of 2,4-hexadiene are there?

4. Write structures for the products of the following reactions:

$$CH_2{=}CH_2 + Br_2 \longrightarrow$$
$$CH_3CH{=}CHCH_3 + HI \longrightarrow$$
$$CH_2{=}CH_2 + HOCl \longrightarrow$$
$$CH_2{=}CH_2 + H_2SO_4 \longrightarrow$$
$$CH_2{=}C(CH_3)_2 + H_2 \xrightarrow{cat.}$$

5. Show by equations all products of the reaction of propylene with hydrogen bromide, sulfuric acid, hypochlorous acid, and sulfur dichloride (SCl_2).

6. What is meant by Markovnikov's rule? Does it always hold true? If not, when does it not apply?

7. What is the principal product of the additions of hydrogen iodide, sulfuric acid, and hypochlorous acid to isobutylene?

8. What is meant by ozonolysis? Baeyer's test? The oxo reaction? Polymerization?

9. A sample of an olefin, C_6H_{12}, was treated with ozone in acetic acid, and then with powdered zinc. The only product isolated was propanone. What was the structure of the original compound?

10. In the preparation of pure 1-butene by dehydration of an alcohol with sulfuric acid, which is the better alcohol to use, 1-butanol or 2-butanol? Why?

11. Write the formulas of three hexadienes, one having a cumulated double-bond system, one a conjugated double-bond system, and one an isolated double-bond system.

12. Illustrate 1,4-addition by writing the products of the reaction of isoprene with bromine and with hydrogen iodide.

13. Show by equations how acetylene can be converted into: 1,1,2,2-tetrachloroethane, ethyl bromide, ethane, butane, ethanal.

14. What are the chief industrial uses of acetylene? How is it manufactured industrially?

15. Illustrate the reaction of acetylene with metals and metal ions. Of what practical use is this reaction?

Advanced Reading References

Essential Principles of Organic Chemistry, James Cason, Prentice-Hall, Inc., Englewood Cliffs, N. J., 1956, Chapters 7, 8, and 9.

Organic Chemistry, 3rd Ed., R. Q. Brewster and W. E. McEwen, Prentice-Hall, Inc., Englewood Cliffs, N. J., 1961, Chapters 3 and 4.

Chemistry of Organic Compounds, 2nd Ed., C. R. Noller, W. B. Saunders, Philadelphia, 1957, Chapters 3 and 7.

Advanced Organic Chemistry, E. Earl Royals, Prentice-Hall, Inc., Englewood Cliffs, N. J., 1954, Chapter 4.

new terms & concepts

Aromatic compounds occur in coal tar.
The properties of benzene, C_6H_6, require a new structural concept.
The original Kekule formula has been modified to a resonance hybrid.
Aromatic compounds are named as substituted benzenes.
Ortho-, meta-, and para-isomers can exist.
Addition reactions can occur, but substitution reactions are
most important in the aromatic series.
These reactions include nitration, sulfonation, halogenation, and Friedel-Crafts.
Aromatic rings are resistant to oxidation.
Substituents on aromatic compounds exhibit an orientation effect.
Meta-directing groups usually contain an unsaturated bond;
para-directing groups usually contain only single bonds.
Benzene is a major industrial raw material.
Carcinogenic hydrocarbons are aromatic compounds which can induce cancer in mice.

5

Aromatic hydrocarbons

When coal is heated in the absence of air, it is converted into coke, and a small quantity of *coal tar* is distilled out. This coal tar contains many important chemical compounds, and is processed to separate these. It is one of the principal sources of the hydrocarbon, *benzene,* and contains many of its homologs and relatives. Since these frequently have a pleasant odor, they have been classed as *aromatic* hydrocarbons. Benzene is the simplest member of this class.

Historically, benzene has been a classical puzzle in chemical structure which is not completely understood even today. Analysis and molecular weight determination show it to have the formula C_6H_6. It is a colorless liquid of aromatic odor, boiling at 80°C and freezing at 6°C. Benzene does not give a positive Baeyer's test, nor does it decolorize bromine water, both tests for unsaturation. It does react with bromine in the presence of a catalyst, such as iron or iodine, by *substitution:*

5.01 $$C_6H_6 + Br_2 \xrightarrow{\text{Fe}} C_6H_5Br + HBr$$

Only one isomer of bromobenzene, C_6H_5Br, exists, showing that all hydrogen atoms are equivalent. Try to arrange six carbon atoms, each with a valence of four, and six hydrogen atoms, each with a valence of one, into a molecule which does not contain a double or triple bond, and you will see the problem which the chemists had to solve.

Some light was shed on this problem by the discovery that under pressure in the presence of catalysts, chlorine could be made to *add* to benzene:

5.02 $$C_6H_6 + 3\,Cl_2 \longrightarrow C_6H_6Cl_6$$

Also, benzene could be reduced by hydrogen at several thousand pounds pressure over a catalyst to form the known compound, cyclohexane.

5.03
$$C_6H_6 + 3\,H_2 \xrightarrow[\text{1500 lb psi}]{\text{Ni}} H_2C\begin{array}{c} H_2C-CH_2 \\ \diagdown \quad \diagup \\ H_2C-CH_2 \end{array}CH_2$$

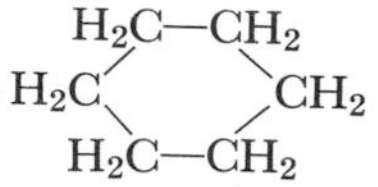

These facts suggested to Kekule, in 1865, that benzene could best be represented by a ring of six carbon atoms containing three conjugated double bonds. To explain the absence of unsaturated properties in such a molecule, Kekule assumed that in this conjugated system without reactive ends the double bonds could shift from position to position, and the true formula of benzene was then represented by a dynamic equilibrium between two static formulas:

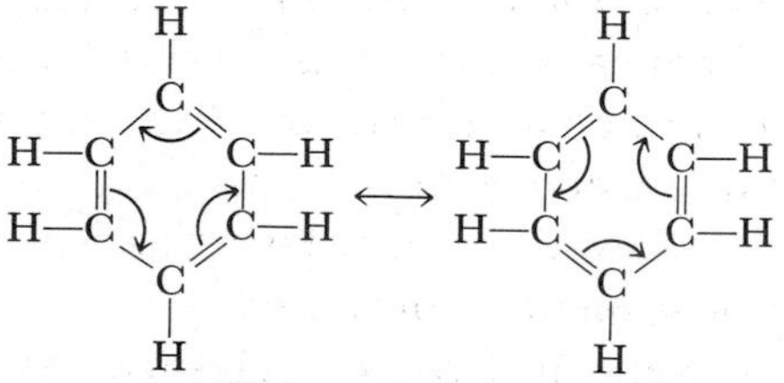

The curved arrows represent the movements of a pair of electrons from position to position. This phenomenon became known as *resonance*. The double bonds were assumed to be vibrating or *resonating* between two positions, and they were therefore never fixed long enough for an addition reagent to attack. The situation may be compared to a wheel with three spokes. When it is still, a stick may be easily thrust through it, but when it is spinning at a high rate, it becomes for all practical purposes a disc (Figure 5.01), and nothing can pass through it unless driven with great force at high speed. The spokes of the wheel are never in any specific position, but may be regarded as spread over the whole surface of the wheel. In the same way, the electrons of the double bonds in aromatic compounds (called *pi*-electrons) are spread over the circumference of the benzene rings, rather than being partly in one position and partly in the other.

It should not be assumed that at any given instant a single mole-

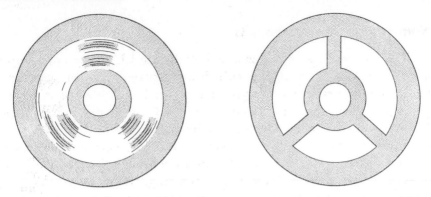

Fig. 5.01. The standing wheel is quite open, but the spinning wheel is impenetrable.

cule of benzene has one of the Kekule structures, above. Modern organic chemists believe all molecules of benzene are alike, and have a single structure. This structure is intermediate between the two Kekule structures. Instead of alternating single and double bonds in rapid motion, all bonds between carbon atoms in benzene are alike, and may be regarded as "one and one-half" bonds. Indeed this is borne out by measurement of the carbon-to-carbon bond distances in benzene, and by comparison of these bond distances to the known carbon-to-carbon double-bond distances, as in ethylene, and the carbon-to-carbon single-bond distance, as in ethane. Each carbon atom in benzene is 1.39 Å from its neighbor. In ethylene, the carbon atoms are 1.34 Å apart, while in ethane they are 1.55 Å apart. Therefore benzene is not composed of partly single and partly double bonds, but rather has an intermediate bond unique to aromatic compounds. Benzene is said to be a *resonance hybrid.* Wheland points out that while a mule is a hybrid of a horse and a donkey, a mule should not be regarded as a horse part of the time, and a donkey the rest of the time. In the same sense, benzene should not be regarded as partly in each of the Kekule formulas, but rather to have a *resonance hybrid* or *aromatic* structure.

$$\text{CH}-\text{CH}_2-\text{CH}_3$$
$$\text{CH}_3$$

benzene   2-phenylbutane

Chemists represent the benzene ring by a simple hexagon containing three double bonds, and the simple radical C_6H_5- is called *phenyl.* Since R— represents the alkyl radical, Ar— may be used to represent any aromatic radical.

Naming aromatic compounds

The common name benzene is used in the I.U.C. system. Simple alkyl derivatives are named as substituted benzenes, but in more complex cases the benzene ring may be indicated as a substituent by the name *phenyl* or substituted phenyl. Table 5.01 gives the common and I.U.C. names of some representative aromatic hydrocarbons.

Since all hydrogens in benzene are equivalent, when one is replaced the derivative formed need not be numbered since this automatically designates the number 1 carbon of the ring. When more than one hydrogen is substituted, the other substituents are assigned the lowest possible numbers—for example:

bromobenzene   1,3-dibromobenzene   1,2,4-tribromobenzene
              (meta-dibromobenzene)

When only two substituents are present, the trivial names may still be used without numbers by the designation of the positions by the prefixes, *ortho-*, *meta-*, and *para-*, for the 2-, 3-, and 4-positions, as in:

o-chlorotoluene   m-dinitrobenzene   p-bromostyrene

The student should notice the existence of isomers in the aromatic series also. For example, *o-*, *m-*, and *p*-xylene and ethylbenzene are all isomers of C_8H_{10}.

Physical properties of aromatic compounds

Most of these compounds have rather high boiling points, and are insoluble in water. The liquids are colorless, and the solids white. As the hydrocarbons increase in molecular weight, the boiling point increases. The boiling points of isomers are close together (compare *ortho-*, *meta-*, and *para*-xylene with ethylbenzene). The rule that the more symmetrical molecules melt higher is nicely illus-

TABLE 5.01   NAMES AND PHYSICAL CONSTANTS OF SOME COMMON AROMATIC HYDROCARBONS

Formula	Common name	I.U.C. name	M.P. °C	B.P. °C
	Benzene	Benzene	6	80
CH_3	Toluene	Methylbenzene	-95	111
CH_3 CH_3	*ortho*-Xylene	1,2-Dimethyl-benzene	-25	144
CH_3 CH_3	*meta*-Xylene	1,3-Dimethyl-benzene	-48	139
CH_3 CH_3	*para*-Xylene	1,4-Dimethyl-benzene	13	138
CH_2CH_3	Ethylbenzene	Ethylbenzene	-95	136
$CH=CH_2$	Styrene	Vinylbenzene	-30	145
CH_3 $CH(CH_3)_2$	Cymene	1-Methyl-4-isopropylbenzene	-69	175
	Biphenyl	Phenylbenzene	70	255
	Naphthalene	Naphthalene	80	218
	Anthracene	Anthracene	218	340
	Phenanthrene	Phenanthrene	100	340

trated in the aromatics series. Benzene, which is very symmetrical, melts 100°C higher than its next higher homolog, toluene. *Para*-xylene is more symmetrical than its isomer, ethylbenzene, and melts over 100° higher. Anthracene is more symmetrical than its isomer, phenanthrene, and melts more than 100° higher.

Reactions of benzene

Although the aromatic hydrocarbons under special vigorous conditions may undergo *addition* reactions, they most commonly react by substitution, usually in the presence of some catalyst, to replace one or more of the hydrogen atoms. For example, chlorine or bromine, in the presence of catalysts like iron or iodine, react with benzene to form the halobenzene.

5.04
$$C_6H_6 + Br_2 \xrightarrow{Fe} C_6H_5Br + HBr$$

The alkylbenzenes, like toluene, have two kinds of hydrogen atoms which may be substituted; the aromatic hydrogens are preferentially replaced by a halogen in the presence of a catalyst in the dark, while the hydrogens on the methyl group are aliphatic and therefore more easily replaced in sunlight.

5.05 $\langle\!\!\!\bigcirc\!\!\!\rangle$ $CH_3 + Br_2 \xrightarrow{Fe} CH_3\langle\!\!\!\bigcirc\!\!\!\rangle Cl + HCl$ (+ some *o*- and *m*-isomer)

5.06 $\langle\!\!\!\bigcirc\!\!\!\rangle$ $CH_3 + Cl_2 \xrightarrow{\text{sunlight}} \langle\!\!\!\bigcirc\!\!\!\rangle CH_2Cl + HCl$

Benzene is easily *nitrated*, with nitric acid in concentrated sulfuric acid, to form *nitrobenzene* (oil of mirbane), or *sulfonated*, in fuming sulfuric acid, to form *benzenesulfonic acid*.

5.07 $C_6H_5—H + HO—NO_2 \xrightarrow{\text{conc. } H_2SO_4} C_6H_5NO_2 + H_2O$

5.08 $C_6H_5—H + HO—SO_2OH \xrightarrow{\text{conc. } H_2SO_4} C_6H_5SO_2OH + H_2O$

Notice that in each case water is produced, and the reaction is promoted by the strong dehydrating agent, concentrated sulfuric acid.

Aromatic hydrocarbons react with alkyl halides in the presence of anhydrous aluminum chloride to form alkylated aromatic compounds. This useful reaction is known by the name of its discoverers, *Friedel* and *Crafts*, and has a wide application in organic syntheses.

5.09 $C_6H_5—H + Cl—CH_3 \xrightarrow{AlCl_3} C_6H_5—CH_3 + HCl$

5.10 $Ar—H + X—R \xrightarrow{AlCl_3} Ar—R + HX$

The alkylation reaction may also be accomplished, using an olefin as the alkylating agent, with aluminum chloride (compare "forming" process, p. 89).

5.11 $\langle\!\!\!\bigcirc\!\!\!\rangle$ $H + CH_2{=}C(CH_3)_2 \xrightarrow{AlCl_3}$ $\langle\!\!\!\bigcirc\!\!\!\rangle$ $-\overset{\displaystyle CH_3}{\underset{\displaystyle CH_3}{\overset{|}{\underset{|}{C}}}}-CH_3$

Notice that this is an *addition* of the aromatic hydrocarbon to the olefin.

The aromatic ring is very stable toward oxidizing conditions. Benzene, naphthalene, and other simple aromatic hydrocarbons burn with a very smoky flame, as a result of incomplete combustion. The ring is not oxidized by chemical oxidizing agents which will convert paraffins to carbon dioxide and water. When alkyl groups are present on aromatic rings, they may be oxidized to carboxyl groups by such reagents as alkaline potassium permanganate or dichromic acid solutions. Aromatic acids can be prepared in this way.

5.12

$$\text{C}_6\text{H}_5\text{—CH}_3 \xrightarrow[\substack{\text{K}_2\text{Cr}_2\text{O}_7 \\ \text{H}_2\text{SO}_4}]{\text{KMnO}_4/\text{OH}^- \text{ or}} \text{C}_6\text{H}_5\text{—COOH}$$

benzoic acid

Any and all side-chains are converted into carboxyl groups by this treatment. For example, ethylbenzene is also oxidized to benzoic acid, while its isomer, o-xylene, gives 1,2-dicarboxybenzene (phthalic acid).

5.13

$$\text{C}_6\text{H}_5\text{—CH}_2\text{CH}_3 \xrightarrow{\text{(ox.)}} \text{C}_6\text{H}_5\text{—COOH}$$

5.14

$$\text{C}_6\text{H}_4(\text{CH}_3)_2 \xrightarrow{\text{ox.}} \text{C}_6\text{H}_4(\text{COOH})_2$$

phthalic acid

Notice how this provides a method for distinguishing between the two isomers.

Orientation in substituted aromatic compounds

Attention has already been called to the fact that no matter which of the six hydrogen atoms on benzene is replaced, only one monosubstituted benzene is possible. On the other hand, if benzene is already substituted, three possible disubstituted benzenes may be obtained, depending on the relative position of the second substituent to the first. For example, bromination of benzene produces only bromobenzene, but bromination of toluene produces three isomers, o-, m-, and p-bromotoluene.

5.15

ortho-   meta-   para-

5.16

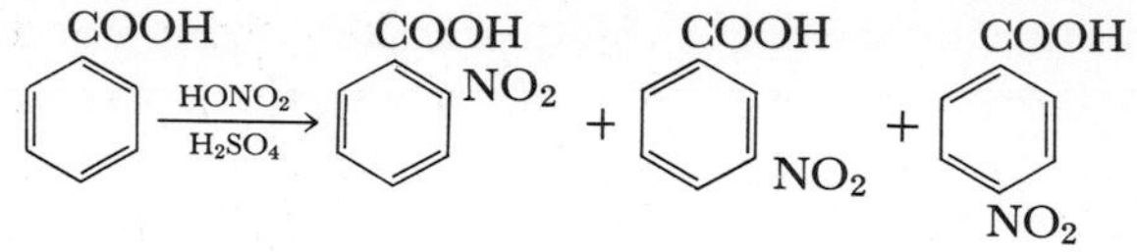

$$\text{COOH} \xrightarrow[\text{H}_2\text{SO}_4]{\text{HONO}_2} \text{COOH}-\text{NO}_2 + \text{COOH} \text{ }_{\text{NO}_2} + \text{COOH} \text{ }_{\text{NO}_2}$$

In the same way, nitration of benzoic acid produces a mixture of *o-, m-,* and *p*-nitrobenzoic acids. In a monosubstituted benzene there are five replaceable hydrogens, two *ortho-*, two *meta-*, and one *para-*. On the basis of chance alone, one would expect to obtain a mixture of 40 per cent *ortho-*, 40 per cent *meta-*, and 20 per cent *para*-bromotoluenes or nitrobenzoic acids in the above reactions. Laboratory experiments prove, however, that only one of the above isomers is formed in high concentration while the other two are present as impurities. Table 5.02 lists the percentage composition of isomers in the products of nitration of several monosubstituted benzenes. It is apparent that with toluene and the halobenzenes, the principal substitution product is the *para*-isomer, while nitrobenzene, benzoic acid, and benzenesulfonic acid yield chiefly the *meta*-substitution product. This must be due to the influence of the group already present on the ring, called the "orienting" influence.

TABLE 5.02   PER CENT COMPOSITION OF MONONITRO-PRODUCTS OF SOME SUBSTITUTED BENZENES

Substance nitrated	Formula	% ortho-	% meta-	% para-
Toluene	$CH_3-C_6H_4-NO_2$	35	5	60
Chlorobenzene	$Cl-C_6H_4-NO_2$	29	1	70
Bromobenzene	$Br-C_6H_4-NO_2$	36	1	63
Iodobenzene	$I-C_6H_4-NO_2$	40	1	59
Benzenesulfonic acid	$HOSO_2-C_6H_4-NO_2$	21	72	6
Benzoic acid	$HOOC-C_6H_4-NO_2$	12	83	5
Nitrobenzene	$NO_2-C_6H_4-NO_2$	7	93	0

Substituent functional groups on aromatic rings may be divided into two classes, those which are *para*-directors, and those which are *meta*-directing. The important *para*-directors usually make the ring more active than benzene to substitution. These are hydroxy (—OH), alkoxy (—OR), amino (—NH$_2$, —NR$_2$), alkyl (—R), and halogen (—X). The important *meta*-directors usually make the ring less active than benzene. These are nitro (—NO$_2$), sulfo (—SO$_2$OH), carboxy (—COOH), cyano (—CN), and keto (—COR). A simple empirical rule for remembering which groups are *meta*-directors is that these contain an unsaturated bond attached to the first atom of the group (—A=B), i.e.,

$$\overset{\overset{\text{O}}{\|}}{-\text{N}}=\text{O} \qquad \overset{\overset{\text{OH}}{|}}{-\text{S}}=\text{O} \qquad \overset{\overset{\text{OH}}{|}}{-\text{C}}=\text{O} \qquad -\text{C}\equiv\text{N} \qquad \overset{\overset{\text{R}}{|}}{-\text{C}}=\text{O}$$

When two groups are already present on the ring, they may supplement or hinder one another in their influence on a third entering substituent. For example, in the preparation of the explosive T.N.T. (trinitrotoluene), by the direct nitration of toluene, almost 100 per cent of the desired product is obtained, owing to the reinforcement of the directive effects of the methyl group by each entering nitro group (Eq. 5.17).

5.17

T.N.T.

Note that the first nitro group, entering the 4-position, directs the next group to the 2- and 6-positions, *meta* to itself, which is also *ortho* to the methyl group. Thus these two groups reinforce one another. In 2,4-dinitrotoluene, the replaceable hydrogens are at 3, 5, and 6. The methyl group, an *ortho-para* director, activates the 6-position. Each of the nitro groups, *meta*-directors, deactivates the 3- and 5-positions, thus forcing the third nitro group into the 6-position. The deactivating influence of the nitro groups is apparent from the increasing temperatures necessary to bring about the reactions.

Mechanism of aromatic substitution

Benzene contains 6 *pi*-electrons, not directly involved in bonding, which form a layer of negative charge on the faces of the benzene ring. To a lesser degree than olefins, benzene is susceptible to attack by electron-seeking (electrophilic) reagents. Bromine, for example, easily reacts to form bromobenzene. The bromonium ion is adsorbed on the face of the benzene ring forming a complex which decomposes by expulsion of a proton.

5.18

It has been shown that nitration occurs by way of the highly electrophilic nitronium ion formed when nitric and sulfuric acid are mixed. Alkylation involves attack on the aromatic ring by the highly electro-

5.19 $$HONO_2 + H_2SO_4 \longrightarrow NO_2^+ + H_2O + HSO_4^-$$

5.20 $$(CH_3)_2C{=}CH_2 + AlCl_3 \longrightarrow (CH_3)_2\overset{+}{C}{-}CH_2AlCl_3^-$$

philic carbonium ion formed when the catalyst, aluminum chloride, attacks the olefin.

Orientation effects are now readily understandable. The hydroxy group is a strong *para*-director which increases the ease of substitution. Oxygen has extra electrons, which may resonate with the *pi*-electrons of the ring, thus increasing the electron density on the ring. These electrons may be localized at the *ortho*- and *para*-positions, thus enhancing these sites to attack by an electrophilic (positively charged) reagent. Note that a positively charged agent is most apt to attack as far away from the positively charged oxygen as possible (i.e., in the

para-position). Similar arguments can be made for ethers, amines, and halogens, all of which have extra unshared electrons which can resonate with the *pi*-electrons, and all of which are *para*-directing groups.

Meta-directors deactivate the ring to electrophilic attack by withdrawal of electrons. These groups usually contain a double bonded electronegative atom such as oxygen, which tends to pull electrons away from the ring, thus decreasing the electron-density and making the ring less susceptible to attack by positively charged agents. Since the electrons at the *ortho*- and *para*-positions are most affected, any reaction which does occur is usually at a *meta*-position, which cannot bear a positive charge.

Similar resonance structures can be written for other *meta*-directors, like the carboxylic group, ketones, or cyano groups.

Some important aromatic hydrocarbons

Benzene is by far the most important aromatic compound. About 300 million gallons are produced annually, both from coal tar and by the hydroforming process (see Chapter 6). Although benzene has some use as an industrial solvent, it is used chiefly as a raw material for the manufacture of plastics, drugs, dyes, and explosives. The major products from benzene are styrene (plastics, synthetic rubber), phenol (plastics, drugs), and aniline (dyes and drugs).

Toluene, ethylbenzene, and cymene are used in motor fuels. Naphthalene has a characteristic odor, and is used as an industrial germicide and antiseptic, as well as in moth balls. Naphthalene has a

naphthalene

fused aromatic ring system, meaning that two carbons are shared between the two rings. It is present in high concentration in coal tar, which is its chief source. *Toluene* and *xylene* are frequently used as preservatives for urine and saliva samples for clinical laboratory tests.

Certain polycyclic hydrocarbons found in soot and tar are known to cause skin cancer in mice when painted on the skin for long periods.

Three of the most active of these carcinogenic hydrocarbons are shown below.

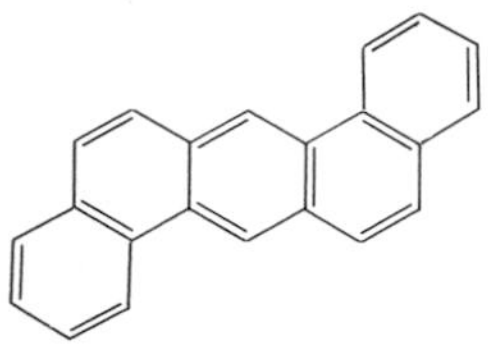

1,2,5,6-dibenzanthracene 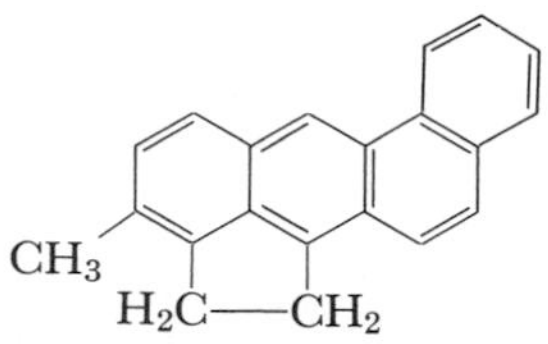   methylcholanthrene 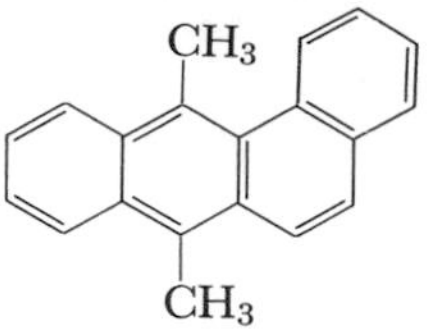   7,12-dimethyl-1,2-benzanthracene

Study Questions

1. There are eight isomers of the aromatic compound C_9H_{12}. Draw their structures and name them.

2. Ozonolysis of o-xylene yields a mixture of biacetyl ($CH_3COCOCH_3$), glyoxal ($HCOCHO$), and methylglyoxal (CH_3COCHO). Does this observation support the hybrid structure for benzene?

3. Clearly show your understanding of resonance in aromatic chemistry.

4. Show by equation two *addition* reactions of benzene, and two *substitution* reactions.

5. n-Propylbenzene melts at $-99°C$, and boils at $160°$. Predict the melting and boiling points of ortho-, meta-, and para-ethyltoluene within $10°$.

6. What conditions are necessary, in the bromination of toluene, to yield chiefly p-bromotoluene? benzyl bromide?

7. Illustrate by equations the following reactions of aromatic compounds:
   a) nitration;   b) sulfonation;
   c) alkylation;   d) reduction.

8. Show by equations the products of the oxidation of the following with alkaline potassium permanganate: toluene, isopropylbenzene, o-xylene, p-xylene, p-bromoethylbenzene.

9. What are the expected principal products in the bromination of ethylbenzene? of chlorobenzene? of benzoic acid? of acetophenone ($C_6H_5COCH_3$)?

10. Show by equations how each of the following conversions may be accomplished:
    a) benzene to p-chloronitrobenzene;
    b) toluene to p-nitrobenzoic acid;

c) toluene to *m*-nitrobenzoic acid;
d) benzene to *p*-bromobenzyl bromide;
e) toluene to 1,2-diphenylethane;
f) benzene to benzoic acid;
g) toluene to T.N.T. (trinitrotoluene);
h) benzene to 3-nitro-4-bromobenzenesulfonic acid;
i) benzene to 3-nitro-5-bromobenzenesulfonic acid.

11. Compound *A*, C_8H_8, is a colorless oil boiling at 143–145°C. It gave a Baeyer's test, decolorized bromine solution rapidly, and upon oxidation with permanganate formed benzoic acid. Write the structure of *A*, and give your reasoning.

12. Compound *B*, $C_{14}H_{14}$, does not give a Baeyer's test, and reacts slowly with bromine to liberate hydrogen bromide. Upon oxidation, only benzoic acid is isolated. What is compound *B*? Give your reasons.

Advanced Reading References

Essential Principles of Organic Chemistry, James Cason, Prentice-Hall, Inc., Englewood Cliffs, N. J., 1956, Chapters 21 and 22.

Organic Chemistry, 3rd Ed., R. Q. Brewster and W. E. McEwen, Prentice-Hall, Inc., Englewood Cliffs, N. J., 1961, Chapter 22.

Chemistry of Organic Compounds, 2nd Ed., C. R. Noller, W. B. Saunders Co., Philadelphia, 1957, Chapters 18 and 20.

Organic Chemistry, 3rd Ed., L. F. Fieser and Mary Fieser, D. C. Heath and Co., Boston, 1957, Chapters 22, 23, and 24.

Advanced Organic Chemistry, E. Earl Royals, Prentice-Hall, Inc., Englewood Cliffs, N. J., 1954, Chapter 5.

Resonance in Organic Chemistry, G. W. Wheland, John Wiley and Sons, Inc., New York, 1955.

new terms & concepts

*Crude oil consists of hydrocarbons and impurities containing
oxygen, nitrogen, and sulfur.
Distillation of crude oil separates gaseous methane, ethane, propane, and butanes.
Petroleum ether, or ligroin, is a low-boiling mixture of pentanes and hexanes.
Gasoline, kerosene, gas oil are obtained from successively higher-boiling fractions.
Residues include the waxes, coke, and asphalt.
The octane number measures the burning rate of gasoline.
Branching hydrocarbons increases octane numbers.
. . . Cracking . . . converts high-molecular-weight paraffins into a mixture of
lower-molecular-weight paraffins and olefins.
"Alkylation" converts low-molecular-weight olefins and paraffins into
higher-molecular-weight branched-chain paraffins.
Both of these processes lead to increased gasoline production.
"Hydroforming" produces aromatics from paraffins.
The Bergius and Fischer-Tropsch processes can be used to convert carbon
into liquid fuels.
Rubber is made from coagulated latex, the milky exudate of the Hevea tree.
The crude rubber, known as caoutchouc to the Indians, is modified by vulcanizing
and by the addition of substances which improve its properties to produce the
substance we use in automobile tires and many other manufacturing processes.
Rubber is an unsaturated polymer of isoprene.*

6

Petroleum and rubber

The two most important naturally occurring hydrocarbon types are petroleum and rubber. Petroleum, or "rock oil," is a fossil substance, produced from fossil plants under conditions of great pressure and reduction in rock strata. It represents a major source of fuel and in recent years has become important as a source of chemicals. Rubber is a plant product, formed by treatment of the natural latex to form the elastic polymer we know as rubber. Each of these cases represents major contribution of organic chemists to the building of great industries. Much of the chemistry described in the previous chapters of this book was developed by researchers in the fields of petroleum or rubber.

PETROLEUM

In the early days, the Indians in Pennsylvania knew of certain ponds and springs where mineral oil formed a film on the surface of the water. A blanket drawn across this surface became saturated with the oil, and could be wrung out to produce the celebrated "Indian Medicine Oils." In 1858 Colonel Titus had a well drilled at what is now Titusville, Pennsylvania, which began to produce crude oil. This was the origin of our great petroleum industries. At present there are about four hundred thousand wells in operation in this country. They are found in four major fields—Pennsylvania, the Midcontinent (Ohio, Michigan, Indiana, and Illinois), the Gulf (Louisiana, Texas, and Oklahoma), and the Western (California). Crude petroleum is a black, smelly, viscous oil which consists chiefly of hydrocarbons, but also contains some sulfur, oxygen, and nitrogen compounds. It is separated by distillation into various fractions. The light gases, including propane and the butanes, are sold as *LPG* (liquified petroleum gas) in tanks for home fuel. Some *petroleum ether* or ligroin is separated, and then a large fraction consisting of seven- to ten-carbon alkanes, heptane up to branched-chain ten-carbon alkanes boiling between 75° and 200°C, is collected as *gasoline*. *Kerosene* is heavier than gasoline, boiling between 175° and 325°C, and *gas oil* (fuel oil) is heavier still, boiling from about 275° to 400°C. Lubricating oils, vaseline, and the residues of coke and asphalt are obtained above these temperatures, and by further chemical treatment.

In the beginning, kerosene was the most important fraction, used in "coal-oil" lamps and for fuel. But the availability of gasoline stimulated the development of the internal combustion engine and the automotive industries. This in turn has increased the demand for better motor fuels. Thomas Midgely, who began a study of this problem in the early 1920's, found that "knocking" in a gasoline engine was caused by an explosion in the cylinders. By using a series of pure paraffins as fuels, he was able to demonstrate that the continuous-chain compounds burned explosively, causing knocking, while the branched-chain compounds burned more slowly, thus developing pressure on the pistons without knocking. In an experimental engine, heptane caused the most knocking, while 2,2,4-trimethylpentane (isooctane) caused the least, as measured by a specially designed bouncing ball gauge. Heptane was therefore assigned an antiknock value or *octane number* of 0, and isooctane an octane number of 100. These two substances provided the extremes of a bouncing ball gauge, and mixtures of these

$$\begin{array}{ccc} & CH_3 & CH_3 \\ & | & | \\ CH_3-C-CH_2-CH-CH_3 \\ & | \\ & CH_3 \end{array}$$

isooctane

formed the intermediate graduations. The *octane number* of a gasoline is the per cent of isooctane in a mixture of isooctane and heptane which burns like the gasoline in question. A further study by Midgely showed that the octane numbers of gasolines could be improved by the addition of other substances, such as iodine or aromatic amines. Lead tetraethyl, $Pb(C_2H_5)_4$, was the most effective of these, and mixed with ethylene bromide, it is added to all "Ethyl" gasolines to improve their performance.

Petroleum cracking

Distillation gives about one barrel of gasoline from each three barrels of crude petroleum. Because gasoline is the most important product, it is desirable to increase the yield of gasoline, which may be done by "cracking." When ethane is passed through a hot iron tube, maintained at about 485°C, it is split into ethylene and hydrogen. At slightly lower temperatures, propane gives a mixture of propene, hydrogen, ethylene, and methane. At still lower temperatures, butane is split to butenes, hydrogen, propene, ethene, methane, and ethane (see Chapter 3). In this reaction, carbon-carbon bonds are broken to form

6.01 $\qquad CH_3CH_3 \xrightarrow{485°} CH_2{=}CH_2 + H_2$

6.02 $\qquad CH_3CH_2CH_3 \xrightarrow{460°}$
$\begin{cases} \rightarrow CH_3CH{=}CH_2 + H_2 & 45\% \\ \rightarrow CH_2{=}CH_2 + CH_4 & 55\% \end{cases}$

6.03 $\qquad CH_3CH_2CH_2CH_3 \xrightarrow{435°}$
$\begin{cases} \rightarrow C_4H_8 + H_2 & 12\% \\ \rightarrow C_3H_6 + CH_4 & 50\% \\ \rightarrow C_2H_4 + C_2H_6 & 38\% \end{cases}$

lower-molecular-weight paraffins and olefins. A paraffin of formula

6.04 $\qquad C_{14}H_{30} \xrightarrow{400°} C_{14-n}H_{28-2n} + C_nH_{2n+2}$

$C_{14}H_{30}$ would yield a variety of olefins and paraffins, where n varies from 0 to 12—for example,

$$C_7H_{14} + C_7H_{16}, \qquad C_6H_{12} + C_8H_{18}, \qquad \text{etc.}$$

Thus the heavy distillate fractions of kerosene and gas oil can be cracked to increase the gasoline. This process provides a source of olefins. The low-molecular-weight ethene, propene, and butenes are therefore available for chemical synthesis and manufacture. Catalysts have been found which greatly accelerate the cracking process at lower temperatures, and promote the formation of fragments which are in the gasoline range—that is, the C_7 to C_{10} compounds.

Alkylation or the "forming" process

In the presence of certain catalysts, such as sulfuric acid or anhydrous aluminum chloride, a paraffin will add to an olefin to form a higher-molecular-weight, and usually branched-chain, paraffin. The reaction is complicated by the fact that these same catalysts bring about isomerization (p. 39) so that the products are rearranged to paraffin mixtures. By this process the lower-molecular-weight olefins from the cracking towers can be alkylated by paraffins from the same source, in what is known as a gasoline *forming* process, thus increasing

$$CH_3-\underset{\underset{CH_3}{|}}{\overset{\overset{CH_3}{|}}{C}}-H + CH_2=CH-CH_3 \xrightarrow{AlCl_3}$$

6.05

$$CH_3-\underset{\underset{CH_3}{|}}{\overset{\overset{CH_3}{|}}{C}}-CH_2-CH_2-CH_3 \ (+CH_3-\underset{\underset{CH_3}{|}}{CH}CH_2-\underset{\underset{CH_3}{|}}{CH}CH_3, \text{ etc.})$$

the available gasoline still further. Because of chain-branching, this *formed* gasoline has a higher octane number than straight-run gasoline, and is used as aviation fuel. By *cracking* and *forming*, the yield can be increased to nearly two barrels of gasoline from each three barrels of crude oil.

Hydroforming

Most aromatic hydrocarbons which boil in the same range as gasoline have octane numbers above 100. These substances can be mixed with alkanes to form high-octane gasoline. Catalytic processes for the conversion of alkanes and cycloalkanes to aromatic hydrocarbons have been developed. Since a great deal of hydrogen is produced, the process has been called "hydroforming." Cyclohexane is readily dehydrogenated to benzene (Eq. 6.06). Other cycloparaffins

6.06

$$H_2C \overset{CH_2-CH_2}{\underset{CH_2-CH_2}{\diagup}} CH_2 \xrightarrow[500°C]{cat.} \langle \rangle + 3 H_2$$

may also be converted to aromatics, since isomerization also occurs (Eq. 6.07). It has even been found possible to convert the six-, seven-, and eight-carbon alkanes into aromatics, using catalysts which promote isomerization and dehydrogenation (Eq. 6.08 and 6.09).

6.07

$$\begin{matrix} H_2C\text{———}CH_2 \\ | \qquad | \\ H_2C \qquad CHCH_3 \\ \diagdown CH_2 \diagup \end{matrix} \xrightarrow[500°C]{cat.} C_6H_6 + 3 H_2$$

6.08

$$CH_3(CH_2)_5CH_3 \xrightarrow[510°C]{cat.} \langle \rangle CH_3 + 4 H_2$$

6.09
$$CH_3(CH_2)_6CH_3 \xrightarrow[510°C]{cat.} C_6H_4(CH_3)_2 + 4\,H_2$$
xylenes

The hydroforming process may therefore serve as a major source of benzene, toluene, and the xylenes for chemical synthesis. The by-product hydrogen is available for further reduction of higher-molecular-weight olefins to paraffins, or for reductive processes on crude oils to remove sulfur.

Synthetic fuels

Most countries do not have the wealth of natural petroleum that is available to the United States. They have therefore been interested in processes for converting coal and other carbonaceous materials into liquid fuels of the gasoline type. Germany has been a pioneer in this research, but the inevitable depletion of oil reserves makes synthetic fuels important to all nations.

The *Bergius* process converts coal to gasoline by hydrogenation over a catalyst (Eq. 6.10).

6.10
$$n\,C + (n+1)\,H_2 \xrightarrow{cat.} C_nH_{2n+2}$$

Powdered coal is mixed with heavy oil residues and catalyst, and then hydrogenated at high pressure to produce heavy oils, which are further cracked reductively to produce gasoline.

The *Fischer-Tropsch* process is more versatile, since it depends on carbon monoxide, which may be made from any carbonaceous material such as wood or algae, as well as coal. Carbon monoxide and hydrogen with suitable catalysts react at relatively low pressures to produce paraffins and water (Eq. 6.11).

6.11
$$n\,CO + (2n+1)\,H_2 \xrightarrow{cat.} C_nH_{2n+2} + n\,H_2O$$

By-products in this process include various oxygenated compounds, such as alcohols, ketones, aldehydes, and carboxylic acids. The process may be modified to increase the amounts of these by-products, which are therefore a potential source of chemicals.

RUBBER

During the sixteenth century, the Spaniards brought to Europe a vegetable product known to the South American Indians as caout-

Fig. 6.01. In the fraction towers shown in the center of this photo ethane, propane, butane, and other hydrocarbons are separated by fractional distillation. (Courtesy of Industrial Chemicals Company, Division of National Distillers and Chemical Corporation.)

chouc, a gummy yellowish-white substance made from the sap of Hevea trees. This substance was used to rub out marks on paper, and thus acquired the name "rubber." In the 1820's, Charles MacIntosh marketed a rubberized cloth raincoat, but the rubber used in these was sticky and soft at ordinary temperatures, and brittle in the cold. At temperatures above 70°C it lost its elasticity and took on the properties of hot taffy. In 1838, Charles Goodyear accidentally discovered that when rubber and sulfur were heated together, a new product was formed which had the desirable properties of rubber—flexibility and elasticity—and retained these properties over a much wider range of temperature, so that it was no longer sticky in hot weather or brittle in freezing weather, and was more wear-resistant. The new product was called *vulcanized* rubber, and was manufactured into hundreds of useful articles, like boots and buggy tires. With the advent of the automobile, the tire industry assumed major importance, and the chemistry of rubber was studied more intensely. Many improvements, like the addition of carbon black or zinc oxide, increased the hardness, strength, and resistance to abrasion and cutting, thus increasing the life of the rubber tire. It is not unusual for a tire to last 30,000 miles today, while 5000 was a good average in 1925.

In 1876, seeds of the Hevea tree were shipped from Brazil to England, planted in hothouses, and the young plants then shipped to Ceylon. This was the beginning of the East Indian rubber plantations. Grafting and other good agricultural practices have raised the yield of latex from 500 to as much as 2000 lb/acre/year. Tapping starts when the tree is five to seven years old. A narrow strip of bark is cut from the tree to a depth of about $\frac{1}{4}$ inch, about 3 or 4 feet from the ground. This cut runs about $\frac{1}{3}$ of the way around the tree, and slants towards the ground to let the latex run down a spout into a cup. Every other day a new cut is made below the old one, until the base is reached. Tapping is then started on the other side of the tree, while new bark covers the old cuts. The latex from the cups is collected and taken to a central location. Here it is treated with acid to coagulate it to a spongy mass, which is pressed dry and then smoked. These so-called crepe rubber "pigs" are then ready for shipment.

Other plants produce latex, such as goldenrod, the Russian dandelion, or quayule, a shrub native to northern Mexico and southwestern United States. These may be used for rubber production, but the low acre yield (50–100 lb/acre/year) makes them uneconomical.

Structure of rubber

Chemical analysis of rubber revealed the following facts. The empirical formula was C_5H_8. The molecular weight of different samples varied between 260,000 and 400,000. When a rubber sample was

Fig. 6.02. Rubber tapper at work, tapping Havea tree for natural latex. (Courtesy of Goodyear Tire and Rubber Company, Akron, Ohio.)

heated strongly in the absence of air, it was nearly all converted to *isoprene,* which was collected by condensation. On treatment with hydrochloric acid, the isoprene could be again polymerized to a rubberlike substance having a molecular weight of about 8000. Since isoprene has the formula C_5H_8, it is apparent that natural rubber is composed of large molecules of addition polymers of isoprene (p. 96).

Rubber is unsaturated, adding one mole of hydrogen catalytically, or one mole of bromine, for each moiety of isoprene present. Therefore rubber has one double bond for each unit of isoprene in the

Fig. 6.03. Ox-drawn trolley taking bales of natural crepe rubber to a railway shipping point on the Dolok Merangir Estate of the Goodyear Rubber Company in Indonesia. (Courtesy of Goodyear Tire and Rubber Company, Akron, Ohio.)

molecule. Ozonolysis of rubber (p. 61) leads to the formation of levu-linic aldehyde (4-ketopentanal) in 90 or more per cent yield (Eq. 6.12).

$$
CH_2{=}CH{-}\underset{\underset{CH_3}{|}}{C}{=}CH_2 \longrightarrow
$$

$$
(-CH_2{-}CH{=}\underset{\underset{CH_3}{|}}{C}{-}CH_2{-}CH_2{-}CH{=}\underset{\underset{CH_3}{|}}{C}{-}CH_2{-})_{n/2}
$$

6.12

rubber

$$
\xrightarrow[\text{2. Zn/HCl}]{\text{1. O}_3} CH_3\overset{\overset{O}{\|}}{C}CH_2CH_2CHO
$$

Rubber is therefore an unsaturated linear polymer, formed by addition polymerization of isoprene in a 1,4-manner, containing three to six thousand isoprene units per molecule.

With the seizure of our natural rubber sources in Borneo and the Indonesian Archipelago at the beginning of World War II, the need for a synthetic substitute became pressing. This was not a new prob-lem, having been studied earlier by German chemists under the same kind of pressure. During World War I, the Germans had learned how to polymerize 2,3-dimethyl-1,3-butadiene with alkali to form a polymer called *methyl rubber*. Although it was used for tires during World War I,

6.13 $\quad CH_2{=}\underset{\underset{CH_3}{|}}{\overset{\overset{CH_3}{|}}{C}}{-}C{=}CH_2 \xrightarrow{\text{KOH}} (-CH_2{-}\underset{\underset{CH_3}{|}}{\overset{\overset{CH_3}{|}}{C}}{=}C{-}CH_2{-})_n$

it was not a satisfactory substitute for natural rubber. Shortly after the war, in 1927, these same workers developed *Buna* rubber, so called because it was made by polymerizing *but*adiene with sodium (*Na*). Buna rubber was not the equal of natural rubber as a soft flexible polymer, but when properly treated formed a superior *hard* rubber, used in instrument and radio panels, handles for special instruments, etc.

6.14 $\quad CH_2{=}CH{-}CH{=}CH_2 \xrightarrow{\text{Na}} (-CH_2{-}CH{=}CH{-}CH_2{-})_n$

The development of useful synthetic elastomers, and their relation to the plastics industry, are described in Chapter 18.

Study Questions

1. Describe the fractional distillation of crude oil.

2. What is meant by the octane number of a gasoline? What does it measure? How is it possible to have an octane number greater than 100?

3. What would be the expected products of cracking of 2-methyl-butane?

4. Why is isomerization a useful reaction in petroleum technology? How will isomerization improve the quality of octane as a fuel?

5. What would be the expected products of the hydroforming process on octane? How can you account for the various products obtained?

6. What steps are necessary to convert algae into gasoline?

7. What chemical reactions prove the structure of rubber? Illustrate by equations.

8. What kinds of monomers form elastic polymers? Write the structure of four different monomers which might be converted to elastic polymers.

9. What is meant by the following terms?
   a) caoutchouc;   *b*) vulcanization;
   c) Hevea tree;   *d*) isoprene;
   e) quayule;   *f*) latex;
   g) crepe rubber;   *h*) elastomer.

Advanced Reading References

Chemistry of Organic Compounds, 2nd Ed., C. R. Noller, W. B. Saunders and Co., Philadelphia, 1957, Chapters 4 and 32.

Organic Chemistry, 3rd Ed., L. F. Fieser and Mary Fieser, D. C. Heath and Co., Boston, 1957, Chapters 5 and 13.

new terms & concepts

Compounds of carbon and hydrogen with chlorine, fluorine, bromine, or iodine
are called organic halogen compounds.
They react with metals in the Wurtz, Wurtz-Fittig, and Grignard reactions.
The replacement reaction introduces many functional groups in place of the halogens.
Allyl halides are more reactive, vinyl halides less reactive than aliphatic halides.
Aromatic halides are relatively unreactive;
they are produced by direct halogenation.
Alkyl halides can be prepared by addition of hydrohalides to unsaturated bonds
and by replacement of hydroxyl groups in alcohol.
There are many useful and industrially important organic halogen compounds,
such as chloroform, carbon tetrachloride, ethyl chloride,
Gammexene, D.D.T., p-dichlorobenzene, Freon, and ethylene bromide.

7

Organic halogen compounds

This class of compounds, the aliphatic members of which may be represented by R—X and the aromatics by Ar—X, are rarely found in nature. They are, nevertheless, one of the most important classes of organic compounds. Many of them have useful properties and have found important industrial applications in their own right, while many others are used in the manufacture of synthetic organic compounds. In physical properties, they resemble their parent hydrocarbons. The lower-molecular-weight members are colorless, odorless gases, while the higher members are water-insoluble, colorless oils or, in the aromatic halides, white solids.

Common names

The organic halogen derivatives are commonly named as salts of the organic radicals—for example, methyl chloride, CH_3Cl, and methylene dichloride, CH_2Cl_2. Table 7.01 lists the common and I.U.C. names of a few representative halogenated hydrocarbons.

Reactions of the halogenated hydrocarbons

The halogen compounds are useful in the synthesis of various hydrocarbons, as has already been described. The Wurtz synthesis (p. 40) may be modified for use in the synthesis of alkylated aromatics. In this case, more vigorous conditions are required, but aromatic bro-

TABLE 7.01   SOME HALOGENATED HYDROCARBONS

Compound	Common name	I.U.C. name	M.P. °C	B.P. °C
CH_3Cl	Methyl chloride	Chloromethane	−98	−24
CH_2Cl_2	Methylene dichloride	Dichloromethane	−97	40
$CHCl_3$	Chloroform	Trichloromethane	−63	61
CHI_3	Iodoform	Triiodomethane	119	(sublimes)
CCl_4	Carbon tetrachloride	Tetrachloromethane	−23	77
CH_3CH_2Cl	Ethyl chloride	Chloroethane	−139	12
CH_3CHCl_2	Ethylidene chloride	1,1-Dichloroethane	−97	57
$BrCH_2CH_2Br$	Ethylene bromide	1,2-Dibromoethane	10	132
$CH_2{=}CHCl$	Vinyl chloride	Chloroethene	−160	−12
$CH_2{=}CHCH_2Br$	Allyl bromide	3-Bromopropene	−119	70
CF_2Cl_2	Freon	Dichlorodifluoromethane	−155	−30
C_6H_5I	Phenyl iodide	Iododenzene	−31	188
$C_6H_5CH_2Cl$	Benzyl chloride	Chloromethylbenzene	−39	179
ClC_6H_4Cl	p-Dichlorobenzene	1,4-Dichlorobenzene	53	173

mides, when refluxed with alkyl halides in the presence of sodium, give satisfactory yields of alkylated aromatics. This is known as the *Wurtz-Fittig* reaction. The aliphatic halogen compounds undergo the *elimina-*

7.01 $C_6H_5Br + 2\,Na + ClCH_2CH_3 \longrightarrow C_6H_5CH_2CH_3 + NaCl + NaBr$

tion reaction (p. 64) to form the olefins and acetylenes. Both aliphatic and aromatic halides form the *Grignard reagents* (p. 41) by reacting with magnesium in the presence of dry ether. The aromatic fluoro derivatives are not sufficiently reactive to be useful in this reaction, but bromo and iodobenzene form the Grignard reagents quite readily. These reagents are extremely reactive, and are very useful in the preparation of other compounds. Grignard reagents are reduced to the hydrocarbons by water, and oxidized to the hydroxyl derivatives by air or oxygen. For this reason they must be protected from air and moisture with great care during their preparation and use.

7.02 $C_6H_5I + Mg \xrightarrow{Et_2O} C_6H_5MgI \xrightarrow{H_2O} C_6H_6$

$\qquad\qquad C_6H_5MgI \xrightarrow{O_2} C_6H_5{-}O{-}MgI \xrightarrow{H_2O} C_6H_6OH$

The displacement reaction, in which the halogen atom is displaced by some other functional group by reaction with a metal salt of this functional group, occurs with the aliphatic halides and certain especially reactive aromatic compounds, and is one of the most important and versatile of all organic reactions. It may be generalized thus:

7.03 $R-X + Z^- \longrightarrow RZ + X^-$

Any metal salt of a function Z will react with an alkyl halide in a polar solvent, usually water, alcohol, or liquid ammonia, to replace the halide.

Table 7.02 shows that practically any of the important functional groups can be introduced into the alkyl chain by the displacement reaction. Even the nitroparaffins can be prepared, using the special reagent silver nitrite (reaction 7).

Displacements at saturated carbon

One of the most common types of organic reactions is displacement of one negative group by another at a saturated carbon atom. This is called a nucleophilic substitution and may be generalized:

7.04 $A{:}C + {:}B \longrightarrow C{:}B + A{:}$ (S_N)

The negative group B (for *base*) displaces group A (with its electrons) by attack on carbon atom C. This is nucleophilic because it involves attack on the nucleus of the carbon atom. Note that all the reactions listed in Table 7.02 can be described in this way. Many other reactions yet to be described, such as conversion of alcohols to alkyl halides (p. 114) and hydrolysis of ethylene oxide (p. 133), are also displacements at saturated carbon.

The nucleophilic substitution (S_N) reaction in Eq. 7.04 may occur

TABLE 7.02   REPLACEMENT REACTIONS OF ALKYL HALIDES

Reaction			Product
1. $R-X + OH^-$	$\xrightarrow{H_2O}$ $R-OH$	$+ X^-$	alcohols
2. $R-X + OR'^-$	$\xrightarrow{alc.}$ $R-OR'$	$+ X^-$	ethers
3. $R-X + SH^-$	$\xrightarrow{alc.}$ $R-SH$	$+ X^-$	thiols
4. $R-X + SR'^-$	$\xrightarrow{alc.}$ $R-SR'$	$+ X^-$	sulfides
5. $R-X + \bar{O}COR'$	$\xrightarrow{H_2O}$ $R-OCOR'$	$+ X^-$	esters
6. $R-X + CN^-$	$\xrightarrow{alc.}$ $R-CN$	$+ X^-$	nitriles
7. $R-X + Ag^+NO_2^-$	$\xrightarrow{alc.}$ $R-NO_2$	$+ AgX$	nitroparaffins
8. $R-X + NH_2^-$	$\xrightarrow{NH_3}$ $R-NH_2$	$+ X^-$	amines
9. $R-X + I^-$	$\xrightarrow{alc.}$ $R-I$	$+ X^-$	alkyl iodides
10. $R-X + {}^-SO_3Na$	$\longrightarrow$ $R-SO_2O^-Na^+$	$+ X^-$	alkanesulfonic acids
11. $R-X + {}^-C{\equiv}CR$	$\xrightarrow{NH_3}$ $R-C{\equiv}CR$	$+ X^-$	acetylenes

in two ways. Sometimes, in strongly polar solvents $A:C$ dissociates to form a carbonium ion (Eq. 7.05). This carbonium ion then can recom-

7.05
$$A:C \rightleftharpoons A:^- + C^+$$
$$C^+ + B:^- \longrightarrow C:B \qquad (S_N 1)$$

bine with the negative group $A:^-$ or with $B:^-$. Since the reaction rate depends only on the concentration of C^+ in solution, it is a first-order reaction, and is called $S_N 1$ (substitution, nucleophilic, first order). Reactions involving tertiary carbon atoms frequently occur by this mechanism, since tertiary carbonium ions are most stable and easily formed.

7.06 $\qquad A:C + :B^- \rightleftharpoons [A:C:B]^- \rightleftharpoons A:^- + C:B \qquad (S_N 2)$

Sometimes, in least polar solvents, $A:C$ associates with $B:$ to form a transition-state complex, which then may decompose in one of two ways (Eq. 7.06). Since the reaction rate depends on the concentration of both $A:C$ and $:B^-$ it is bi-molecular or second order, and the reaction is said to be $S_N 2$ (substitution, nucleophilic, second order). In typical $S_N 2$ reactions a stronger base usually displaces a weaker base. In general, the rate of $S_N 2$ displacements increases with the strength of the base B, and with decrease of electron density on the carbon atom. The rate decreases with the basicity of the negative group being displaced. (This will tend to reverse the equilibriums shown in Eq. 7.06.) Reactions involving primary carbon atoms, such as hydrolysis of ethyl bromide to ethanol, are usually $S_N 2$ reactions, but many basic displacement reactions are intermediate between the two types, and probably proceed in both ways.

Relative reactivity of organic halides

When nitro groups are present in the *ortho* or *para* position to an aromatic halogen, the halogen is more reactive than usual, and may be replaced by reaction with metal salts. In this case two nitro groups are more effective than one. In general, iodine is more easily replaced than bromine, which is more easily replaced than chlorine. Fluorine

7.07 $\qquad$ NO$_2$ ⟨ring⟩ (NO$_2$ / NO$_2$) X + K$^+$OH $\xrightarrow{\text{alc.}}$ NO$_2$ ⟨ring⟩ (NO$_2$ / NO$_2$) OH + K$^+$X$^-$

is somewhat anomalous in its reactivity. One fluoro atom on an alkyl chain is more easily replaced than chlorine, but two fluoro atoms on the same carbon ($-CF_2-$) are quite stable, and three fluorine atoms in $-CF_3$ is the most stable halogen group known. The presence of the trifluoromethyl group in an organic molecule stabilizes the whole molecule toward oxidation, and has been used in dyes to prevent fading.

In general, tertiary halides are more easily replaced than secondary, and secondary more easily replaced than primary. However, carbon-carbon double bonds have a strong influence on the reactivity of the halides. The ethenyl halides (vinyl halides) are unreactive, but the halides which have a double bond on the second carbon (allyl halides) are much more reactive than the simple alkyl halides. For example, in the replacement of chlorine by iodide ion (reaction 9), allyl chloride reacts 80 times as fast as propyl chloride, and benzyl chloride 200 times as fast, as shown in Table 7.03.

TABLE 7.03   RATE OF REPLACEMENT OF CHLORIDES BY IODIDE

Reaction	Rate
$CH_3CH_2CH_2Cl + I^- \xrightarrow{\text{acetone}} CH_3CH_2CH_2I + Cl^-$	1
$CH_2{=}CH{-}CH_2Cl + I^- \xrightarrow{\text{acetone}} CH_2{=}CH{-}CH_2I + Cl^-$	80
$\bigcirc{-}CH_2Cl + I^- \xrightarrow{\text{acetone}} \bigcirc{-}CH_2I + Cl^-$	200

In general, the order of reactivity of organic halides to replacement may be indicated as follows, from least reactive to most reactive.

a) $R{-}Cl < R{-}Br < R{-}I$

b) $I°{-}X < II°{-}X < III°{-}X$

c) $C{=}C{-}X < C{-}C{-}X < C{=}C{-}C{-}X$

d) $\bigcirc{-}X < \bigcirc{-}C{-}C{-}X < \bigcirc{-}C{-}X$

e) $\bigcirc{-}X < \underset{NO_2}{\bigcirc}{-}X < NO_2\underset{NO_2}{\bigcirc}{-}X < NO_2\overset{NO_2}{\underset{NO_2}{\bigcirc}}{-}X$

Preparation of organic halides

The direct substitution reaction in the paraffin series (p. 37) is not very useful in preparing pure compounds. Industrially, methane may be chlorinated to form a mixture of methyl chloride, methylene dichloride, chloroform, and carbon tetrachloride. Some other paraffins

7.08 $CH_4 + Cl_2 \xrightarrow{\text{cat.}} CH_3Cl + CH_2Cl_2 + CHCl_3 + CCl_4 + HCl$

may be chlorinated to form useful chloro compounds. For example, a mixture of all the isomeric pentanes (from petroleum) is chlorinated, and distilled to give a complex mixture of monochloropentanes useful as an industrial solvent. In the laboratory, this reaction is only useful as a preparative method in the aromatic series (p. 78). The alkyl halides may also be prepared by addition of hydrohalides to olefins (p. 56), and to acetylenes (p. 67).

7.09 $C_6H_6 + Br_2 \xrightarrow{\text{Fe}} C_6H_5Br + HBr$

7.10 $R-CH=CH-R + HI \longrightarrow R-CH_2-CHI-R$

7.11 $HC \equiv CH + 2 HCl \longrightarrow CH_3-CHCl_2$

The most useful method of preparing aliphatic halides is by the replacement of carbon-oxygen bonds. This may be brought about in the the loss of water between these reagents, i.e.,

7.12 $CH_3CH_2-OH + H-Br \xrightarrow{H_2SO_4} CH_3CH_2-Br + H_2O$

Hydrogen bromide reacts with an alcohol in the presence of sulfuric acid to form the alkyl bromide. In the same way, a solution of anhydrous zinc chloride in concentrated hydrochloric acid, called the *Lucas reagent,* reacts readily with alcohols to form the alkyl chlorides.

7.13 $(CH_3)_3COH + HCl \xrightarrow{ZnCl_2} (CH_3)_3CCl + H_2O$

The phosphorus trihalides and thionyl chloride ($SOCl_2$) are also effective reagents in replacing C—O bonds by C—X bonds, as the following equations show.

7.14 $3 CH_3CH_2CH_2OH + PI_3 \longrightarrow$

$3 CH_3CH_2CH_2I + P(OH)_3$ (phosphorous acid, H_3PO_3)

7.15 $(CH_3)_2C=O + PCl_3 \longrightarrow CH_3C(Cl)_2CH_3 + POCl_3$

7.16 $C_4H_9OH + SOCl_2 \longrightarrow C_4H_9Cl + HCl + SO_2$

The alkyl fluorides may be obtained by reactions similar to the above, but are most readily formed in an exchange reaction between antimony trifluoride and alkyl halides. For example, carbon tetrachloride reacts to form *freon*, CF_2Cl_2, which is a remarkably inert, nontoxic gas, boiling at $-30°C$. It is so inert that several generations of mice have been raised in an atmosphere of 80 per cent freon, 20 per cent oxygen with no unusual effects! For this reason it has largely replaced sulfur dioxide or ammonia as a refrigerant gas.

7.17 $$3\,CCl_4 + 2\,SbF_3 \longrightarrow 3\,CF_2Cl_2 + 2\,SbCl_3$$

The fluorocarbons are a new class of completely fluorinated hydrocarbons, C_nF_{2n+2}, which promises to have industrial importance. They are very stable toward oxidation, decomposition, and attack by alkali or acid, and hence should prove useful in aviation lubricating oils, etc. Tetrafluoroethene, $CF_2{=}CF_2$, can be polymerized (p. 277) to form a very stable polymer, *Teflon* $(-CF_2-CF_2-)_n$, which is a waxy solid especially effective as an insulator, and, as a material for the manufacture of bearings and valves used in working with corrosive chemicals.

Useful organic halides

Many of the chloromethanes and ethanes are used as commercial solvents. Carbon tetrachloride and tetrachloroethane ($CHCl_2CHCl_2$) especially have been used in dry cleaning because they are nonflammable. Carbon tetrachloride has been used as a fire-extinguisher also, but is dangerous because of its toxic properties. The chlorinated paraffins all have anesthetic properties which increase with the number of halogens present. They also are rather toxic, having a depressant action on the heart, and causing kidney and especially liver damage. The toxicity also increases with the number of halogen atoms in the molecule. All of the compounds CH_3Cl, CH_2Cl_2, $CHCl_3$, and CCl_4 have been used as general anesthetics, but chloroform has the widest ratio between the effective anesthetic dose and the toxic dose. However, its clinical use has been discontinued in favor of other less toxic general anesthetics. The use of chloroform and especially carbon tetrachloride by people with extensive liver damage (alcoholics, for example) is dangerous.

Chloroform ($CHCl_3$) is a colorless liquid with a characteristic sweet odor and burning taste, boiling at $61°C$, and only slightly soluble in water, but soluble in organic solvents. It is used in troches and lozenges as a cough sedative, and as a counterirritant in liniments for external application. *Carbon tetrachloride* (CCl_4) boils at $78°C$, and is a heavy colorless liquid, practically insoluble in water, but soluble in the common organic solvents. Its chief medicinal use is as an anthelminthic in the treatment of hookworm. *Ethyl chloride* (CH_3CH_2Cl) is a very volatile liquid, b.p. 12°C, which may be stored under low pressure in metal cylinders. Owing to its great volatility, it is used as a topical anesthetic; a stream of the liquid is sprayed on the surface and, by evaporation, "freezes" the tissues. *Tetrachloroethylene* (perchloroethylene, $CCl_2=CCl_2$) boils at 121°C, and is considered to be less toxic than carbon tetrachloride, and therefore more useful as an industrial solvent. It is stable, nonflammable, and a good solvent for fats and oils.

Ethylene bromide ($BrCH_2CH_2Br$) is a colorless oil boiling at 131°C. It is mixed with tetraethyl lead to prevent lead deposits in engines using "leaded" gasoline, and is also used in agriculture as a soil fumigant and nematocide. *Iodoform* (triiodomethane, CHI_3) is a yellow crystalline solid, melting at 121°C, with a characteristic iodine-like odor. (It has been described as a "hospital" odor.) It has been used as an antiseptic in petrolatum ointments, impregnated in wound dressings, and as a dusting powder. Its effect seems to be due to the slow liberation of iodine on contact with proteins. Since its odor is thought objectionable by some, its use has largely been discontinued.

Allyl chloride (3-chloro-1-propene, $CH_2=CHCH_2Cl$) is a colorless oil boiling at 44°C. It was originally prepared by treating allyl alcohol ($CH_2=CHCH_2OH$) with PCl_3. It is a very reactive compound, having both a double bond and a highly reactive chlorine. The discovery that direct high-temperature chlorination of propylene leads not to 1,2-dichloropropane, as might be expected, but rather to allyl chloride, has opened the way to the economical large-scale production

7.18 $CH_2=CH-CH_3 + Cl_2 \xrightarrow{500-600°} CH_2=CH-CH_2Cl + HCl$

of allyl chloride. Among the important products made commercially from allyl chloride are allyl alcohol, glycerol (p. 123), cyclopropane, epichlorohydrin, and trichloropropane.

A number of aromatic halogen derivatives have proved useful as *insecticides*. *p-Dichlorobenzene* (dichloricide, $p\text{-}ClC_6H_4Cl$) is a white crystalline solid resembling naphthalene in odor and in its effect on moth larvae. It is used as a dusting powder on vermin-infested livestock and plants. Chlorophenothane (dichlorodiphenyltrichloroethane, D.D.T.) was developed during World War II as an effective delousing agent for humans, and proved to be a particularly effective insecticide against the common house fly. It is a white crystalline substance, melting at 109°C, insoluble in water, and readily absorbed through the skin, especially in kerosene solutions. Two other powerful insecticides which are chlorinated hydrocarbons have recently been developed and are widely used in agricultural work against corn borers, boll weevils, grasshoppers, etc. These are gammexane and chlordane, and the structures are shown below. Gammexane is the *gamma*-form of hexachlorocyclohexane.

$$\left(Cl\langle\bigcirc\rangle\right)_2 CH—CCl_3$$

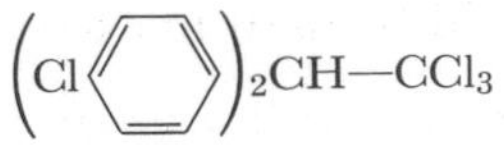

D.D.T.

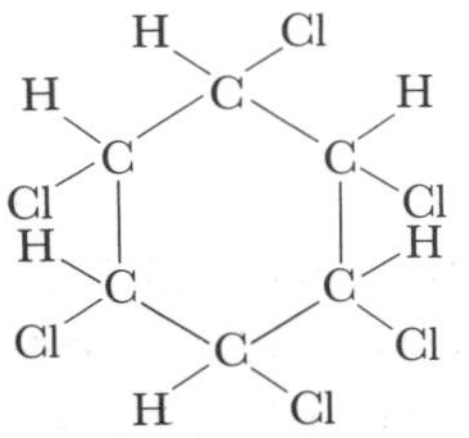

gammexane 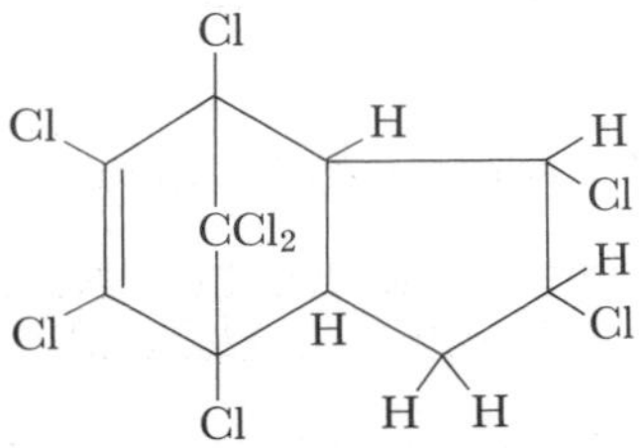   chlordane

The insecticide consists of a mixture of the *alpha, beta, gamma, delta,* and *epsilon* forms, but the activity is due largely to the *gamma*-form. These isomers are the various possible combinations of axial and equatorial chlorine atoms of hexachlorocyclohexane (see p. 53).

Study Questions

1. Draw the structural formulas and give the correct I.U.C. names for each of the following: chloroform, ethyl chloride, methylene dibromide, vinyl chloride, benzyl iodide, iodoform, allyl chloride.

2. Show by equations how ethyl iodide could be converted to ethanol, ethyl ether, propanonitrile, dimethylaminoethane, and ethyl acetate.

3. Show how ethyl bromide could be prepared from ethane, ethylene, and ethanol. Which of these methods would you choose to prepare ethyl bromide in the laboratory?

4. What are the principal uses of each of the following: *a*) chloroform, *b*) carbon tetrachloride, *c*) tetrachloroethane, *d*) dichlorodifluoromethane, *e*) 1,2-dibromoethane, *f*) hexachlorocyclohexane?

5. Write structural formulas and common names of three chlorinated hydrocarbons used as insecticides.

6. Allyl chloride, CH_2=CH—CH_2Cl, is a useful industrial raw material. Illustrate by equations how allyl chloride might be converted into some useful compounds.

7. Discuss the use and limitations of the substitution reaction in the preparation of halogenated hydrocarbons.

8. In the conversion of ethane to ethyl chloride by direct chlorination, which reagent should be used in excess? Why?

9. Which of the following will give an immediate precipitate with silver nitrate in aqueous alcohol: bromobenzene, *n*-butyl chloride, or benzyl iodide? Explain.

Advanced Reading References

Organic Chemistry, 3rd Ed., R. Q. Brewster and W. E. McEwen, Prentice-Hall, Inc., Englewood Cliffs, N. J., 1961, Chapters 5 and 23.

Chemistry of Organic Compounds, 2nd Ed., C. R. Noller, W. B. Saunders Co., Philadelphia, 1957, Chapters 6 and 19.

Organic Chemistry, 3rd Ed., L. F. Fieser and Mary Fieser, D. C. Heath and Co., Boston, 1957, Chapters 7 and 29.

new terms & concepts

Aliphatic hydroxy compounds are called alcohols.
Aromatic hydroxy derivatives are called phenols.
Alcohols may be primary, secondary, or tertiary, depending on the number of carbon atoms attached to the hydroxylated carbon.
Hydroxylated hydrocarbons are more soluble in water than the hydrocarbons.
Phenols are stronger acids than alcohols.
Alcohols lose the hydroxyl group more readily than phenols.
Alcohols may eliminate water to form olefins, or replace the hydroxyl group to form ethers or alkyl halides.
Alcohols and phenols lose the hydrogen of the hydroxyl group to form salts and esters.
Alcohols may be oxidized to aldehydes or ketones.
Phenols are easily substituted in the ortho- and para-positions.
Alcohols are prepared by hydrolysis of alkyl halides, hydrolysis of alkyl sulfates, or by reduction of aldehydes, ketones, acids, or esters.
Carbonyl compounds react with Grignard reagents to produce alcohols.
Phenols are formed by hydrolysis of aromatic sulfonic acids or aryl halides.
Industrially important syntheses of specific alcohols include methanol from carbon monoxide, ethanol by fermentation, glycerol from allyl chloride, and phenol from benzene.

8

Oxygenated hydrocarbons

i. alcohols and phenols

As has already been seen (p. 14), oxygen, with its two valence bonds, can combine with carbon and hydrogen to form several functional groups. The aliphatic *alcohols* and aromatic *phenols* contain the hydroxy (—OH) group, *ethers* have a carbon atom attached to each of the oxygen valences (R—O—R), *aldehydes* and *ketones* contain the carbonyl group (—CO—), and the *carboxylic acids* combine both the hydroxy and the carbonyl group on the same carbon to form the *carboxyl* group (—COOH). Compounds of these types are found widely distributed in nature, and are very important in medicine and industry.

The aliphatic paraffins and olefins are converted to *alcohols* by substitution of one or more hydrogen atoms by hydroxyl groups (R—OH), while substitution of hydrogen by hydroxyl in the aromatic series leads to *phenols* (Ar—OH). The simplest members of the two series are methanol and phenol.

$$CH_3OH \qquad \langle\!\bigcirc\!\rangle OH$$

methanol   phenol

Alcohols are classified as primary (I°), secondary (II°), or tertiary (III°), depending on the number of carbon atoms attached to the hydroxylated carbon.

$CH_3CH_2CH_2CH_2OH$ $CH_3—CH—CH_3$ $CH_3—C—OH$ (with CH_3 above and CH_3 below the central C)
with OH below the central CH

1-butanol   isopropanol   2-methyl-2-propanol
(a I° alcohol)   (a II° alcohol)   (a III° alcohol)

Naming the alcohols and phenols

The alcohols are commonly named by naming the radical and adding the word "alcohol," e.g., CH_3OH, methyl alcohol, $CH_3CH_2CH_2OH$, propyl alcohol, etc. The phenols, on the other hand, are named entirely by a series of unrelated trivial names (see Table 8.01).

Physical properties of alcohols and phenols

The alcohols and phenols are generally colorless substances with relatively high boiling points. The hydroxy group increases the solu-

TABLE 8.01   NAMES AND PHYSICAL PROPERTIES OF SOME ALCOHOLS AND PHENOLS

I.U.C. name	Common name	Formula	M.P. °C	B.P. °C
Methanol	Methyl alcohol	CH_3OH	−98	65
Ethanol	Ethyl alcohol	CH_3CH_2OH	−114	78
Propanol	n-Propyl alcohol	$CH_3CH_2CH_2OH$	−126	97
Isopropanol	Isopropyl alcohol	$CH_3CHOHCH_3$	−90	82
1-Butanol	n-Butyl alcohol	$CH_3CH_2CH_2CH_2OH$	−90	118
2-Butanol	sec-Butyl alcohol	$CH_3CH_2CHOHCH_3$	−115	100
2-Methyl-1-propanol	Isobutyl alcohol	$(CH_3)_2CHCH_2OH$	−108	108
2-Methyl-2-propanol	tert-Butyl alcohol	$(CH_3)_3COH$	26	83
1-Pentanol	amyl alcohol	$CH_3(CH_2)_4OH$	−125	138
Hydroxybenzene	Phenol	⬡OH	41	182
1-Methyl-4-hydroxybenzene	para-cresol	CH_3⬡OH	36	202
1,2-Dihydroxybenzene	Catechol	⬡ with OH, OH	104	245
1,3-Dihydroxybenzene	Resorcinol	⬡ with OH, OH	108	276
1,4-Dihydroxybenzene	Hydroquinone	HO⬡OH	170	285

bility in water, so that alcohols and phenols are more soluble than the parent hydrocarbons. Methanol, ethanol, and the propanols are miscible with water in all proportions, while hexanol is soluble only to the extent of 0.6 g/100 ml water at 20°C. This illustrates the rule that "like dissolves like." The lower alcohols have a higher per cent of oxygen and resemble water, while the higher alcohols resemble the hydrocarbons in solubility. The more hydroxy groups present per molecule, the greater the solubility in water. For example, compare the solubilities in 100 parts of water of benzene (0.07 at 22°), phenol (8.2 at 15°), and resorcinol (147 at 12°). The boiling points listed in Table 8.01 illustrate the decrease in boiling point with chain branching of isomers. Again, the melting points of the most symmetrical isomers are highest. (Compare tert-butyl alcohol to its isomers, and hydroquinone to its isomers.)

Reactions of the alcohols and phenols

The hydroxy compounds react as more or less weak acids, RO—H, losing a hydrogen atom as a proton by breaking an oxygen-hydrogen bond. Alkali metals, like sodium, dissolve in alcohols liberating hydrogen.

8.01 $$2\ ROH + 2\ Na \longrightarrow 2\ RONa + H_2$$

Phenols are much stronger acids than alcohols, and are soluble in strong bases such as sodium hydroxide.

8.02 $$C_6H_5OH + NaOH \longrightarrow C_6H_5ONa + H_2O$$

Even though phenol is acidic enough to react with strong bases, it is still a weak acid, weaker than carbonic acid, present in soda water (H_2CO_3). Phenol is often called *carbolic acid*, and is used as an antiseptic agent.

The carbon-oxygen bond in alcohols may be easily broken, forming the halogen derivatives with hydrohalides, thionyl chloride, or the phosphorus halides (p. 104). In this reaction a tertiary alcohol reacts much more rapidly than a secondary alcohol, which in turn reacts more rapidly than a primary. This is the basis of the *Lucas test,* in which an alcohol is shaken with the *Lucas reagent* (HCl/ZnCl₂). If an oily layer of alkyl chloride separates immediately, it is a III° alcohol. If about 5 or 10 minutes is required for separation of the oily layer, a II° alcohol is indicated, while several hours may be required before the reaction is observed with a I° alcohol. Replacement of the hydroxy group in phenols is much more difficult.

8.03 $R—OH + H—Cl \xrightarrow{ZnCl_2} R—Cl + H_2O$

The displacement of OH in alcohols by halide ion is a typical S_N reaction (p. 101) and may be either S_N1 or S_N2. The reaction involves alkylhydronium ion, ROH_2^+, which is formed immediately when acids and alcohols are allowed to react. Reactions with tertiary alcohols involve tertiary carbonium ions, which are stable, easily formed, and proceed rapidly. S_N2 reactions usually occur with primary alcohols, and are slower. Secondary alcohols probably react both ways at intermediate rates, hence the order observed by the Lucas test. With

8.04 $ROH + HCl \longrightarrow ROH_2^+ + Cl^-$

8.05 $ROH_2^+ \longrightarrow R^+ + H_2O$ (S_N1)

8.06 $R^+ + Cl^- \longrightarrow RCl$

8.07 $ROH_2^+ + Cl^- \rightleftharpoons [RO\overset{+}{H}_2Cl^-] \rightleftharpoons RCl + H_2O$ (S_N2)

acids forming weak nucleophiles, like sulfuric acid, the alcohols react to form ethers. This involves nucleophilic displacement on alkylhydronium ion by alcohol:

8.08 $CH_3CH_2—\overset{..}{\underset{H}{O}}: + CH_3CH_2\overset{+}{O}H_2 \xrightarrow{H_2SO_4} CH_3CH_2\overset{+}{\underset{H}{O}}CH_2CH_3 + H_2O$

The carbon-oxygen bond in alcohols is also easily broken in the elimination reaction (p. 63), forming water and olefins:

8.09 $H—\overset{\overset{\displaystyle H}{|}}{\underset{\underset{\displaystyle H}{|}}{C}}—\overset{\overset{\displaystyle H}{|}}{\underset{\underset{\displaystyle OH}{|}}{C}}—H \xrightarrow[160°]{H_2SO_4} H_2C{=}CH_2 + H_2O$

This reaction follows the same order as the Lucas test, and olefins are most readily formed from tertiary alcohols, least readily from primary alcohols. This is not surprising, since the olefin is formed by an alternate decomposition of the carbonium ion, most easily formed from the tertiary alcohol. Carbonium ions tend to eliminate a proton where possible (Eq. 8.10), forming the olefin. The rate of this reaction at any

8.10 $CH_3—\overset{\overset{\displaystyle CH_3}{|}}{\underset{\underset{\displaystyle CH_3}{|}}{C}}{}^+ \rightleftharpoons CH_2{=}\overset{\overset{\displaystyle CH_3}{|}}{\underset{\underset{\displaystyle CH_3}{|}}{C}} + H^+$ (E_1)

temperature depends only on the concentration of carbonium ion present, hence is E_1 (elimination, first order). Phenols cannot be dehydrated in this manner.

Both alcohols and phenols react with carboxylic acids to form *esters,* with the loss of water, but alcohols form more stable esters than do phenols. The *esterification* reaction is catalyzed by acids and dehydrating agents.

$$8.11 \quad CH_3\overset{\overset{\displaystyle O}{\parallel}}{C}\!-\!OH + H\!-\!O\!-\!C_4H_9 \xrightarrow{H_2SO_4} CH_3\overset{\overset{\displaystyle O}{\parallel}}{C}\!-\!O\!-\!C_4H_9 + H_2O$$

butyl acetate

$$CH_3CH_2COOH + HOC_6H_5 \longrightarrow CH_3CH_2CO\!-\!OC_6H_5 + H_2O$$

8.12
phenyl propionate

The esters are named as acid salts of the organic radicals. The esterification reaction is reversible: esters react with water to form alcohols again.

$$8.13 \qquad CH_3CO\!-\!OC_4H_9 + HOH \longrightarrow HOC_4H_9 + CH_3COOH$$

$$8.14 \qquad CH_3COOH + OH^- \longrightarrow CH_3COO^- + H_2O$$

This reaction is promoted by the use of alkali, which neutralizes the acid formed by the hydrolysis. Since the salts of the aliphatic carboxylic acids are soaps, this reaction is known as the *saponification* reaction. Alcohols occur in nature as esters, so this reaction is important in the preparation of soaps, and of alcohols and acids from natural sources.

Alcohols may be easily oxidized to aldehydes and ketones. A primary alcohol loses two hydrogen atoms to form the aldehyde (Eq. 8.15), while a secondary alcohol similarly is converted to a ketone.

$$8.15 \qquad CH_3\!-\!\overset{\overset{\displaystyle H}{|}}{\underset{\underset{\displaystyle H}{|}}{C}}\!-\!O\!-\!H + CuO \longrightarrow CH_3\!-\!\overset{\overset{\displaystyle H}{|}}{C}\!\!=\!\!O + H_2O + Cu$$

$$8.16 \qquad CH_3\!-\!\overset{\overset{\displaystyle CH_3}{|}}{\underset{\underset{\displaystyle O-H}{|}}{C}}\!-\!H + CuO \longrightarrow CH_3\!-\!\overset{\overset{\displaystyle O}{\parallel}}{C}\!-\!CH_3 + H_2O + Cu$$

(Eq. 8.16). The oxidizing agents may be rather mild, like copper oxide or air. Stronger oxidizing agents will further oxidize the aldehydes and ketones, and should be avoided. Tertiary alcohols and phenols are not oxidized under these conditions. The lower-molecular-weight alcohols burn with a clear blue flame, and are frequently used in heating lamps.

The presence of a hydroxy group on the aromatic ring greatly increases the ease of substitution. For example, phenol reacts readily with a solution of bromine in water to form *tribromophenol* (Eq. 8.17), and it is not possible to form a monobromophenol by direct bromination, since the molecule is so reactive.

8.17

$$\text{(ring)}-OH + 3\ Br_2 \longrightarrow Br-\text{(ring)}-OH + 3\ HBr$$

The hydroxy group is, of course, one of the strongest *ortho-para*-directing groups known. The phenols form colored complexes with the ferric (Fe^{+++}) ions, and if a dilute aqueous solution of a phenol is shaken with ferric chloride a colored solution which is characteristic of the phenol is formed, and is a test for its presence.

Preparation of alcohols and phenols

Two general methods for preparing alcohols have already been described. Olefins add sulfuric acid, and the alkyl sulfate so formed can be hydrolyzed to the alcohol (p. 56). This reaction is particularly use-

8.18

$$R-CH=CH_2 \xrightarrow{H_2SO_4} R-CH-CH_3 \xrightarrow{H_2O} R-CH-CH_3$$
$$\qquad\qquad\qquad OSO_2OH \qquad\qquad OH$$

ful for the preparation of II° and III° alcohols and has industrial application (see Figure 8.01). The replacement of alkyl halides in aqueous alkali (p. 101) is useful for the preparation of I° alcohols.

8.19

$$R-X + OH^- \xrightarrow{H_2O} R-OH + X^-$$

Reduction of the carbonyl group in aldehydes and ketones provides another useful source of alcohols. Hydrogen is readily taken up by both aldehydes and ketones in the presence of an active metal catalyst such as platinum or nickel. The aldehydes yield I° alcohols, and the

8.20

$$CH_3CHO + H_2 \xrightarrow{cat.} CH_3CH_2OH$$

8.21

$$R-CHO + H_2 \xrightarrow{cat.} R-CH_2OH$$

8.22

$$R-\overset{O}{\overset{\|}{C}}-R + H_2 \xrightarrow{cat.} R-\overset{OH}{\underset{|}{C}H}-R$$

ketones yield II° alcohols. Carboxylic acids and esters may be reduced to I° alcohols with lithium aluminum hydride. Esters can also be re-

Fig. 8.01. In these towers at Houston, Texas, tons of ethylene are converted into ethyl alcohol. (Courtesy of Shell Chemical Company.)

duced with hydrogen at high pressure over metal catalysts. This reaction provides an industrial source for certain alcohols from naturally occurring esters. Coconut oil, for example, contains esters of lauric acid which yield lauryl alcohol on reduction (Eq. 8.25).

8.23 $2 \text{ R—COOH} + \text{LiAlH}_4 + 2 \text{ H}_2\text{O} \longrightarrow 2 \text{ R—CH}_2\text{OH} + \text{Al(OH)}_3 + \text{LiOH}$

8.24 $\text{R—COOC}_2\text{H}_5 + 2 \text{ H}_2 \xrightarrow{\text{cat.}} \text{R—CH}_2\text{OH} + \text{C}_2\text{H}_5\text{OH}$

8.25 $(\text{C}_{11}\text{H}_{23}\text{COO})_3\text{C}_3\text{H}_5 \xrightarrow[\text{4000 psi}]{\text{H}_2/\text{Ni}}$

        glyceryl trilaurate $3 \text{ C}_{12}\text{H}_{25}\text{OH} + \text{CH}_2\text{OHCHOHCH}_2\text{OH}$

                            lauryl alcohol   glycerol

The *Grignard* reagent provides a useful source of many alcohols and some phenols. This reagent adds rapidly to all sorts of carbonyl compounds in the following manner:

8.26 $\underset{\displaystyle \overset{\displaystyle \text{O}}{\|}}{\text{R—C—R}^1} + \text{R}^2\text{—MgX} \longrightarrow \text{R—}\underset{\text{R}^2}{\overset{\text{O—MgX}}{\text{C}}}\text{—R}^1 \xrightarrow{\text{H}_2\text{O}} \text{R—}\underset{\text{R}^2}{\overset{\text{OH}}{\text{C}}}\text{—R}^1 + \text{Mg(OH)X}$

The organic part of the Grignard reagent adds to the carbon, and the positive magnesium adds to the negative oxygen, of the carbonyl group. The salt thus formed must be hydrolyzed to the alcohol. By a proper choice of carbonyl compound and Grignard reagent, almost any desired alcohol may be synthesized. The following examples illustrate the preparation of I°, II°, and III° alcohols.

8.27 $\text{CH}_3\text{CH}_2\text{—MgBr} + \text{H}_2\text{C}{=}\text{O} \longrightarrow$

                 $\text{CH}_3\text{CH}_2\text{CH}_2\text{—O—MgBr} \xrightarrow{\text{H}_2\text{O}} \text{CH}_3\text{CH}_2\text{CH}_2\text{OH}$

8.28 $\text{CH}_3\text{—MgI} + \text{CH}_3\text{—CH}{=}\text{O} \longrightarrow$

                 $\text{CH}_3\text{—}\underset{\text{O—MgI}}{\text{CH}}\text{—CH}_3 \xrightarrow{\text{H}_2\text{O}} \text{CH}_3\text{CHOHCH}_3.$

8.29 $\text{CH}_3\text{CH}_2\text{CH}_2\text{—MgBr} + \text{CH}_3\text{—}\overset{\displaystyle \overset{\displaystyle \text{O}}{\|}}{\text{C}}\text{—CH}_3 \longrightarrow$

                 $\text{CH}_3\text{CH}_2\text{CH}_2\text{—}\underset{\text{CH}_3}{\overset{\text{O—MgBr}}{\text{C}}}\text{—CH}_3 \xrightarrow{\text{H}_2\text{O}} \text{CH}_3\text{CH}_2\text{CH}_2\underset{\text{CH}_3}{\overset{\text{CH}_3}{\text{C}}}\text{OH}$

Grignard reagents react with oxygen or air to form the magnesium salt of the alcohol or phenol. This reaction can be used to prepare phenols.

8.30 $\text{C}_6\text{H}_5\text{—MgX} + \text{O}_2 \longrightarrow \text{C}_6\text{H}_5\text{—O—MgX} \xrightarrow{\text{H}_2\text{O}} \text{C}_6\text{H}_5\text{OH}$

The reaction of acetylene with carbonyl derivatives forms the acetylenic alcohols. This reaction may be catalyzed by alkali metals. Acetylene reacts with formaldehyde to give propargyl alcohol (2-propyne-1-ol), or with 2 moles of formaldehyde to produce 2-butyne-1,4-diol. Both of these compounds are important raw materials for industrial syntheses. For example, 2-butyne-1,4-diol may be reduced to butane-1,4-diol (tetramethylene glycol) which is useful in the manufacture of polymers such as nylon.

8.31 $HC\equiv CH + CH_2O \xrightarrow[Na]{NH_3} HC\equiv C-CH_2OH$

8.32 $HC\equiv CH + 2\,CH_2O \longrightarrow HOCH_2-C\equiv C-CH_2OH$

8.33 $HOCH_2C\equiv C-CH_2OH \xrightarrow[cat.]{2\,H_2} HOCH_2CH_2CH_2CH_2OH$

The reaction of acetylene with ethyl methyl ketone produces 3-methyl-1-pentyne-3-ol, which is a useful hypnotic (induces sleep).

8.34 $HC\equiv CH + CH_3\overset{\overset{\displaystyle O}{\|}}{C}CH_2CH_3 \longrightarrow HC\equiv C-\underset{\underset{\displaystyle CH_3}{|}}{\overset{\overset{\displaystyle OH}{|}}{C}}-CH_2CH_3$

Most of the common phenols used in industry, such as the cresols, etc., are obtained by alkaline extraction of coal-tar distillates. The demand for phenol itself is so great that it must be synthesized from benzene. The Grignard method is far too expensive for industrial application, but phenol can be obtained by two different hydrolysis reactions. Benzene may be sulfonated in concentrated sulfuric acid to benzenesulfonic acid or chlorinated to form chlorobenzene in good yield (p. 78). Each of these may be cheaply converted to phenol. The sodium salt of benzenesulfonic acid, when fused in an iron vessel with sodium hydroxide, forms sodium phenolate according to Eq. 8.35.

8.35 $C_6H_5-SO_2ONa + 2\,NaOH \longrightarrow C_6H_5-ONa + Na_2SO_3 + H_2O$

Chlorobenzene may be hydrolyzed by treatment with a superheated solution of sodium hydroxide under pressure:

8.36 $C_6H_5-Cl + 2\,NaOH \longrightarrow C_6H_5-ONa + NaCl + H_2O$

The sodium phenolate is easily converted to phenol by any cheap acid:

8.37 $C_6H_5-ONa + H^+ \longrightarrow C_6H_5OH + Na^+$

These same reactions may be applied to manufacture other hydroxybenzene derivatives.

Some useful alcohols and phenols

Many alcohols and phenols of various sorts have important industrial uses. Only a relatively few examples can be given here. Other examples may be found in more advanced organic texts. *Methanol* (wood alcohol, CH_3OH) is found in many natural esters, such as *oil of wintergreen* (methyl salicylate), but seldom occurs free in nature. It was formerly obtained by the destructive distillation of maple wood, but the industrial demand for millions of gallons has forced its synthesis by the catalytic hydrogenation of carbon monoxide:

8.38 $$CO + 2\,H_2 \xrightarrow{\text{cat.}} CH_3OH$$

Methanol is a nerve poison, being especially toxic to the optic nerve, causing blindness in rather small doses; it is therefore used to *denature* (make unfit for internal use) ethanol when it is to be used as an industrial solvent. Methanol has extensive use as an antifreeze, and to manufacture formaldehyde.

Ethanol (ethyl alcohol, alcohol, grain neutral spirits, C_2H_5OH) may be manufactured by the hydration of ethylene (p. 56) but is more commonly obtained by the fermentation of sugar or starch solutions in the presence of yeast or other sources of enzymes. The reaction may be represented as follows:

8.39 $$C_6H_{12}O_6 \xrightarrow{\text{zymase}} 2\,C_2H_5OH + 2\,CO_2$$
glucose

Blackstrap molasses, a by-product of sugar refining, is treated with yeast which contains the enzyme invertase. Invertase splits the sugar to glucose, and a second enzyme in the yeast, zymase, brings about the fermentation to alcohol and carbon dioxide. The alcohol solution so obtained contains from 6 to 12 per cent alcohol, and must be distilled as an azeotropic mixture of 95 per cent alcohol and 5 per cent water (190 proof spirits). In addition to its many uses as an industrial solvent, ethyl alcohol has several important medicinal applications. It is a useful antiseptic in concentrations of 50 to 70 per cent, and it has a stimulating followed by depressant action on the central nervous system, also causing anesthesia and lowering of body temperature. Indeed all alcohols have a degree of narcotic action which increases with chain branching, so that some of the III° alcohols have been used as hypnotics. The production and distribution of ethanol is controlled by the Federal government, and that used for industrial application is rendered unfit for human consumption by denaturing and is not taxed (Figure 8.02). Pure (95 per cent) ethanol may be obtained under a tax per proof gallon, or tax-free by certain legally authorized bodies, such as hospitals and research laboratories. Approximately one million tons of ethanol were produced in the United States in 1960, and were consumed by such divergent industries as plastics, foods, textiles, agricultural, paints, ferrous and nonferrous metallurgy, refrigeration, and explosives.

Isopropyl alcohol ($CH_3CHOHCH_3$) is used as a substitute for ethanol in many of its applications, since it is more toxic and is not useful as a beverage. It is a good solvent and a somewhat better antiseptic than ethanol. Isopropanol is used to sterilize instruments, as an astringent in lotions, and as rubbing alcohol. Isopropyl alcohol is manufactured by the hydration of propylene, from the petroleum cracking process, or by the reduction of acetone (propanone).

8.40 $$CH_3-CH=CH_2 \xrightarrow{H_2SO_4} CH_3-\underset{OSO_2OH}{\underset{|}{CH}}-CH_3 \xrightarrow{H_2O} CH_3-\underset{OH}{\underset{|}{CH}}-CH_3$$

8.41 $$CH_3-\underset{\text{acetone}}{CO-CH_3} + H_2 \xrightarrow{\text{cat.}} CH_3CHOHCH_3$$

Allyl alcohol (2-propene-1-ol, $CH_2=CH-CH_2OH$) is a colorless liquid which boils at 97°C, and has an acrid, irritating odor. It has both a double bond and an alcohol group, and exhibits reactions of both. For example, treatment with bromine converts it to 2,3-dibromo-1-propanol, while phosphorus tribromide converts it to allyl bromide.

8.42 $$CH_2BrCHBrCH_2OH \xleftarrow{Br_2} CH_2=CHCH_2OH \xrightarrow{PBr_3} CH_2=CHCH_2Br$$

Allyl alcohol and its derivatives may be polymerized (p. 278). It is most conveniently prepared by the hydrolysis of allyl chloride.

8.43 $$CH_2=CHCH_2Cl \xrightarrow[OH^-]{H_2O} CH_2=CHCH_2OH$$

Amylene hydrate (dimethylethylcarbinol, $CH_3CH_2C(CH_3)_2OH$) is a colorless liquid, boiling about 100°C, with a camphorlike odor and burning taste, used as a mild sedative in capsules or by enema. *Tribromoethanol* (avertin, CBr_3CH_2OH) is sometimes used as a general anesthetic, administered rectally in oil solution. *Cyclohexanol* (hexalin) is a colorless liquid boiling at 162°C, which is made by catalytic hydrogenation of phenol under pressure. It reacts as an ordinary II° alcohol, and is produced commercially as a solvent and as a chemical intermediate. Cyclohexanol is easily oxidized to cyclohexanone.

Fig. 8.02. Large quantities of ethyl alcohol are denatured for industrial use. The alcohol scale tanks shown are used for measuring ethyl alcohol, with which denaturants are combined to produce specially denatured alcohol formulas, authorized for use in numerous preparations, including certain pharmaceuticals. (Courtesy of Commercial Solvents Corporation.)

8.44

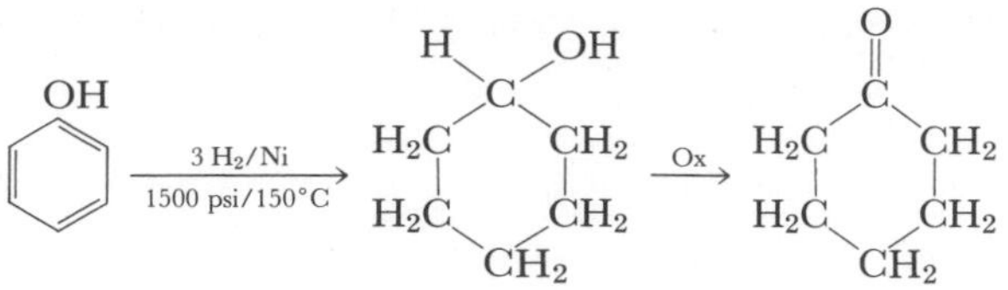

$$\text{OH} \xrightarrow[\text{1500 psi}/150°\text{C}]{3\ \text{H}_2/\text{Ni}} \begin{array}{c} \text{H} \quad \text{OH} \\ \text{C} \\ \text{H}_2\text{C} \quad \text{CH}_2 \\ \text{H}_2\text{C} \quad \text{CH}_2 \\ \text{CH}_2 \end{array} \xrightarrow{\text{Ox}} \begin{array}{c} \text{O} \\ \text{C} \\ \text{H}_2\text{C} \quad \text{CH}_2 \\ \text{H}_2\text{C} \quad \text{CH}_2 \\ \text{CH}_2 \end{array}$$

Several naturally occurring hydroxycyclohexane derivatives are important. *Menthol* (mint camphor, $C_{10}H_{20}O$) occurs in peppermint oil, and is a crystalline solid, m.p. $41°C$, with a mintlike odor. When rubbed on the skin, it causes a refreshing cool sensation, followed by slight burning. It has a counterirritant stimulating effect on mucous membranes, and is used in nasal sprays, inhalators, and mentholated cigarettes. It is a cyclic alcohol, related in structure to the dihydroxy compound, *terpin hydrate*, which is used as an expectorant in bronchitis.

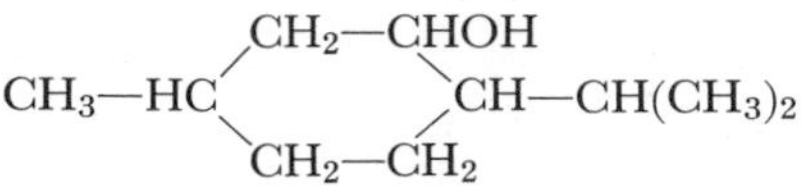

$$\text{CH}_3\!-\!\text{HC} \begin{array}{c} \text{CH}_2\!-\!\text{CHOH} \\ \\ \text{CH}_2\!-\!\text{CH}_2 \end{array} \!\!\! \text{CH}\!-\!\text{CH(CH}_3)_2 \qquad\qquad \text{CH}_3\!-\!\text{C} \begin{array}{c} \text{CH}_2\!-\!\text{CH}_2 \\ \text{OH} \\ \text{CH}_2\!-\!\text{CH}_2 \end{array} \!\!\! \begin{array}{c} \text{OH} \\ | \\ \text{CH}\!-\!\text{C}\!-\!\text{CH}_3 \cdot \text{H}_2\text{O} \\ | \\ \text{CH}_3 \end{array}$$

menthol 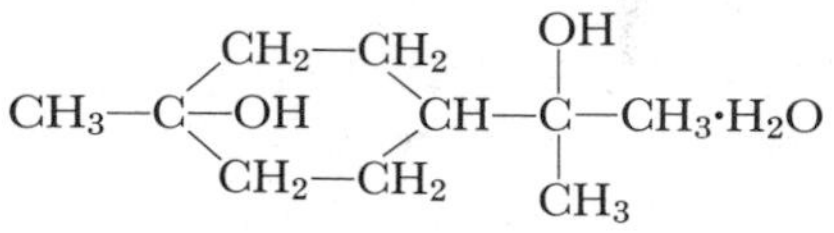   terpin hydrate

Several other polyhydroxy compounds are of interest. *Ethylene glycol*, $HOCH_2CH_2OH$, may be manufactured from ethylene by reaction with hypochlorous acid and replacement of the chloro group with alkali, or by hydrolysis of ethylene oxide (p. 133).

8.45 $\quad CH_2\!=\!CH_2 + HOCl \longrightarrow HOCH_2CH_2Cl \xrightarrow[\text{H}_2\text{O}]{OH^-} HOCH_2CH_2OH$

Ethylene glycol is a high-boiling ($196°C$) oily colorless liquid, very hygroscopic and completely miscible with water. It is used as a humectant, in antifreeze, as an industrial solvent, and in the manufacture of polyester fibers (dacron) and films (mylar). *Glycerol* (glycerin, 1,2,3-propanetriol, $CH_2OHCHOHCH_2OH$) is obtained as a byproduct in the manufacture of soap by the saponification of fats. It is also manufactured from allyl chloride by the following scheme:

8.46 $\quad CH_2\!=\!CH\!-\!CH_2Cl \xrightarrow{HOCl} ClCH_2CHOHCH_2Cl \xrightarrow[\text{H}_2\text{O}]{2\ OH^-} \begin{array}{ccc} CH_2\!-\!CH\!-\!CH_2 \\ | \quad\quad | \quad\quad | \\ OH \quad OH \quad OH \end{array}$

Glycerol has a sweet taste, characteristic of polyhydroxy compounds, and is harmless to humans. It is a constituent of fats. It is slightly antiseptic in concentrations above 25 per cent. Since it is hygroscopic it is used as a humectant to keep tobacco humid. Glycerol is also added to toothpastes in order to provide "body" for the product. Liquid soaps contain glycerol as a solvent.

$$CH_2—O—NO_2 \qquad CH_2—O—NO_2$$
$$CH—O—NO_2 \qquad CH—O—NO_2 \qquad CH_3—CH—CH_2—CH_2—O—NO$$
$$CH_2—O—NO_2 \qquad CH—O—NO_2 \qquad \qquad \qquad CH_3$$
$$\qquad \qquad \qquad \qquad CH_2—O—NO_2$$

glyceryl   erythrityl   amyl nitrite
trinitrate   tetranitrate

Several of the alcohols have important medicinal uses as their nitrates or nitrites. *Glyceryl trinitrate* (nitroglycerin) is used in tablets or in alcohol solution as a vasodilator to reduce arterial tension in heart disease. It is also an explosive, detonating with great violence when heated or sharply jarred. Erythrityl tetranitrate is similar to nitroglycerin in its medicinal action, which is less marked but more prolonged. It is also administered in the form of tablets. *Amyl nitrite* is a pale yellow flammable volatile liquid having a characteristic etherlike odor. It is used in heart disease to prevent spasm and dilate the blood vessels. It is sometimes employed as restorative in heart failure during anesthesia, and is usually administered by inhalation. Amyl nitrite is marketed in little thin-walled glass or plastic vessels called "pearls" which can be quickly broken in a handkerchief and the fumes inhaled. *Ethyl nitrite* (CH_3CH_2ONO) is more volatile and has the same effect, being used in alcohol solution as *sweet spirits of niter*.

The most characteristic property of the phenolic compounds is their antiseptic power. Lister, about 1865, began the practice of sterilizing instruments and working surfaces with solutions of phenol, but it was soon found that the alkylated phenols, such as the cresols, had a higher antiseptic action. Thus *hexylresorcinol* (S.T. 37, caprokol) was found to be from 50–150 times as effective as phenol against the common bac-

HO —〈 〉— OH, $CH_2CH_2CH_2CH_2CH_2CH_3$ CH_3 —〈 〉— OH, $CH(CH_3)_2$

hexylresorcinol   thymol

teria. *Thymol*, found in oil of thyme, is somewhat more effective than phenol, and in dilute solution has a pleasant taste, so that it is frequently used in mouthwashes, gargles, and in toothpaste.

Phenol (carbolic acid, C_6H_5OH) is by far the most important member of this class. Its manufacture from chlorobenzene and benzenesulfonic acid has been described. Phenol is used extensively as a preservative, owing to its antiseptic action, and also has a mild local anesthetic effect. It is used in dilute solution as an antiseptic and mild anesthetic in such preparations as calamine lotion. The itching is reduced by the anesthetic action, while the infection or irritation of parasites is prevented by the antiseptic effect. In higher concentrations, phenol causes ulceration and blisters, owing to its general protoplasmic toxic action. Phenol is used extensively in the manufacture of the phenol-formaldehyde plastics, such as Bakelite (Chapter 18). *Ortho-,* *meta-,* and *para*-cresol are the principal constituents of the coal-tar extract *creosote,* which is used as a wood-preservative on telegraph poles and railroad ties, as well as in the treatment of livestock for skin infestations.

8.47

guaiacol   catechol

Catechol (ortho-dihydroxybenzene, pyrocatechol) occurs naturally as the methyl ether, guaiacol, in beech wood. Cleavage of the ether with hydrogen iodide yields catechol. Guaiacol is used in medicine for its analgetic, antipyretic, and antiseptic action. The nucleus of catechol occurs in the hormone adrenalin. *Resorcinol (meta-*dihydroxybenzene) is obtained by fusion of sodium *m*-benzenedisulfonate with alkali. It is used in the manufacture of hexylresorcinol and the fluore-

8.48

cein dyes. *Hydroquinone* (para-dihydroxybenzene, quinol) occurs naturally as a glycoside, arbutin ($HOC_6H_4-O-C_6H_{11}O_5$) in *arbutus.* Hydroquinone is easily oxidized to *quinone.* It is therefore a good reducing agent, and as such is used in photographic developers and as an anti-oxidant.

8.49

Study Questions

1. Write structural formulas and I.U.C. names for all the isomeric 5-carbon alcohols, $C_5H_{11}OH$. Try to predict the melting point and boiling point of each of the eight isomers. Compare your predictions to the actual values in a handbook. Which of these are I°, which II°, and which III° alcohols?

2. Without using distillation, how could you separate a mixture of cyclohexanol and phenol? What color test would distinguish pure samples of cyclohexanol and phenol?

3. What single test would distinguish which of four pure samples was tertiary butyl alcohol from cyclohexanol, phenol, and 1-butanol?

4. How could you convert phenol into cyclohexene?

5. Illustrate by equations the esterification and saponification reactions.

6. Show by equations how isopropanol could be converted into a) propane, b) acetone (2-propanone), c) 2-bromopropane, d) 2,3-dimethylbutane, and e) 1,2-dibromopropane.

7. Indicate by equations one industrial method for the preparation of each of the following:
   a) isopropanol;   b) phenol;
   c) ethylene glycol;   d) ethanol;
   e) methanol;   f) glycerol.

8. What is meant by "denatured" alcohol? Grain neutral spirits? 100 proof alcohol? Wood alcohol? Sweet spirits of nitre?

9. Show clearly your understanding of the difference between sulfates and sulfonates, and between nitro compounds and nitrates.

10. Show by equations how allyl alcohol would react with a) excess HBr, b) bromine, c) dilute $KMnO_4$, d) PBr_3, and e) HOCl.

11. What are the alcohols formed when ethylmagnesium bromide reacts with a) formaldehyde, b) acetone, c) acetaldehyde, and d) cyclohexanone?

12. When phenol is produced industrially by hydrolyzing chlorobenzene with aqueous sodium hydroxide under pressure with superheated steam, some diphenyl ether, C_6H_5—O—C_6H_5 is formed. How can you account for this by-product?

13. An aromatic compound, A, C_7H_7OCl, reacts to decolorize bromine water. The compound gives a white precipitate when shaken with

a solution of silver nitrate in alcohol. Oxidation with alkaline permanganate gave a white solid, B, which was soluble in sodium bicarbonate with foaming, gave a purple color in ferric chloride solution, and had the formula $C_7H_6O_3$. What are the possible formulas of A and B? B melted at $215°C$. What are the formulas of A and B?

14. Give one practical application for each of the following: a) menthol, b) ethylene glycol, c) glycerol, d) amyl nitrite, e) hexylresorcinol, f) hydroquinone, and g) creosote.

Advanced Reading References

Essential Principles of Organic Chemistry, James Cason, Prentice-Hall, Inc., Englewood Cliffs, N. J., 1956, Chapters 4, 5, and 25.

Organic Chemistry, 3rd Ed., R. Q. Brewster and W. E. McEwen, Prentice-Hall, Inc., Englewood Cliffs, N. J., 1961, Chapters 6 and 28.

Chemistry of Organic Compounds, 2nd Ed., C. R. Noller, W. B. Saunders Co., Philadelphia, 1957, Chapters 5 and 24.

Principles of Organic Chemistry, 2nd Ed., J. English and H. G. Cassidy, McGraw-Hill, New York, 1956, Chapter 8.

Advanced Organic Chemistry, R. C. Fuson, John Wiley and Sons, New York, 1950, Chapter V.

new terms & concepts

Ethers contain oxygen bonded to different carbon atoms.
Simple ethers have two identical radicals in R—O—R.
Mixed ethers have different radicals bonded to oxygen as in Ar—O—R.
Ethers are prepared by dehydration of alcohols or by the Williamson synthesis,
which is the reaction of an alkoxide or phenoxide with an alkyl halide.
Ethers are not very reactive, but may be cleaved by strong acids.
Ethers form peroxides on exposure to air.
Ethyl ether is an anesthetic.
Ethylene oxide is an important industrial raw material, manufactured from
ethylene by air oxidation or from the chlorohydrin.
Ethylene oxide is very reactive because of a strained ring.
This oxide adds exothermically to compounds having a labile hydrogen,
such as water, alcohol, and ammonia.

128

9

Oxygenated hydrocarbons
ii. ethers

The ethers are represented by the formulas R—O—R or Ar—O—R, with both valences of oxygen bound to different carbon atoms. Ethers are low-boiling, relatively inert compounds which resemble in many ways the hydrocarbons in which an oxygen atom has replaced a methylene group. For example, propane, CH_3—CH_2—CH_3, and methyl ether, CH_3—O—CH_3, are both inert gases, highly flammable, and cause general anesthesia on inhalation. Compare the boiling points of the ethers (Table 9.01) with those of the paraffins having the same number of atoms in the chain (Table 3.01). The ethers are widely used as industrial solvents, and several have been used as general anesthetics, particularly ethyl ether. When both carbon groups are identical, they are said to be simple ethers, and are named as radical ethers; e.g., $CH_3CH_2OCH_2CH_3$, ethyl ether, $C_6H_5OC_6H_5$, phenyl ether. If the two radicals are different they are said to be mixed ethers, and are named as alkoxy derivatives of the larger carbon group; for example, $C_6H_5OCH_3$, methoxybenzene, $(CH_3)_2CHOCH_3$, 2-methoxypropane.

Preparation

As has been mentioned, the simple ethers may be obtained by dehydrating primary alcohols under less vigorous conditions than are

TABLE 9.01 SOME COMMON ETHERS

I.U.C. name	Common name	Formula	B.P. °C
Methyl ether	Methyl ether	$CH_3—O—CH_3$	−25
Methoxyethane	Methyl ethyl ether	$CH_3—O—CH_2CH_3$	8
Ethyl ether	Ethyl ether	$CH_3CH_2—O—CH_2CH_3$	35
Propyl ether	n-Propyl ether	$CH_3CH_2CH_2—O—CH_2CH_2CH_3$	89
Isopropyl ether	Isopropyl ether	$(CH_3)_2CH—O—CH(CH_3)_2$	69
Butyl ether	n-Butyl ether	$CH_3(CH_2)_3—O—(CH_2)_3CH_3$	141
Ethenyl ether	Vinyl ether	$CH_2{=}CH—O—CH{=}CH_2$	39
Methoxybenzene	Anisole	$C_6H_5—O—CH_3$	154
Ethoxybenzene	Phenetole	$C_6H_5—O—CH_2CH_3$	172
Phenyl ether	Phenyl ether	$C_6H_5—O—C_6H_5$	259
Epoxyethane	Ethylene oxide	$H_2C{\overset{}{-\!-\!-}}CH_3$ $\diagdown O \diagup$	14
1,2-Epoxypropane	Propylene oxide	$CH_3—CH{-\!-\!-}CH_2$ $\diagdown O \diagup$	35
1,4-Dioxacyclohexane	1,4-Dioxane	$CH_2{-\!-\!-}CH_2$ $O \qquad O$ $CH_2{-\!-\!-}CH_2$	101
Oxacyclopentane	Tetrahydrofuran	$H_2C{-\!-\!-}CH_2$ $H_2C \qquad CH_2$ $\diagdown O \diagup$	66

required to form olefins. Ethanol reacts at about 140°C in the presence of sulfuric acid to form ethyl ether and water.

9.01 $CH_3CH_2—OH + H—OCH_2CH_3 \xrightarrow[140]{H_2SO_4} CH_3CH_2—O—CH_2CH_3 + H_2O$

Industrially this reaction is carried out by passing the alcohol vapors over an alumina catalyst.

9.02 $2\,CH_3CH_2OH \xrightarrow[250°]{Al_2O_3} C_2H_5—O—C_2H_5 + H_2O$

Dehydration of secondary and tertiary alcohols to form ethers is less successful, since these compounds are much more readily dehydrated to form olefins.

A more generally useful reaction is the replacement of alkyl halides by the alkoxide group (p. 101) known as the *Williamson synthesis*.

9.03 $CH_3CH_2CH_2Br + Na^{+-}OCH_2CH_3 \longrightarrow$

          $CH_3CH_2CH_2—O—CH_2CH_3 + Na^+Br^-$

An alcohol is converted into its sodium salt, and then refluxed with the appropriate alkyl halide. Mixed ethers of known composition can thus be obtained. For example, methyl butyl ether may be readily formed by the reaction of sodium methoxide with butyl chloride.

9.04 $\qquad$ $C_4H_9Cl + Na^+{}^-OCH_3 \longrightarrow C_4H_9-O-CH_3 + NaCl$

In the same way, the phenoxide ion reacts readily with alkyl halides to form alkoxybenzenes. The reverse process of allowing chloroben-

9.05

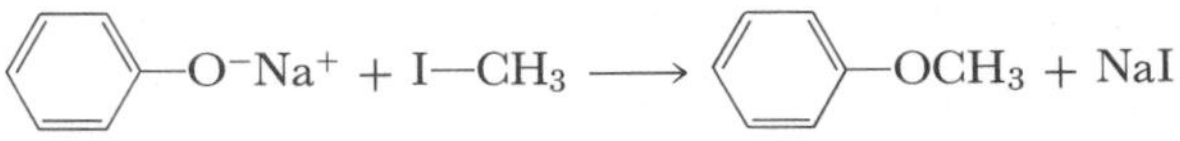

zene to react with sodium methoxide does not produce anisole owing to the unreactivity of the aromatic halide. However, phenyl ether is a by-product in the industrial process for converting chlorobenzene to phenol, since phenoxide ion competes with hydroxide ion.

9.06

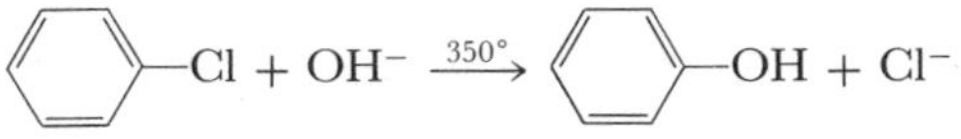

9.07

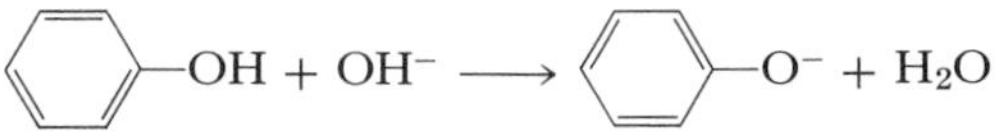

9.08

Reactions of ethers

Ethers are not highly reactive, a property which makes them useful as solvents. Cleavage of the carbon-oxygen bond can be brought about with strong acids. Boiling an ether with hydrogen iodide cleaves it to the alcohol and alkyl iodide.

9.09 $\qquad$ $CH_3CH_2-O-CH_2CH_3 + HI \longrightarrow CH_3CH_2-OH + CH_3CH_2I$

9.10

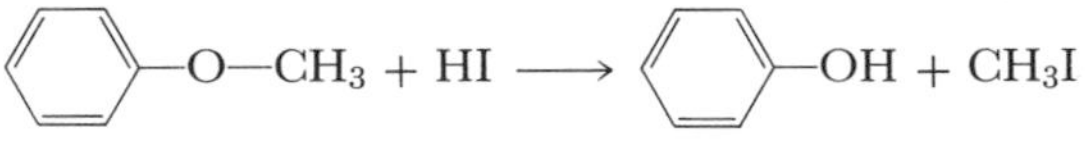

Hydrogen chloride is employed industrially to convert tetrahydrofuran to 4-chloro-1-butanol or directly to 1,4-dichlorobutane, which has use in the manufacture of nylon. The reaction is catalyzed by aluminum chloride. Tetrahydrofuran is a cyclic ether manufactured indirectly from corn cobs and oat hulls.

9.11

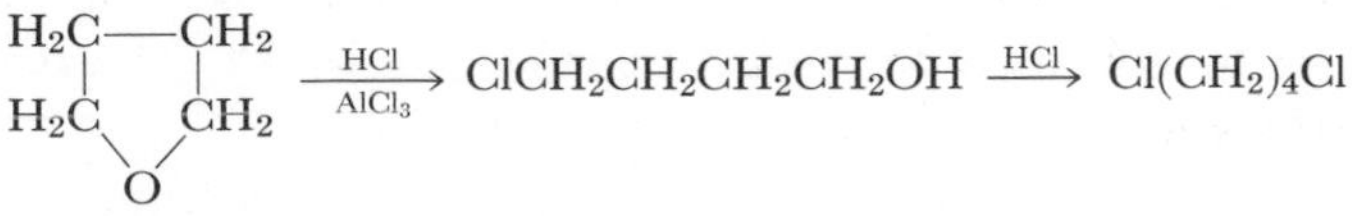

Ethers form highly explosive peroxides upon exposure to air.

9.12
$$2\,C_2H_5OC_2H_5 + O_2 \longrightarrow 2\,C_2H_5-\overset{\overset{O}{\uparrow}}{O}-C_2H_5 \longrightarrow C_2H_5-O-O-C_2H_5$$

The peroxide is less volatile than ether and is concentrated by evaporation or distillation. Distillation of ether which is old and has been exposed to the air several times may result in a violent explosion. Metals, acting as reducing agents, prevent the formation of peroxides. Ether is therefore stored in metal cans, or with iron wire, to prevent peroxide formation.

Some useful ethers

Ether (ethyl ether, $CH_3CH_2OCH_2CH_3$) is a colorless, sweet-smelling liquid boiling at $35\,°C$, extremely flammable, used as an industrial solvent and as a general anesthetic. It is soluble to the extent of 12 parts/hundred in water. Ether was first introduced as an anesthetic about 1850 by Crawford Long in Georgia and Avery Morton in Boston almost simultaneously. It is easily administered and in general has advantages over the anesthetics previously mentioned (ethylene, cyclopropane), so that it is more widely used. *Vinyl ether* (vinethene, $CH_2{=}CH-O-CH{=}CH_2$) is about four times as effective as a general anesthetic than ethyl ether, and was actually predicted to be an anesthetic by Leake before it was made. It involves both the olefin and ether structures, each of which is an anesthetic by itself.

Ethylene oxide is a cyclic ether, prepared from 2-chloroethanol by treatment with alkali, or more cheaply industrially by the oxidation of ethylene over a silver catalyst. Ethylene oxide is a good general

9.13
$$\underset{\underset{OH \quad Cl}{|\quad\;\;|}}{CH_2-CH_2} + NaOH \longrightarrow H_2C\underset{O}{\diagdown\diagup}CH_2 + NaCl + H_2O$$

9.14
$$CH_2{=}CH_2 + O_2 \xrightarrow{\text{cat.}} H_2C\underset{O}{\diagdown\diagup}CH_2$$

anesthetic, but there is danger of explosion as it is very reactive. It has found much greater use in chemical manufacture, owing to its great reactivity. Nearly 800 million pounds were produced in 1960. Ethylene oxide resembles cyclopropane, in that the strained ring reacts by addition with opening of the ring. It adds water in the presence of acid to form ethylene glycol.

9.15
$$H_2C\!\!-\!\!CH_2 + H\!-\!OH \xrightarrow{H^+} HOCH_2CH_2OH$$
(O bridge)

More than 50 per cent of the ethylene oxide production goes to manufacture of ethylene glycol, which is used in antifreeze, brake fluid, paint solvent, and in the manufacture of plastics. Further reaction of ethylene glycol with ethylene oxide yields the polyethylene glycols, which are useful solvents, water-soluble lubricants, plasticizers, and emulsifying agents.

$$HOCH_2CH_2OH + H_2C\!\!-\!\!CH_2 \longrightarrow$$

9.16
$$HOCH_2CH_2OCH_2CH_2OH \xrightarrow{H_2C\!\!-\!\!CH_2}$$
diethylene glycol

$$HOCH_2CH_2OCH_2CH_2OCH_2CH_2OH \longrightarrow \text{etc.}$$
triethylene glycol

Ethylene oxide reacts exothermically with other compounds having a labile hydrogen atom, such as alcohols, phenols, amines, ammonia, and acids, to produce a variety of useful substances. In addition to ethylene glycol and the polyethylene glycols, ethylene oxide serves as an industrial source of anhydrous ethylene chlorohydrin, acrylonitrile, ethanolamine, triethanolamine, diethylaminoethanol, and the industrial solvents known as cellosolves and carbitols.

9.17
$$H_2C\!\!-\!\!CH_2 + HCl \longrightarrow HOCH_2CH_2Cl$$
ethylene chlorohydrin

9.18
$$H_2C\!\!-\!\!CH_2 + HCN \longrightarrow HOCH_2CH_2CN \xrightarrow{-H_2O} CH_2\!\!=\!\!CH\!\!-\!\!CN$$
acrylonitrile

$$H_2C\!\!-\!\!CH_2 + NH_3 \longrightarrow HOCH_2CH_2NH_2 \xrightarrow{H_2C\!\!-\!\!CH_2}$$
ethanolamine

9.19
$$(HOCH_2CH_2)_2NH \xrightarrow{H_2C\!\!-\!\!CH_2} (HOCH_2CH_2)_3N$$
diethanolamine   triethanolamine

9.20
$$H_2C\!\!-\!\!CH_2 + (C_2H_5)_2NH \longrightarrow (CH_3CH_2)_2NCH_2CH_2OH$$
diethylaminoethanol

9.21
$$H_2C\!\!-\!\!CH_2 + CH_3OH \longrightarrow CH_3OCH_2CH_2OH \xrightarrow{H_2C\!\!-\!\!CH_2}$$
methylcellosolve
$$CH_3OCH_2CH_2OCH_2CH_2OH$$
methylcarbitol

Ethylene oxide reacts readily with Grignard reagents to form primary alcohols. For example, β-phenylethanol, or *oil of roses,* can be made from ethylene oxide and bromobenzene.

9.22
$$\text{C}_6\text{H}_5\text{—Br} \xrightarrow[(\text{C}_2\text{H}_5)_2\text{O}]{\text{Mg}} \text{C}_6\text{H}_5\text{—MgBr} \xrightarrow[2.\ \text{H}_2\text{O/H}^+]{1.\ \text{H}_2\text{C}\overset{\text{O}}{\diagdown}\text{CH}_2} \text{C}_6\text{H}_5\text{—CH}_2\text{CH}_2\text{OH}$$

All these reactions are nucleophilic displacements of oxygen from carbon. They are acid-catalyzed, and may be summarized by the following:

9.23
$$\text{CH}_2\text{—CH}_2 + \text{H}^+ \longrightarrow \text{CH}_2\text{—CH}_2$$

9.24
$$\text{CH}_2\text{—CH}_2 + \text{B:} \longrightarrow \text{BCH}_2\text{CH}_2\text{OH}$$

(Compare this to the reaction of cyclic bromonium ion, p. 59.)

Dioxane is a high-boiling ether completely soluble in water, and having good solvent properties. It is made indirectly from ethylene oxide by dehydrating diethylene glycol.

9.25
$$\text{HOCH}_2\text{CH}_2\text{OCH}_2\text{CH}_2\text{OH} \xrightarrow[250°]{\text{Al}_2\text{O}_3} \text{O}\underset{\text{CH}_2\text{—CH}_2}{\overset{\text{CH}_2\text{—CH}_2}{\diagup\diagdown}}\text{O}$$

Study Questions

1. Write structural formulas and names (common or I.U.C.) for all isomeric ethers of the formula $C_6H_{14}O$. There are 15.

2. Show by equations how ethanol could be converted to *a*) ethylene, *b*) ethyl ether, *c*) ethylene chlorohydrin, *d*) ethylene oxide, *e*) ethylene glycol, and *f*) dioxane.

3. What is meant by the Williamson synthesis? Show how it can be employed to synthesize anisole, phenetole, and methyl isopropyl ether.

4. What is the industrial or medicinal value of the following substances? *a*) vinethane, *b*) ethylene oxide, *c*) ethylene glycol, *d*) tetrahydrofuran, and *e*) acrylonitrile.

5. Propylene oxide reacts in the same way as ethylene oxide. Show what products might be expected from the reaction of propylene oxide with water, hydrogen chloride, ethanol, ammonia, and methylmagnesium chloride.

6. A substance A, C_7H_8O, when treated with bromine reacted slowly to liberate hydrogen bromide, and a substance B, C_7H_7OBr, was formed. When A was boiled with HI, methyl iodide was obtained, and a substance C, C_6H_6O, which gave a purple color with ferric chloride. What are the structures of A, B, and C?

7. How could you distinguish between the following pairs of isomers?
   a) ethanol and dimethyl ether;
   b) vinyl ethyl ether and tetrahydrofuran;
   c) *p*-methoxybenzyl alcohol and *p*-ethoxyphenol.

Advanced Reading References

Organic Chemistry, 3rd Ed., R. Q. Brewster and W. E. McEwen, Prentice-Hall, Inc., Englewood Cliffs, N. J., 1961, Chapter 7.

Principles of Organic Chemistry, 2nd Ed., J. English and H. G. Cassidy, McGraw-Hill, New York, 1956, Chapter 10.

Chemistry of Organic Compounds, 2nd Ed., C. R. Noller, W. B. Saunders, Philadelphia, 1957, Chapter 8.

new terms & concepts

Aldehydes and ketones contain the carbonyl (—CO—) group.
The carbonyl group reacts by addition.
Reagents with active hydrogen atoms such as hydrogen cyanide, sodium bisulfite,
alcohols, amines, hydroxylamine, and hydrazine add to the carbonyl group.
Grignard reagents add readily to the carbonyl group to form alcohols.
The carbonyl group can be reduced to alcohols, or completely to
the methylene (—CH$_2$—) group.
Aldehydes differ from ketones in ease of oxidation.
Aldehydes react with mild oxidizing agents such as Fehling's or Benedict's
solution (copper oxide) or Tollens' reagent (silver oxide).
Carbonyl groups activate α-hydrogens.
Methyl ketones produce haloforms in alkaline halogen solutions.
In alkaline solution, aldehydes undergo aldol condensation *if α-hydrogens*
are present, and the Cannizzaro reaction if α-hydrogens are absent.
Carbonyl groups are formed by oxidation of alcohols or by hydrolysis of 1,1-dihalides.
Ketones are obtained by pyrolysis of calcium salts of carboxylic acids
or by the Friedel-Crafts reaction in the aromatic series.
The oxo process is an important industrial source for alphatic aldehydes.
Formaldehyde, acetaldehyde, and benzaldehyde are aldehydes used industrially.
Acetone and cyclohexanone are useful solvents for manufacture of intermediates.
Aromatic aldehydes occur in flavoring oils.
Large-ring ketones are important in the perfume industry.
The aldehydes and ketones possess the functional group of oxygen linked
by a double bond to carbon (C$=$O), called the carbonyl *group.*
Aldehydes have a hydrogen atom attached to the carbonyl group
forming the carboxaldehyde group, —CHO,
which is more reactive than the carbonyl group in ketones.
The ketones have both free valences of the carbonyl group attached to organic radicals.
Like the ethers, ketones are simple if both groups are the same in R—CO—R,
but are mixed ketones in R—CO—R′ or Ar—CO—R.
These compounds have proved very useful in organic syntheses,
and as industrial solvents and manufacturing materials.

10

Oxygenated hydrocarbons
iii. aldehydes and ketones

Naming the aldehydes and ketones

Many aldehydes and ketones are known by common names. Some of these, along with their I.U.C. names for comparison, are listed in Table 10.01.

TABLE 10.01   NAMES AND PROPERTIES OF SOME COMMON ALDEHYDES AND KETONES

Compound	Common name	I.U.C. name	M.P. °C	B.P. °C
$H_2C{=}O$	Formaldehyde	Methanal	−92	−21
$CH_3{-}CHO$	Acetaldehyde	Ethanal	−123	20
$CH_3CH_2{-}CHO$	Propionaldehyde	Propanal	−81	48
$CH_3CH_2CH_2{-}CHO$	Butyraldehyde	Butanal	−99	75
$(CH_3)_2CH{-}CHO$	Isobutyraldehyde	2-Methylpropanal	−66	65
$CH_3(CH_2)_3{-}CHO$	Valeraldehyde	Pentanal		103
$C_6H_5{-}CHO$	Benzaldehyde	Benzaldehyde	−56	179
$CH_3{-}CO{-}CH_3$	Acetone	Propanone	−95	56
$CH_3{-}CO{-}CH_2CH_3$	Methyl ethyl ketone	Butanone	−87	80
$CH_3{-}CO{-}CH_2CH_2CH_3$	Methyl propyl ketone	2-Pentanone	−78	102
$CH_3CH_2{-}CO{-}CH_2CH_3$	Diethyl ketone	3-Pentanone	−42	103
$C_6H_5{-}CO{-}CH_3$	Acetophenone	Ethanoylbenzene	20	202
$C_6H_5{-}CO{-}C_6H_5$	Benzophenone	Benzoylbenzene	49	306
$H_2C{\begin{smallmatrix}CH_2-CH_2\\ \\CH_2-CH_2\end{smallmatrix}}C{=}O$	Cyclohexanone	Cyclohexanone	−45	155

Physical properties of aldehydes and ketones

The presence of an oxygen atom in a molecule increases the boiling point and the solubility in water over that of the parent hydrocarbon. This effect is somewhat less in the carbonyl compounds than in the corresponding alcohols. Compare, for example, butane, butanal, and 1-butanol. Butane boils at $-1°C$, and is soluble 2 parts/100 in water; butanal boils at $75°C$, and is soluble 4 parts/100 in water; while 1-butanol boils at $117°C$, and is soluble 9 parts/100 in water. The effect of symmetry of the molecule on the melting point may still be observed in the melting points of butyraldehyde and isobutyraldehyde (Table 10.01) and of 2-pentanone and 3-pentanone.

The lower members of the aliphatic aldehydes have stinging unpleasant odors (formaldehyde, for example) but the higher-molecular-weight aldehydes and ketones have pleasant flowery odors which make them valuable as perfumes and flavors. Many of these occur in nature as essential oils of flowers and spices.

Reactions of the carbonyl group

In the presence of metal catalysts at low pressure, aldehydes and ketones are easily reduced to I° or II° alcohols by adding hydrogen (p. 116). The carbonyl group is unsaturated, and therefore undergoes a number of *addition* reactions. Since oxygen is more electronegative than carbon (p. 7) it will attract the electrons of the double bond strongly. Addition to the carbonyl group then occurs by attack of a

$$-\overset{|}{C}{=}\overset{\frown}{O}\colon \longleftrightarrow -\overset{|}{\underset{}{C}}-\overset{+}{\underset{}{O}}\colon^{-}$$

nucleophilic (electron-rich) reagent, B:, on the carbon. B: in the equation may be any electron-rich reagent, such as

$$:NH_3, \quad :CN^-, \quad NaSO_3^-, \quad R-\overset{..}{\underset{..}{O}}-H, \quad R-\overset{..}{\underset{..}{S}}-H$$

$$R:^- \text{ (the Grignard carbanion)}, \; :NH_2OH, \quad \text{or} \quad :NH_2NH_2$$

$$B: + \overset{|}{\underset{|}{C}}{=}O \longrightarrow B-\overset{|}{\underset{|}{C}}-O^- \overset{H^+}{\longrightarrow} B-\overset{|}{\underset{|}{C}}-OH$$

The important step in additions to carbon-oxygen double bonds is the forming of a bond to carbon. The reaction may be catalyzed by acids, since addition of a proton to oxygen renders the carbon more positive. Since the nucleophilic reagents are usually bases which can react with

$$-\overset{|}{\underset{|}{C}}\!\!=\!\!O + H^+ \longrightarrow -\overset{|}{\underset{|}{C}}\!-OH$$

protons, a delicate balance of protons and nucleophilic base must be maintained. Thus the formation of oximes and hydrazones is catalyzed by the addition of some hydrochloride or sulfate salts of the base.

Ammonia adds to the carbonyl group forming a group of hydroxy-amines called aldehyde-ammonias, or other more complex products. Hydrogen cyanide and sodium bisulfite add to form the cyanohydrins and bisulfite addition compounds.

10.01
$$R-CHO + NH_3 \longrightarrow R-\underset{NH_2}{\overset{|}{C}HOH} \qquad \text{aldehyde-ammonia}$$

10.02
$$R-\overset{O}{\overset{\|}{C}}-CH_3 + H-CN \longrightarrow R-\underset{OH}{\overset{CH_3}{\overset{|}{\underset{|}{C}}}}-CN \qquad \text{cyanohydrin}$$

10.03
$$R-CHO + HSO_2ONa \longrightarrow R-\underset{OH}{\overset{|}{C}H}-SO_2ONa \qquad \begin{array}{l}\text{bisulfite addition} \\ \text{product}\end{array}$$

Alcohols will add to aldehydes in a reversible reaction to form hemiacetals, which further react in the presence of acid catalysts by loss of water to form the 1,1-di-ethers, called *acetals*.

10.04
$$CH_3-\overset{H}{\overset{|}{C}}\!\!=\!\!O + H-OCH_2CH_3 \rightleftharpoons CH_3-\underset{O-CH_2CH_3}{\overset{H}{\overset{|}{\underset{|}{C}}}}-OH \xrightarrow[H^+]{HOCH_2CH_3}$$

hemiacetal

$$CH_3C\overset{H}{\underset{OCH_2CH_3}{\overset{OCH_2CH_3}{\diagdown}}} + H_2O$$

acetaldehyde
diethyl acetal

Mercaptans add to the carbonyl group of both aldehydes and ketones to form the hemimercaptal, which then reacts further to lose water and form the *mercaptal*.

$$(CH_3)_2C{=}O + H{-}SCH_3 \rightleftharpoons (CH_3)_2C{\overset{OH}{\underset{SCH_3}{\big<}}} \xrightarrow{H-SCH_3}$$

10.05

$$(CH_3)_2C{\overset{SCH_3}{\underset{SCH_3}{\big<}}} + H_2O$$

The addition of the *Grignard reagent* to carbonyl compounds to form the alcohol (p. 118) also illustrated addition to the >C=O group (Eq. 10.06).

10.06
$$C_6H_5{-}\overset{\overset{\displaystyle CH_3}{|}}{C}{=}O + XMg{-}CH_3 \longrightarrow C_6H_5{-}\overset{\overset{\displaystyle CH_3}{|}}{\underset{\underset{\displaystyle CH_3}{|}}{C}}{-}O{-}MgX \xrightarrow{H_2O}$$

$$C_6H_5{-}\overset{\overset{\displaystyle CH_3}{|}}{\underset{\underset{\displaystyle CH_3}{|}}{C}}{-}OH + MgX(OH)$$

When a hydrogen atom of ammonia is replaced by a negative oxygen or nitrogen atom, as in *hydroxylamine*, NH_2OH, or *hydrazine*, NH_2NH_2, these compounds react much more readily with carbonyl compounds, first adding reversibly to form an unstable intermediate, which loses water to form a stable product containing a $C{=}N$ group

10.07
$$CH_3{-}\overset{\overset{\displaystyle H}{|}}{C}{=}O + H{-}\overset{\overset{\displaystyle H}{|}}{N}{-}OH \rightleftharpoons \left[CH_3{-}\overset{\overset{\displaystyle H}{|}}{\underset{\underset{\displaystyle HO}{|}}{C}}{-}\overset{}{\underset{\underset{\displaystyle H}{|}}{N}}{-}OH \right] \longrightarrow$$

$$CH_3{-}\overset{\overset{\displaystyle H}{|}}{C}{=}NOH + H_2O$$
acetaldoxime

10.08
$$(CH_3)_2C{=}O + H{-}NHNH_2 \rightleftharpoons \left[(CH_3)_2\overset{}{\underset{\underset{\displaystyle HO}{|}}{C}}{-}\overset{}{\underset{\underset{\displaystyle H}{|}}{N}}NH_2 \right] \longrightarrow$$

$$(CH_3)_2C{=}NNH_2 + H_2O$$
acetone hydrazone

(Eqs. 10.07 and 10.08). Hydroxylamine reacts with aldehydes and ketones to form *oximes,* and hydrazine forms *hydrazones.* These reactions are important because the oximes and hydrazones are useful derivatives suitable for identifying the aldehydes and ketones by melting points. This is particularly true of the substituted hydrazines. For example, phenylhydrazine, $C_6H_5NHNH_2$, is a special reagent for identifying sugars, reacting with their aldehyde or ketone groups to form characteristic crystals of osazones which can be identified from previously determined patterns (see p. 264). It forms *phenylhydrazones* with simple carbonyl compounds.

10.09

$$C_6H_5-\overset{\overset{H}{|}}{C}=O + H-NHNHC_6H_5 \rightleftharpoons \left[C_6H_5-\overset{\overset{H}{|}}{\underset{\underset{HO}{|}}{C}}-\overset{|}{\underset{\underset{H}{|}}{N}}-NHC_6H_5 \right] \longrightarrow$$

$$C_6H_5-CH=N-NHC_6H_5 + H_2O$$
benzaldehyde
phenylhydrazone

Reactions at the alpha-carbon atom

The strongly polar carbonyl group activates its neighboring carbon atoms (the *alpha*-carbons) so that they tend to lose their hydrogens (the *alpha*-hydrogens) more easily than is common for simple aliphatic C-H bonds. For example, simple aldehydes and ketones can exist in two isomeric forms which can change one into the other because of the labile *alpha*-hydrogen. These are called *tautomers,* and the phenomenon of two tautomers changing back and forth is called *tautomerism.*

$$H-\overset{\overset{H}{|}}{\underset{\underset{H}{|}}{C}}-\overset{\overset{O}{\|}}{C}-H \rightleftharpoons \overset{H}{\underset{H}{}}C=C\overset{OH}{\underset{H}{}}$$
enol

The hydroxy-olefin form is called the *enol* form, according to the I.U.C. nomenclature. The carbonyl, or *keto,* form is the most stable form, but the shift is promoted by alkali, and reactions of the *alpha*-hydrogens are favored in alkaline solution. It is because of this equilibrium between keto and enol forms that acetylene can be hydrated to produce

10.10 $\quad H-C\equiv C-H + H-OH \xrightarrow[H_2SO_4]{Hg^+} H_2C=CHOH \rightleftharpoons CH_3-CHO$

acetaldehyde (p. 68). *Alpha*-hydrogens are easily replaced by halogens in alkaline solution. Propionaldehyde reacts with chlorine in sodium carbonate solution to form 2-chloropropanal. Methyl ketones, containing the CH_3-CO- group, are a special case, and react rapidly

10.11 $CH_3CH_2CHO + Cl_2 + OH^- \longrightarrow CH_3CHClCHO + H_2O + Cl^-$

with an alkaline solution of a halogen. All of the methyl hydrogens are replaced by halogen atoms, forming a trihalomethyl ketone, which is unstable in alkali and is split in a second reaction to the haloform. When iodine is used, iodoform is precipitated in the solution as a yellow solid which is easily seen, thus serving as a test for the CH_3—CO— group. This reaction, called the *haloform reaction,* may also be used to manufacture *chloroform* and *bromoform* ($CHBr_3$).

10.12 $CH_3-\overset{\overset{\displaystyle O}{\|}}{C}-CH_3 + 3\,I_2 + 3\,OH^- \longrightarrow CH_3-\overset{\overset{\displaystyle O}{\|}}{C}-CI_3 + 3\,H_2O + 3\,I^-$

10.13 $CH_3-CO-CI_3 + OH^- \longrightarrow CH_3-COO^- + CHI_3$

                       iodoform

In alkaline solution, carbonyl compounds having an ionizable *alpha*-hydrogen will act as nucleophilic reagents adding readily to the carbonyl group of other molecules. For example, acetaldehyde forms 3-hydroxybutanol (aldol) by condensing with itself in alkaline solution (Eq. 10.14). In this way a new carbon-carbon bond is formed,

$$CH_3CHO + OH^- \longrightarrow \left[\bar{C}H_2CHO \right] + H_2O$$

10.14 $CH_3CHO + \left[\bar{C}H_2CHO \right] \longrightarrow CH_3\overset{\overset{\displaystyle O^-}{|}}{\underset{\underset{\displaystyle H}{|}}{C}}-CH_2CHO$

$$CH_3\overset{\overset{\displaystyle O^-}{|}}{\underset{\underset{\displaystyle H}{|}}{C}}-CH_2CHO + H_2O \longrightarrow CH_3\overset{\overset{\displaystyle OH}{|}}{\underset{\underset{\displaystyle H}{|}}{C}}-CH_2CHO + OH^-$$

                      aldol

and this reaction is therefore an important synthetic method for new compounds. The product is called aldol since it has both an aldehyde and an alcohol group. The reaction is called the *aldol condensation,* and is general for both aldehydes and ketones, providing there is at least one hydrogen on the *alpha*-carbon. Ketones are less reactive than aldehydes. The reaction has wide application in industry for the production of higher alcohols and acids. For example, both crotonic acid and 1-butanol are commercially prepared from aldol. 2-ethylhexanediol,

10.15 $CH_3CHOHCH_2CHO \xrightarrow{-H_2O} CH_3CH{=}CHCHO$

       aldol   crotonaldehyde

used in insect-repellants, and 2-ethylhexanol, used as a solvent, are also indirectly available by further aldol condensations (Eq. 10.17).

10.16 $CH_3CH_2CH_2CH_2OH \xleftarrow[cat.]{2 H_2} CH_3CH=CHCHO \xrightarrow{ox} CH_3CH=CHCOOH$

$$\text{crotonic acid}$$

$$CH_3CH_2CH_2CH_2OH \xrightarrow{ox} CH_3CH_2CH_2CHO \xrightarrow{OH^-}$$

10.17
$$\underset{\underset{\displaystyle CH_2CH_3}{|}}{CH_3CH_2CH_2\overset{\displaystyle OH}{\overset{|}{C}HCH}-CHO} \xrightarrow[cat.]{H_2} \underset{\displaystyle CH_2CH_3}{CH_3CH_2CH_2\overset{\displaystyle OH}{\overset{|}{C}HCH}-CH_2OH}$$

$$\downarrow -H_2O$$

$$\underset{\displaystyle CH_2CH_3}{CH_3CH_2CH_2CH=C}-CHO \xrightarrow[cat.]{2 H_2} \underset{\displaystyle CH_2CH_3}{CH_3(CH_2)_3CHCH_2OH}$$

Mixed aldol condensations may be carried out, but the products are complicated, unless one of the aldehydes does not have *alpha*-hydrogens. In this case, it is possible to get good yields of one product. For example, benzaldehyde may be condensed with acetaldehyde to produce cinnamaldehyde (Eq. 10.18). In this case, loss of water is spontaneous,

10.18 $\langle \bigcirc \rangle-CHO + CH_3CHO \xrightarrow{OH^-} \langle \bigcirc \rangle-CH=CHCHO + H_2O$

$$\text{cinnamaldehyde}$$

because of the increased stability of the conjugated system of cinnamaldehyde. In general, aldols (β-hydroxyaldehydes) are easily dehydrated to α,β-unsaturated compounds. This is undoubtedly due to the higher reactivity of *alpha*-hydrogens and the greater stability of conjugated systems.

Oxidation of aldehydes and ketones

The aldehydes differ from the ketones in one important property, the ease of oxidation. Aldehydes are readily oxidized even by air to form the respective acids. In fact, it is difficult to keep an aldehyde unless it is protected from air. The oxidation can also be brought about by mild chemical agents, and use is made of this fact in several

10.19
$$2 R-\overset{\displaystyle O}{\overset{||}{C}}-H + O_2 \longrightarrow 2 R-\overset{\displaystyle O}{\overset{||}{C}}-OH$$

tests for aldehydes. For example, the *silver mirror* test depends on the reduction of the mild oxidizing agent silver ammonium hydroxide

$(Ag(NH_3)_2{}^+OH^-)$, called *Tollens' reagent,* by an aldehyde. The free reduced silver is deposited on a clean glass surface as a mirror. The

10.20
$$RCHO + 2\,Ag(NH_3)_2{}^+OH^- \longrightarrow$$
$$RCOO^-NH_4{}^+ + 2\,\underline{Ag} + 3\,NH_3 + H_2O$$

best mirrors are silvered by this process, using formaldehyde as the reducing agent. Cupric ion (Cu^{++}) is also reduced by aldehydes in alkaline solution, oxidizing the aldehydes according to the equation:

10.21
$$RCHO + 2\,\underset{\text{blue}}{Cu^{++}} + 4\,OH^- \longrightarrow RCOOH + \underset{\text{red}}{\underline{Cu_2O}} + 2\,H_2O$$

Since copper ions form a blue solution, and are reduced to a red precipitate of cuprous oxide, this forms a useful test for the aldehyde group, and for certain sugars which contain the aldehyde group. *Fehling's solution* and *Benedict's solution* are specially prepared copper solutions used for this test, which may be applied to test for the presence of sugars in urine or blood. Since ketones are not oxidized by *Tollens', Fehling's,* or *Benedict's* solutions, these reagents are useful in distinguishing between the aldehydes and ketones.

Ketones are more resistant to oxidation, since carbon-carbon bonds must be broken. When ketones are oxidized by strong oxidizing agents, such as dichromic acid, the bonds on either side of the carbonyl group are broken, and a mixture of acids results. For example, ethyl methyl

10.22
$$CH_3 \overset{a}{\underset{}{|}} CO \overset{b}{\underset{}{|}} CH_2CH_3 \quad \overset{\text{[O]}}{\underset{\text{[O]}/b}{\rightrightarrows}} \quad \begin{matrix} CO_2 + CH_3CH_2COOH \\ 2\,CH_3COOH \end{matrix}$$

ketone when so oxidized produces a mixture of carbon dioxide and propionic acid (Eq. 10.22), formed by oxidation at (a), and acetic acid, formed by oxidation at (b). This reaction is a useful synthetic procedure in the case of cyclic ketones which form only one product, the dicarboxylic acid, by either path of oxidation. Cyclohexanone is a commercial source of adipic acid, used in the manufacture of plastics.

10.23
$$\xrightarrow[\text{a and b}]{\text{[O]}} HOCOCH_2CH_2CH_2CH_2COOH$$
adipic acid

The haloform reaction provides an effective means of oxidizing methyl ketones to the respective acids containing one less carbon atom.

Trimethylacetic acid is obtained in about 75 per cent yield by oxidation of methyl tert-butyl ketone with bromine in sodium hydroxide solution (Eqs. 10.25 and 10.26).

10.24
$$R-CO-CH_3 \xrightarrow[OH^-]{NaOCl} RCOOH + CHCl_3$$

10.25
$$(CH_3)_3C-CO-CH_3 + 4\,NaOH + 3\,Br_2 \longrightarrow$$
$$(CH_3)_3CCOO^-Na^+ + CHBr_3 + 3\,NaBr + 3\,H_2O$$

10.26
$$(CH_3)_3CCOO^-Na^+ + H_2SO_4 \longrightarrow$$
$$(CH_3)_3CCOOH + NaHSO_4$$

Since aldehydes are so readily oxidized and reduced, in strong basic solution aldehydes which do not have *alpha*-hydrogen atoms undergo a disproportionation in which one-half of the molecules are oxidized by the other half, which are reduced. For example, when benzaldehyde is heated with sodium hydroxide, benzoic acid and benzyl alcohol are

10.27
$$2\,RCHO + Na^+OH^- \longrightarrow RCOO^-Na^+ + RCH_2OH$$

10.28 2 ⬡ $CHO + NaOH \longrightarrow$ ⬡ $COO^-Na^+ +$ ⬡ CH_2OH

produced. This reaction is called the *Cannizzaro reaction*. It can be used effectively only with aldehydes having no *alpha*-hydrogens, since other aldehydes would undergo aldol condensations in the presence of alkali more readily than they would undergo the Cannizzaro reaction. Since there is a difference in the ease of oxidation of various aldehydes, mixed Cannizzaro reactions may be carried out. Formaldehyde is most readily oxidized of all aldehydes, and therefore is an effective reducing agent for other aldehyde groups. *para*-Nitrobenzaldehyde can be reduced to *p*-nitrobenzyl alcohol by heating it in an alkaline solution of formaldehyde.

10.29 NO_2 ⬡ $CHO + CH_2O \xrightarrow{OH^-} NO_2$ ⬡ $CH_2OH + HCOO^-$

Reduction of aldehydes and ketones

Conversion of the carbonyl group to the hydroxy group has already been mentioned (p. 116). The carbonyl group may also be converted to the methylene group by two chemical methods. The *Clemmensen* reduc-

$$\overset{\displaystyle O}{\underset{\displaystyle |}{-\!\overset{||}{C}\!-}} \longrightarrow -CH_2-$$

tion (p. 41) involves treatment of the ketone with zinc and hydro-chloric acid. An aldehyde or ketone may be converted to the hydra-

10.30 $R{-}CO{-}R \xrightarrow{Zn/HCl} RCH_2R + H_2O$

zone and heated with strong alkali, in the *Wolff-Kishner* reduction. The hydrazone loses nitrogen under these conditions to form the com-

10.31

$$\underset{\displaystyle R{-}\overset{\displaystyle \overset{O}{\|}}{C}{-}R}{} + H_2N{-}NH_2 \longrightarrow \underset{\displaystyle R{-}\overset{\displaystyle \overset{N{-}NH_2}{\|}}{C}{-}R}{} + H_2O$$

10.32 $R_2C{=}NNH_2 \xrightarrow[OH^-]{\Delta} RCH_2R + N_2$

pletely reduced product. Bi-molecular reduction of ketones occurs when they are treated with magnesium metal in alcohol solution. Acetone, for example, when refluxed with magnesium forms 2,3-dimethyl-butane-2,3-diol (pinacol). Pinacol can be dehydrated to 2,3-dimethyl-1,3-butadiene, which was used in the early efforts to make synthetic rubber (p. 96).

10.33

$$2\ CH_3COCH_3 \xrightarrow{Mg} \underset{\underset{Mg}{\underset{|}{O\ \ \ O}}}{CH_3{-}\overset{\overset{CH_3}{|}}{C}{-}\overset{\overset{CH_3}{|}}{C}{-}CH_3}$$

$$\xrightarrow{H^+} \underset{\underset{OH\ \ OH}{}}{CH_3{-}\overset{\overset{CH_3}{|}}{C}{-}\overset{\overset{CH_3}{|}}{C}{-}CH_3} \xrightarrow{\Delta} CH_2{=}\overset{\overset{CH_3}{|}}{C}{-}\overset{\overset{CH_3}{|}}{C}{=}CH_2$$

pinacol

Preparation of the carbonyl compounds

One of the best sources of the carbonyl compounds is oxidation of alcohols. I° alcohols give aldehydes and II° alcohols yield ketones

10.34 $R{-}CH_2OH + CuO \longrightarrow R{-}CHO + Cu + H_2O$

10.35 $R{-}CHOH{-}R + CuO \longrightarrow R{-}CO{-}R + Cu + H_2O$

(p. 115). Another method involves hydrolysis of the 1,1-dichlorides, to form the unstable 1,1-dihydroxy compounds which lose water to form aldehydes. This method is especially useful in the commercial manu-

10.36 $R{-}CHCl_2 \xrightarrow{2\ OH^-} \left[\underset{\underset{O{-}H}{|}}{R{-}\overset{\overset{H}{|}}{C}{-}OH} \right] \longrightarrow R{-}\overset{\overset{H}{|}}{C}{=}O$

facture of benzaldehyde from toluene by way of chlorination in light.

10.37 $C_6H_5CH_3 \xrightarrow{Cl_2} C_6H_5CHCl_2 \xrightarrow{OH^-} C_6H_5CHO$

Aldehydes may also be obtained by reduction of acid chlorides over a special catalyst.

10.38
$$R-\overset{O}{\overset{\|}{C}}-Cl + H_2 \xrightarrow{cat.} R-\overset{O}{\overset{\|}{C}}-H + HCl$$

An important industrial process for the manufacture of aldehydes developed in recent years is the *oxo* process (Chapter 4). Oxo production was started in the United States in 1948, and something over 75 million pounds of aldehydes and derivatives were manufactured by this process in 1960. The reaction involves condensing olefins with carbon monoxide and hydrogen over cobalt catalysts. The final product is an aldehyde with one more carbon atom than the starting material. Both continuous- and branched-chain aldehydes are produced. When the oxo process is coupled with the aldol condensation, the synthetic

10.39 $CH_3CH=CH_2 + CO + H_2 \xrightarrow{cat.} CH_3CH_2CH_2CHO + CH_3\underset{\underset{CH_3}{|}}{C}HCHO$

possibilities of aliphatic compounds from petroleum are almost unlimited.

The more reactive aromatic compounds may be converted to aldehydes by special methods. For example, in the *Reimer-Tiemann* reaction phenol condenses with chloroform in the presence of a base to form salicylaldehyde. Dimethylformamide, $(CH_3)_2NCHO$, acts as a

10.40

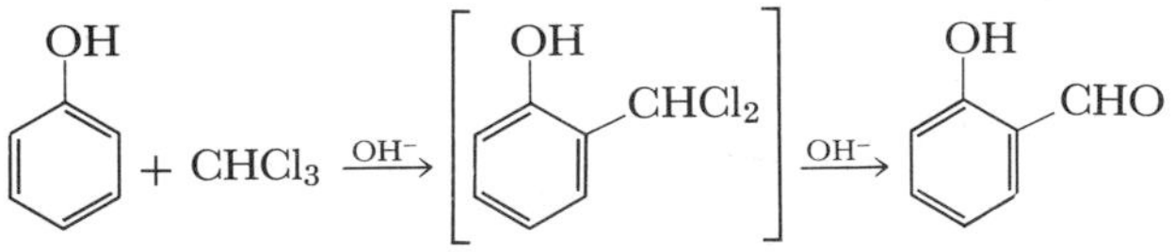

formylating agent for reactive aromatic compounds in the presence of phosphorous oxychloride. *p*-Dimethylaminobenzaldehyde can be obtained in about 85 per cent yield in this reaction.

10.41

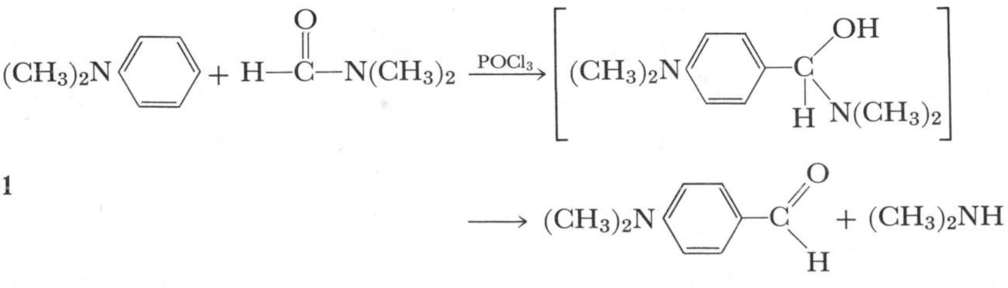

Ketones may be prepared by the action of Grignard reagents on esters or acid chlorides (Eq. 10.42). The aromatic ketones are readily

10.42
$$R-\overset{O}{\overset{\|}{C}}-OC_2H_5 + R'-MgX \longrightarrow \left[R-\overset{OMgX}{\underset{R'}{\overset{|}{\underset{|}{C}}}}-OC_2H_5 \right] \longrightarrow$$

$$R-\overset{O}{\overset{\|}{C}}-R' + C_2H_5OMgX$$

10.43
$$R-\overset{O}{\overset{\|}{C}}-Cl + R'-MgX \longrightarrow \left[R-\overset{OMgX}{\underset{R'}{\overset{|}{\underset{|}{C}}}}-Cl \right] \longrightarrow$$

$$R-\overset{O}{\overset{\|}{C}}-R' + MgClX$$

prepared by a special application of the *Friedel-Crafts* reaction (p. 78), in which an aromatic compound reacts with an acid chloride in the presence of anhydrous aluminum chloride.

10.44
$$\text{⟨⟩}-H + Cl-\overset{O}{\overset{\|}{C}}-R \xrightarrow{\text{AlCl}_3} \text{⟨⟩}-\overset{O}{\overset{\|}{C}}-R + HCl$$

Acids can be converted to ketones by heating the barium or calcium salts in the dry state. This reaction is especially useful in the

10.45
$$\left[\begin{array}{c} CH_3-\overset{O}{\overset{\|}{C}}-O^- \\ CH_3-\overset{}{\underset{O}{\overset{|}{\underset{\|}{C}}}}-O^- \end{array} \right] Ca^{++} \xrightarrow{\Delta} CH_3-\overset{O}{\overset{\|}{C}}-CH_3 + CaCO_3$$

synthesis of cyclic ketones from open-chain dicarboxylic acids. For example, cyclopentanone results when barium salt of adipic acid is heated (Eq. 10.46). This reaction produces a new carbon-carbon bond, and has been used to synthesize rings containing up to 30 carbon atoms. A number of other special methods have been developed for the preparation of aromatic aldehydes and ketones, but the above will serve to illustrate the general processes.

10.46

$$\begin{array}{c} COO^- \\ | \\ (CH_2)_4\ Ba^{++} \\ | \\ COO^- \end{array} \xrightarrow{\Delta} \begin{array}{c} O \\ \parallel \\ C \\ H_2C \quad CH_2 \\ | \qquad | \\ H_2C \text{---} CH_2 \end{array} + BaCO_3$$

Some important aldehydes and ketones

Formaldehyde, or methanal, CH_2O, is a colorless gas with a pungent irritating odor, prepared industrially by oxidizing methanol with air over a catalyst. *Formaldehyde solution* (formalin) contains not less than

10.47 $$CH_3OH + O_2 \xrightarrow{cat.} H_2C{=}O + H_2O$$

37 per cent CH_2O in water, with 10–15 per cent methanol added as a preservative, to prevent polymerization. It is used as a disinfectant and fungicide, chiefly by evaporation of the solution to liberate the gas. Since formaldehyde is a protein poison, it can not be used as an internal antiseptic, but it is commonly used to preserve biological and anatomical specimens. Formaldehyde reacts with ammonia to form a

10.48 $4\,NH_3 + 6\,CH_2O \longrightarrow$

hexamethylenetetramine, $C_6H_{12}N_4$

white crystalline odorless compound, $C_6H_{12}N_4$, called hexamethylene-tetramine, which is used as a urinary antiseptic under the name *Methenamine, U.S.P.,* or Urotropine. Hexamethylenetetramine liberates formaldehyde when treated with acid, and since it has no antiseptic action unless the urine is acidic, it probably acts by slow liberation of formaldehyde in the bladder and kidneys. Formaldehyde polymerizes to a linear polymer, $H{-}(OCH_2)_n{-}OH$, called *paraformaldehyde,* a white waxy solid that liberates formaldehyde on heating. It is used to make fumigating candles. Formaldehyde also reacts with phenol and urea to form useful plastics (see Chapter 18).

$$HO{-}CH_2{-}O{-}CH_2{-}O{-}CH_2{-}O{-}CH_2{-}O{-}CH_2{-}O{-}CH_2{-}O{-}CH_2{-}O{-}CH_2 \text{-------} O{-}CH_2{-}OH$$

paraformaldehyde

Acetaldehyde is chiefly important as a chemical intermediate in the manufacture of acetic acid, ethanol, ethyl acetate, etc. Since it can be readily made from acetylene, which in turn is made from coke, it pro-

$$CaO + C \xrightarrow{\Delta} CaC_2 \xrightarrow{H_2O} H-C{\equiv}C-H$$

10.49
$$\xrightarrow[Hg/H^+]{H_2O} CH_3CHO \begin{array}{l} \xrightarrow{H_2} CH_3CH_2OH \\ \xrightarrow{O_2} CH_3COOH \\ \xsearrow[alumina] CH_3COOCH_2CH_3 \end{array}$$

vides a useful path for the preparation of many organic compounds from coal. In the presence of acid, acetaldehyde trimerizes to a ring compound, called para-acetaldehyde or paraldehyde. This compound, *paraldehyde,* is a rapid and effective sedative, but has the disadvantage of imparting a disagreeable odor to the breath. The compound is a liquid with a sharp taste and fernlike odor.

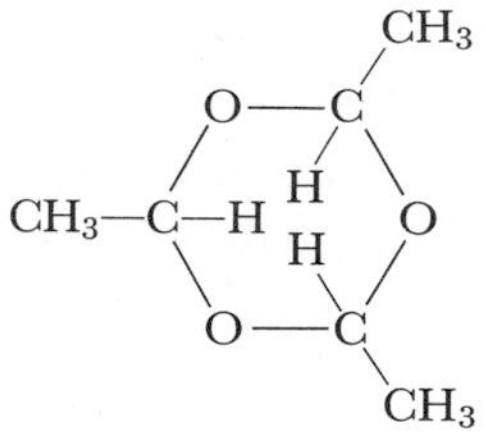

paraldehyde

When all of the hydrogens of acetaldehyde are replaced by chlorine atoms, chloral, Cl_3C-CHO, is formed as an oily liquid which reacts

10.50
$$CH_3CH_2OH + 4\,Cl_2 \longrightarrow Cl_3C-CHO + 5\,HCl$$

with water to form a white crystaline solid, $Cl_3C-CH(OH)_2$, *chloral hydrate.* This substance is a rapid effective hypnotic which is of value in inducing sleep where there is nervous excitement, but it is not effective where pain is severe. Chloral is manufactured directly from ethanol by oxidation with chlorine gas, and condenses with chlorobenzene in the presence of sulfuric acid to produce the insecticide, D.D.T. (p. 107).

10.51

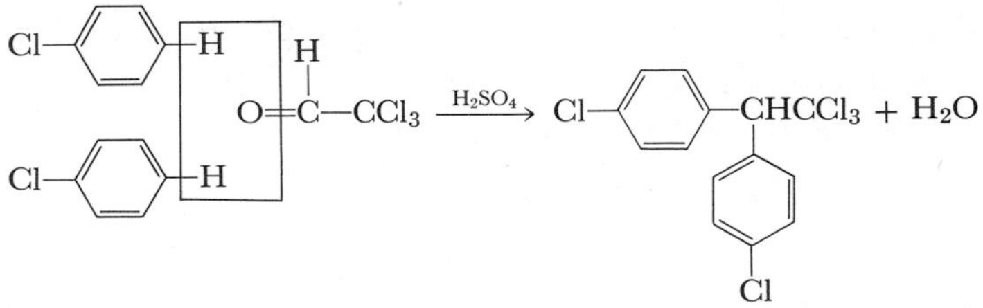

Acetone, $CH_3—CO—CH_3$, is the simplest ketone, and is widely used as an industrial solvent. It can be manufactured by fermentation of corn starch or molasses using special ferments, by the oxidation of isopropanol, or by the distillation of calcium acetate. Acetone is a low-boiling liquid soluble in water and sometimes found in the urine and blood of diabetic patients. Being volatile, it is also excreted through the lungs, and may be detected on the breath of the diabetic by its sweet odor. Acetone is the raw material from which *methyl methacrylate* can be prepared, and this in turn is polymerized by addition polymerization to the clear, hard, glasslike resins such as *Lucite* or *Plexiglass* used in combs, dentures, etc. (Figure 10.01). The chemical reactions of this manufacturing process are shown stepwise in Eq. 10.52.

10.52

$$CH_3—\overset{\displaystyle O}{\overset{\|}{C}}—CH_3 + HCN \longrightarrow CH_3—\underset{\underset{\displaystyle CH_3}{|}}{\overset{\overset{\displaystyle OH}{|}}{C}}—CN \xrightarrow[H^+]{CH_3OH} CH_3—\underset{\underset{\displaystyle CH_3}{|}}{\overset{\overset{\displaystyle OH}{|}}{C}}—COOCH_3$$

$$\xrightarrow{H_2SO_4} CH_2=\underset{\underset{\displaystyle CH_3}{|}}{C}—COOCH_3$$

$$\xrightarrow{polymerize} —CH_2—\underset{\underset{\displaystyle COOCH_3}{|}}{\overset{\overset{\displaystyle CH_3}{|}}{C}}—CH_2—\underset{\underset{\displaystyle COOCH_3}{|}}{\overset{\overset{\displaystyle CH_3}{|}}{C}}—CH_2—\underset{\underset{\displaystyle COOCH_3}{|}}{\overset{\overset{\displaystyle CH_3}{|}}{C}}—CH_2—\underset{\underset{\displaystyle COOCH_3}{|}}{\overset{\overset{\displaystyle CH_3}{|}}{C}}—CH_2—\underset{\underset{\displaystyle COOCH_3}{|}}{\overset{\overset{\displaystyle CH_3}{|}}{C}}—etc.$$

methyl methacrylate resin

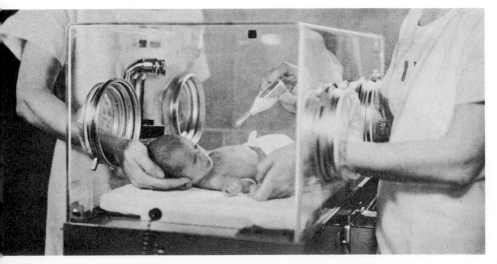

Fig. 10.01. Nursery incubator of Lucite plastic combines clear vision with maximum safety. (Courtesy of Owens-Illinois Company.)

Several cyclic ketones are of interest. Those having 15 or 17 carbons in a ring are used in the perfume industry, and are found naturally in musk glands of certain animals. *Muscone* is obtained from the musk deer, and *civetone* (p. 43) from the civet cat. Similar large-ring com-

muscone

camphor

pounds have been manufactured synthetically for perfumery. *Camphor,* obtained from the camphor tree (China, India, Australia), is a mild antiseptic and irritant often used in liniments and other rubifacients, and as an expectorant in colds and bronchitis.

Several of the aromatic aldehydes are used as flavoring oils and perfumes. *Benzaldehyde,* C_6H_5CHO, is the principle constituent of oil of almonds, and is used as a flavoring. 3-Methoxy-4-hydroxybenzaldehyde is called *vanillin* and is the essential flavor of the vanilla bean. Vanillin is now manufactured as a by-product of the paper industry from waste lignin. It is used in alcohol solution as synthetic extract of vanilla. *Anisaldehyde* (*para*-methoxybenzaldehyde) is found along with *anethole* (*p*-methoxypropenylbenzene, $CH_3OC_6H_4CH=CHCH_3$) in oil of anise, and *cinnamaldehyde* (3-phenylpropenal) is the principal flavoring oil in oil of cinnamon.

The mixed aryl alkyl ketones have definite hypnotic activity which increases with increasing size of the alkyl group, but all of them are toxic, the toxicity increasing in the same way. *Acetophenone* (phenyl methyl ketone, $C_6H_5-CO-CH_3$) was once used in medical practice as a hypnotic, Hypnone, but its use has been discontinued.

Cyclohexanone is used as a solvent and chemical intermediate. It is manufactured from phenol by high-pressure reduction to cyclohexanol, followed by oxidation to cyclohexanone. Because of its manufacture from phenol, it is the cheapest and most common cyclic ketone known.

10.53

Study Questions

1. Write structural formulas for ethanal, 2-methylpropanal, 3-heptanone, 2,3-butanedione, cyclopropanone, and cyclohexyl methyl ketone.

2. What are the two principal sites of reactivity in propionaldehyde? Write a reaction which illustrates each.

3. Do aldehydes and ketones occur in nature? Give two examples of each, and tell where they occur.

4. Write *five* different reactions illustrating addition to the carbonyl group.

5. What is meant by the terms "hydrazone," "phenylhydrazone," and "oxime"? Illustrate these by formulas.

6. Define tautomerism. Write the tautomeric structures of ethyl methyl ketone.

7. An alcohol having the formula C_3H_8O slowly deposited iodoform on standing in an alkaline solution of sodium hypoiodite (NaOI). What is the structure of the alcohol?

8. What are the principal industrial sources of acetaldehyde, acetone, 1-butanol, formaldehyde, and cyclohexanone? Write equations for the reactions involved.

9. What chemical tests could be used to distinguish acetone from propionaldehyde? 2-pentanone from 3-pentanone?

10. What is the basis of Benedict's test?

11. What is meant by the adol condensation? Show by equations how isobutyraldehyde might be converted into 2,2,4-trimethylpentane ("isooctane") using this reaction.

12. What is the "oxo" process? One of the principal products from this process is isoamyl alcohol. Show how it is produced.

13. Using readily available materials, such as ethanol, methanol, acetone, acetic acid, and benzene, show how the following compounds could be made *via* Grignard reagents as intermediates. *a*) *t*-butyl alcohol, *b*) 2-butanol, *c*) acetophenone, *d*) *a*-methylstyrene (2-phenylpropene), *e*) 3-methyl-3-pentanol, *f*) 1,1-diphenylethene.

14. What is the *Cannizzaro* reaction? Show how trimethylacetaldehyde would react with strong base.

15. Pentaerythritol is used to make explosives, and has the formula $C(CH_2OH)_4$. It is formed by the reaction of acetaldehyde and excess formaldehyde in basic solution. Write the reactions involved.

16. Show by equations how you could accomplish each of the following conversions:

    a) acetophenone to ethylbenzene;
    b) ethyl methyl ketone to propionic acid;
    c) acetone to pinacol;
    d) phenol to salicylaldehyde;
    e) benzene to acetophenone;
    f) acetaldehyde to crotonaldehyde;
    g) isobutyraldehyde to 2,2-dimethyl-1,3-propanediol;
    h) acetic acid to tert-butyl alcohol;
    i) 1-butanol to 2-ethyl-1-hexanol;
    j) acetaldehyde to butyraldehyde oxime;
    k) cyclohexanone to cyclopentanone;
    l) acetone to methyl methacrylate;
    m) phenol to adipic acid.

17. Compound A has the formula C_8H_8O. Compound A gives a precipitate with 2,4-dinitrophenylhydrazine, but does not give a silver mirror when treated with Tollens' reagent. Treating A with iodine in basic solution gave a yellow precipitate. Oxidation of A with permanganate gave benzoic acid. What is the formula of A? Show your reasoning.

18. Name and give the formulas of *five* different commercially important aldehydes or ketones, and indicate their sources.

19. Compound A, $C_5H_{10}O_2$, gives a positive Benedict's test, and when treated with acetic anhydride gives a compound B, $C_7H_{12}O_3$, which also gives a positive Benedict's test. Heating compound A in benzene solution caused water to separate, and a compound C, C_5H_8O, was formed which also gave a positive Benedict's test. Compound C decolorized a solution of bromine in water, and was easily oxidized to an acid D, $C_5H_8O_2$. Reduction of D gave isovaleric acid, $(CH_3)_2CHCH_2COOH$. What is the most probable formula of A? Using your formula for A, show the reactions involved and the structures for B, C, and D. What other formulas of A are possible?

Advanced Reading References

Essential Principles of Organic Chemistry, James Cason, Prentice-Hall, Inc., Englewood Cliffs, N. J., 1956, Chapters 14 and 28.

Chemistry of Organic Compounds, 2nd Ed., C. R. Noller, W. B. Saunders Co., Philadelphia, 1957, Chapters 11 and 25.

Organic Chemistry, 3rd Ed., R. Q. Brewster and W. E. McEwen, Prentice-Hall, Inc., Englewood Cliffs, N. J., 1961, Chapters 8 and 29.

new terms & concepts

Carboxylic acids have the characteristic —COOH group.
They are found commonly in nature (chiefly in fats),
hence the name "fatty" acids.
Carboxyclic acids form salts.
They replace the hydroxyl group to form acyl derivatives such as
esters, acid chloride, or amides.
They add reagents to the carbonyl group such as hydrogen
or Grignard reagents.
The carbonyl group is especially reactive in the acid derivatives such as
acids chlorides or esters.
Alpha-hydrogens are reactive and can be replaced by halogens or condensed with
aldehydes in the Perkin reaction.
Acids are synthesized by oxidation of primary alcohols, aldehydes, or side chains in
the aromatic series.
Hydrolysis of nitriles or reaction of Grignard reagents with carbon dioxide are also
important synthetic methods which increase the length of the carbon chain.
Unsaturated acids have properties of both functions.
Alpha-, beta-unsaturated acids add nucleophiles in a 1,4-manner.
The dicarboxylic acids lose carbon dioxide readily if
derivatives of malonic acid. They lose water readily to form anhydrides if 5- or 6-membered rings
are formed and the orientation is favorable.
Malonic acid has very reactive alpha-hydrogens, which are easily replaced.

11

Oxygenated hydrocarbons
iv. carboxylic acids; derivatives

Compounds which contain both the *carbo*nyl and hydr*oxyl* groups on the same carbon atom,

$$-C\overset{O}{\underset{OH}{\diagdown}}$$

are called carboxylic acids. They are an important class of substances, being found widely distributed in nature in the plant and animal kingdoms. One of the chief sources of the open-chain members of this series is animal fats, hence the name "fatty acids," or indirectly, aliphatic acids. The aromatic acids have the carboxyl group directly attached to the ring, Ar—COOH, and many of these are important manufacturing substances. When the hydrogen of the hydroxyl group is replaced by an organic group,

$$-C\overset{O}{\underset{O-R}{\diagdown}}$$

the acid derivatives known as *esters* are formed. These also occur in nature very commonly in fats, waxes, flavoring oils, etc. As with the alcohols, the hydroxyl group may be replaced by halogens to form the acyl and aroyl halides, RCOX, ArCOX, and by the amino group to form amides, $RCONH_2$ and $ArCONH_2$.

Naming the carboxylic acids

The carboxylic acids were among the first organic compounds known, and therefore over the space of many years common names have been given to these substances. Table 11.01 compares the common and I.U.C. names of a few representative acids.

Many of the acid derivatives are formed by replacement of the

$$R-\overset{\overset{\displaystyle O}{\parallel}}{C}-Z$$

—OH group, to form R—C—Z structures, where Z is any other function. The group RCO— is given the general name *acyl*, or in the aromatic series, *aroyl* (ArCO—). The name for any particular acid radical is then derived by changing the ending *-ic* to *-yl*. For example:

RCO—Cl   acyl chlorides $(ArCO)_2CH_2$ diaroylmethanes

$CH_3COOH \longrightarrow CH_3CO-Cl$ $C_6H_5COOH \longrightarrow C_6H_5COCH_2COC_6H_5$

acetic   acetyl   benzoic   dibenzoylmethane
acid   chloride   acid

Physical properties of the acids

The lower-molecular-weight carboxylic acids are colorless liquids with a sharp, penetrating, unpleasant odor. The odor of rancid butter is due to traces of free butyric acid, and isovaleric acid is responsible for the odor of human sweat. The presence of both the carbonyl and hydroxyl groups greatly increases the solubility in water; butyric acid is completely miscible in all proportions (compare p. 138, Chapter 10).

The boiling points and melting points of the first few members of the series appear to be abnormally high. These acids are actually dimers, having molecular weights just twice the theoretical formula weight. This molecular association of low-molecular-weight carboxylic acids is caused by the formation of hydrogen bonds. The electropositive hydrogen atom is attracted to the electron-rich electronegative oxygen of the carbonyl group, forming a weak bond or "hydrogen bridge."

$$CH_3-C\overset{\displaystyle O \rightarrow H-O}{\underset{\displaystyle O-H \leftarrow O}{}}C-CH_3$$

TABLE 11.01   NAMES AND PROPERTIES OF SOME CARBOXYLIC ACIDS

Compound	Common name	I.U.C. name	M.P. °C	B.P. °C
HCOOH	Formic acid	Methanoic acid	8	100
CH₃COOH	Acetic acid	Ethanoic acid	17	118
CH₃CH₂COOH	Propionic acid	Propanoic acid	−22	141
CH₃CH₂CH₂COOH	Butyric acid	Butanoic acid	−8	164
CH₃(CH₂)₃COOH	Valeric acid	Pentanoic acid	−35	187
CH₃(CH₂)₄COOH	Caproic acid	Hexanoic acid	−2	202
CH₃(CH₂)₁₀COOH	Lauric acid	Dodecanoic acid	48	224/100 mm
CH₃(CH₂)₁₂COOH	Myristic acid	Tetradecanoicacid	58	250/100 mm
CH₃(CH₂)₁₄COOH	Palmitic acid	Hexadecanoic acid	64	272/100 mm
CH₃(CH₂)₁₆COOH	Stearic acid	Octadecanoic acid	70	285/100 mm
C₆H₅COOH	Benzoic acid	Benzoic acid	127	250
HOOC—COOH	Oxalic acid	Ethanedioic acid	186 dec.	sublimes
HOOCCH₂COOH	Malonic acid	Propanedioic acid	135 dec.	
HOOCCH₂CH₂COOH	Succinic acid	Butanedioic acid	190	dec.
HOOC(CH₂)₄COOH	Adipic acid	Hexanedioic acid	152	265/10 mm
⬡ COOH COOH (phthalic structure)	Phthalic acid	1,2-Benzenedicarboxylic acid	191	dec.

This association increases the actual molecular weight, and thus serves to increase the melting and boiling points. A similar attraction between molecules causes the alcohols to boil much higher than the ethers or aldehydes of like molecular weight.

The melting points of the carboxylic acids having an even number of carbon atoms are always higher than those next higher and lower neighbors with an uneven number of carbon atoms (see Figure 11.01). These acids provide an excellent illustration of the so-called "saw-tooth" effect, or variation in properties between homologs having odd and even numbers of carbon atoms, mentioned in Chapter 4. Similar "saw-tooth" effects are observed when other properties of homologous series are plotted, such as acid or base strengths, or biological activity.

Reactions of the carboxyl group

Since the carboxylic acids are composed of a carbonyl and a hydroxyl group, one might expect the reactions to be similar to the reactions of these two functions, and in a general way there are resemblances. Like the alcohols, the hydrogen of the —OH may be replaced by metals, or the —OH itself may be replaced. The carbonyl

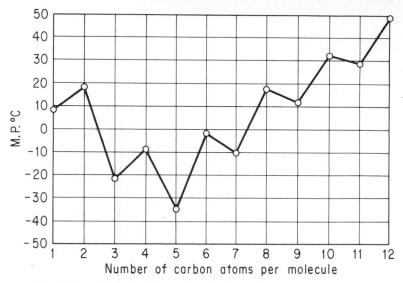

Fig. 11.01. Plot of melting points of a homologous series of acids.

group undergoes addition reactions, and the *alpha*-hydrogens are easily replaced.

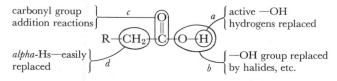

a) Replacement of the active —OH hydrogen is the most characteristic property of the acids. It will be remembered that phenols were much stronger acids than alcohols. In the same way, the carboxylic compounds are much stronger acids than phenols, and will react immediately with even weak bases like sodium bicarbonate or ammonia to form salts.

11.01 $RCOOH + OH^- \longrightarrow RCOO^- + H_2O$

11.02 $RCOOH + HCO_3^- \longrightarrow RCOO^- + H_2O + CO_2$

The salts of the acids are much more soluble in water than the free acids. When the organic portion of the acid is large, the salts are called *soaps*.

b) Replacement of the hydroxyl group by halogens can be brought about by some of the same reagents used in the alcohol series. With phosphorous trichloride or thionyl chloride the acyl and aroyl chlorides are readily formed. The halogen atom in these acid chlorides is very reactive, and the acid chlorides are frequently used to prepare acid derivatives instead of the acids themselves. Alcohols may be dehydrated to form ethers, and, in the same way, acids may be dehydrated to

11.03 $\qquad$ $3\,RCOOH + PCl_3 \longrightarrow 3\,RCOCl + H_3PO_3$

11.04 $\qquad$ $ArCOOH + SOCl_2 \longrightarrow ArCOCl + HCl + SO_2$

form *acid anhydrides*. The reaction between an acid chloride and the sodium salt of an acid to form a simple or mixed anhydride is reminiscent of the Williamson synthesis of ethers. The anhydrides are also

11.05
$$
\underset{}{R-\overset{O}{\overset{\|}{C}}-O-H} + \underset{}{HO-\overset{O}{\overset{\|}{C}}-R} \xrightarrow{P_2O_5} R-\overset{O}{\overset{\|}{C}}-O-\overset{O}{\overset{\|}{C}}-R + H_2O
$$

11.06
$$
R-\overset{O}{\overset{\|}{C}}-O-Na + Cl-\overset{O}{\overset{\|}{C}}-R' \longrightarrow R-\overset{O}{\overset{\|}{C}}-O-\overset{O}{\overset{\|}{C}}-R' + Na^+Cl^-
$$

very reactive, and may be used in the place of acids to bring about more rapid reactions. They react with water to give the acids again.

11.07 $\qquad$ $RCO-O-COR + H-OH \longrightarrow 2\,RCOOH$

c) Addition of polar reagents like water, alcohol, and ammonia to the carbonyl group is a common reaction of carboxylic acids, anhydrides, and acid chlorides. The simple addition reaction is usually followed immediately by the loss of water or some other polar molecule to form a more stable acid derivative. For example, the *esterification* reaction (p. 115) involves first the addition of the alcohol to the carbonyl, as in hemiacetal formation (p. 139) followed by loss of water:

11.08
$$
R-\overset{O}{\overset{\diagup}{C}}_{\diagdown OH} + HOCH_3 \rightleftharpoons \left[R-\overset{OCH_3}{\underset{OH}{\overset{|}{\underset{|}{C}}}}-OH \right] \rightleftharpoons R-\overset{O}{\overset{\diagup}{C}}_{\diagdown OCH_3} + HOH
$$

Each of the two steps is reversible, since water will also add to the carbonyl group of the ester, and alcohol may be split out. If an acid chloride or anhydride is used in this reaction, the reaction is nearly complete because the second step is not so readily reversible.

11.09
$$
R-\overset{O}{\overset{\diagup}{C}}_{\diagdown Cl} + HOCH_3 \rightleftharpoons \left[R-\overset{OCH_3}{\underset{Cl\ H}{\overset{|}{\underset{|}{C}}}}-O \right] \longrightarrow R-\overset{O}{\overset{\|}{C}}-OCH_3 + HCl
$$

11.10
$$R-C{O \atop OCOR} + HOCH_2CH_3 \rightleftharpoons \left[R-C{OCH_2CH_3 \atop \quad | \atop OCOR}-O-H \right] \longrightarrow$$

$$R-\overset{O}{\overset{\|}{C}}-OCH_2CH_3 + RCOOH$$

Ammonia and amines also add to the carbonyl group of acids and their derivatives to form a class of compounds known as *amides*.

11.11 $$R-C{O \atop Cl} + H-NR_2 \longrightarrow \left[R-\overset{OH}{\underset{Cl}{\overset{|}{C}}}-NR_2 \right] \longrightarrow R-CO-NR_2 + HCl$$
$$\text{an amide}$$

This reaction occurs much more readily with acid chlorides, anhydrides, or even with esters, since the free acids form salts with ammonia and amines. The amides are an important class of acid derivatives.

11.12 $$RCOOH + HNR_2 \longrightarrow RCOO^-H_2NR_2{}^+$$

Many of them are found in nature. For example, nitrogen is excreted from animal bodies in the form of amides. Mice excrete *acetamide*, CH_3CONH_2, which is the source of the peculiar dry odor around mouse cages and animal rooms where mice are kept. Humans excrete a diamide of carbonic acid, H_2NCONH_2, called *urea*.

The Grignard reagent will add to the carbonyl group of acid derivatives to form the ketones (p. 148). The acids themselves, having an active acid hydrogen, react to reduce the Grignard reagent and form the magnesium salt of the acid. Esters, acid anhydrides, or

11.13 $$R-C{O \atop Cl} + XMg-R' \longrightarrow \left[R-\overset{OMgX}{\underset{Cl}{\overset{|}{C}}}-R' \right] \longrightarrow R-\overset{O}{\overset{\|}{C}}-R' + MgXCl$$

$$RCOOH + R'-MgX \longrightarrow R'H + RCOO^-Mg^{++}X^-$$

disubstituted amides, $R-CO-NR_2$, all compounds which have a carbonyl group but no acidic hydrogens, will add Grignard reagents to the carbonyl group to form ketones or tertiary alcohols. Dimethyl formamide reacts with Grignard reagent to form an aldehyde.

11.14

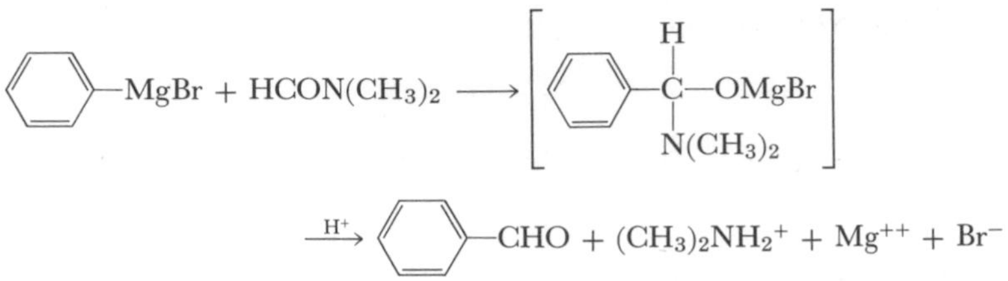

$$\text{C}_6\text{H}_5\text{—MgBr} + \text{HCON(CH}_3)_2 \longrightarrow \left[\begin{array}{c} \text{H} \\ | \\ \text{C}_6\text{H}_5\text{—C—OMgBr} \\ | \\ \text{N(CH}_3)_2 \end{array} \right]$$

$$\xrightarrow{\text{H}^+} \text{C}_6\text{H}_5\text{—CHO} + (\text{CH}_3)_2\text{NH}_2^+ + \text{Mg}^{++} + \text{Br}^-$$

The carboxyl group may be reduced to the alcohol group (p. 118) by various reagents. Since acid derivatives, such as esters and acid chlorides, are more easily reduced by hydrogen over a catalyst, this is also the result of addition to the carbonyl group, by hydrogen in this instance. The free carboxyl group is reduced by lithium aluminum hydride.

11.15 $$\text{RCOOH} \xrightarrow{\text{LiAlH}_4} \text{RCH}_2\text{OH} + \text{H}_2\text{O}$$

Since long-chain fatty acids are available from natural sources, reduction provides a convenient source of long-chain alcohols.

Mechanism of reactions at the carbonyl group

All the above reactions may be generalized in terms of two common steps. First, attack of a nucleophilic (electron-rich) reagent on the carbon of the carbonyl group (see Chapter 10). Second, elimination of a second, less nucleophilic, base from the transition complex.

Step 1:
$$\text{R—C(=O)—A} + \text{B:} \rightleftharpoons \left[\begin{array}{c} \text{O}^- \\ | \\ \text{R—C—A} \\ | \\ \text{B} \end{array} \right]$$

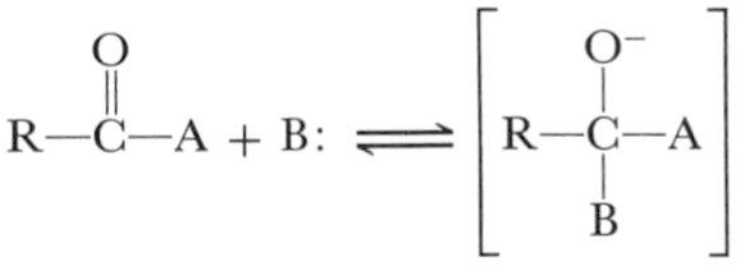

Step 2:
$$\left[\begin{array}{c} \text{O}^- \\ | \\ \text{R—C—A} \\ | \\ \text{B} \end{array} \right] \rightleftharpoons \text{R—C(=O)—B} + \text{A:}$$

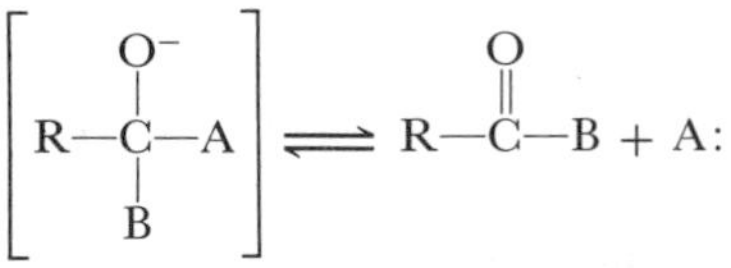

The stronger the attacking nucleophile, B:, and the weaker the displaced base, A:, the faster the reaction. The reaction may be catalyzed by acids, bases, or both. Acid catalysts increase the polarity of the carbonyl group, while basic catalysts increase the base strength of the nucleophile.

Direct reaction:

$$R—\overset{\displaystyle O}{\overset{\|}{C}}—A + HB \xrightarrow{\text{slow}} \left[R—\overset{\displaystyle OH}{\underset{\displaystyle B}{\overset{|}{\underset{|}{C}}}}—A \right] \longrightarrow R—\overset{\displaystyle O}{\overset{\|}{C}}—B + H^A$$

Acid-catalyzed:

$$R—\overset{\displaystyle O}{\overset{\|}{C}}—A + H^+ \xrightarrow{\text{fast}} \left[R—\overset{\displaystyle O}{\underset{+}{\overset{|}{C}}} \cdots \underset{B}{} —A \right] + H^+$$

Base-catalyzed:

$$HB + OH^- \xrightarrow{\text{fast}} B:^- + H_2O$$

$$R—\overset{\displaystyle O}{\overset{\|}{C}}—A + B:^- \xrightarrow{\text{fast}} \left[R—\overset{\displaystyle O^-}{\underset{\displaystyle B}{\overset{|}{\underset{|}{C}}}}—A \right]$$

The carbonyl reactions of the acids and their derivatives can now be summarized as in Table 11.02.

TABLE 11.02   CARBONYL REACTIONS OF THE ACIDS AND THEIR DERIVATIVES

A. Hydrolysis of acid derivatives

Anhydrides $R—\overset{\displaystyle O}{\overset{\|}{C}}—O—\overset{\displaystyle O}{\overset{\|}{C}}—R + H_2O \text{ (or } OH^-) \longrightarrow$

$$R—\overset{\displaystyle O}{\overset{\|}{C}}—OH + R—\overset{\displaystyle O}{\overset{\|}{C}}—OH \text{ (or } R—\overset{\displaystyle O}{\overset{\|}{C}}—O^-)$$

Acid chlorides $R—\overset{\displaystyle O}{\overset{\|}{C}}—Cl + H_2O \text{ (or } OH^-) \longrightarrow$

$$R—\overset{\displaystyle O}{\overset{\|}{C}}—OH + HCl \text{ (or } Cl^-)$$

Esters $R—\overset{\displaystyle O}{\overset{\|}{C}}—OR' + H_2O \text{ (or } OH^-) \longrightarrow$

$$R—\overset{\displaystyle O}{\overset{\|}{C}}—OH + HOR'$$

Amides $R—\overset{\displaystyle O}{\overset{\|}{C}}—NR_2' + H_2O \text{ (or } OH^-) \longrightarrow$

$$R—\overset{\displaystyle O}{\overset{\|}{C}}—OH + NHR_2'$$

TABLE 11.02 CARBONYL REACTIONS OF THE ACIDS AND THEIR DERIVATIVES (CONTINUED)

B. Formation of esters

From acid

$$RC\overset{O}{\overset{\|}{}}{-}OH + R'OH \longrightarrow RCOOR' + H_2O$$

From acid chlorides
$$RCOCl + R'OH \longrightarrow RCOOR' + HCl$$

From anhydrides
$$RCOOCOR + R'OH \longrightarrow RCOOR' + RCOOH$$

Ester interchange
$$RCOOR'' + R'OH \longrightarrow RCOOR' + R''OH$$

C. Formation of amides

From acids
$$R_2'NH + RCOOH \longrightarrow R{-}\overset{O}{\overset{\|}{C}}{-}NR_2' + H_2O$$

From acid chlorides
$$R_2'NH + RCOCl \longrightarrow R{-}\overset{O}{\overset{\|}{C}}{-}NR_2' + HCl$$

From anhydrides
$$R_2'NH + RCOOCOR \longrightarrow R{-}\overset{O}{\overset{\|}{C}}{-}NR_2' + RCOOH$$

From esters
$$R_2'NH + RCOOR' \longrightarrow R{-}\overset{O}{\overset{\|}{C}}{-}NR_2' + R'OH$$

D. Anhydride formation

$$RCOO^- + R\overset{O}{\overset{\|}{C}}{-}Cl \longrightarrow RCOOCOR + Cl^-$$

E. Haloform reaction

$$HO^- + R{-}\overset{O}{\overset{\|}{C}}{-}CCl_3 \longrightarrow RCOOH + Cl_3C^-$$

F. Grignard addition

$$R'{-}\overset{+}{Mg}X + R{-}\overset{O}{\overset{\|}{C}}{-}Cl \longrightarrow R'{-}\overset{O}{\overset{\|}{C}}{-}R + \overset{+}{Mg}XCl^-$$

$$R'{-}\overset{+}{Mg}X + R{-}\overset{O}{\overset{\|}{C}}{-}OR'' \longrightarrow R'{-}\overset{O}{\overset{\|}{C}}{-}R + RO^-\overset{+}{Mg}X$$

d) The *alpha*-hydrogen atoms in acids having the general formula $R_2CHCOOH$ are activated by the adjacent carbonyl group, and may be replaced by halogens. Since acetates, containing the group $CH_3CO{-}$, do not undergo the haloform reaction, it is apparent that the *alpha*-hydrogens in acids are not as reactive as in aldehydes or ketones. The halogenation reaction is promoted by catalysts, such as the phosphorus halides.

11.16 $R_2CHCOOH + Br_2 \xrightarrow{PBr_3} R_2CBrCOOH + HBr$

The *alpha*-hydrogen atoms in acid anhydrides are slightly more re-active, and can be condensed with aromatic aldehydes at high tem-peratures with basic salts as catalysts. This reaction is known as the *Perkin synthesis*. At the reaction temperature, the intermediate alcohol adduct cannot be isolated, but is immediately dehydrated. The water thus formed hydrolyzes the anhydride, producing an unsaturated acid as the final product. The Perkin synthesis is unsuccessful with alde-hydes having an *alpha*-hydrogen, since they condense with themselves too readily.

11.17

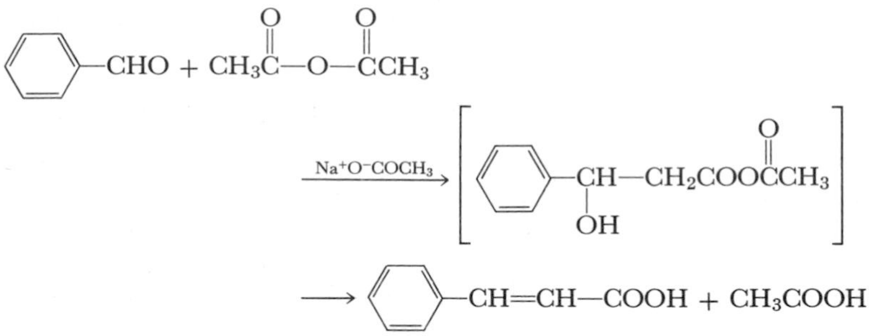

$$\text{C}_6\text{H}_5\text{—CHO} + \text{CH}_3\overset{\text{O}}{\overset{\|}{\text{C}}}\text{—O—}\overset{\text{O}}{\overset{\|}{\text{C}}}\text{CH}_3 \xrightarrow{\text{Na}^+\text{O}^-\text{COCH}_3} \left[\text{C}_6\text{H}_5\text{—}\underset{\text{OH}}{\overset{}{\text{CH}}}\text{—CH}_2\text{COO}\overset{\text{O}}{\overset{\|}{\text{C}}}\text{CH}_3 \right]$$

$$\longrightarrow \text{C}_6\text{H}_5\text{—CH}{=}\text{CH—COOH} + \text{CH}_3\text{COOH}$$

Preparation of the carboxylic acids

Many of the common aliphatic acids are available from natural sources, chiefly by hydrolysis of the esters. However, many of them are manufactured in different ways. For example, oxidation of I° alcohols or aldehydes leads to acids:

11.18 $\text{R—CH}_2\text{OH} \xrightarrow{\text{ox.}} \text{R—COOH}$

11.19 $\text{R—CHO} \xrightarrow{\text{ox.}} \text{R—COOH}$

Oxidation of aromatic compounds containing a side-chain, such as toluene or acetophenone, leads to an aromatic carboxylic acid:

11.20 $\text{C}_6\text{H}_5\text{—CH}_3 \xrightarrow{\text{ox.}} \text{C}_6\text{H}_5\text{—COOH} \xleftarrow{\text{ox.}} \text{C}_6\text{H}_5\text{—COCH}_3$

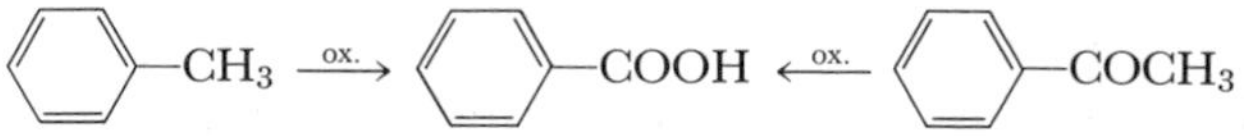

The hydrolysis of nitriles provides a useful method for preparing acids, since the nitriles in turn may be prepared readily. The nitriles have the functional group —C≡N, which is hydrolyzed under acid conditions to form ammonia and the carboxyl group:

11.21 $\text{R—C}{\equiv}\text{N} + 2\,\text{H}_2\text{O} \xrightarrow{\text{H}^+} \text{R—COOH} + \text{NH}_3$

In the alkyl series, nitriles are readily obtained by the replacement of alkyl halides or by the addition of hydrogen cyanide to carbonyls:

11.22 $CH_3CH_2Br \xrightarrow{CN^-} CH_3CH_2CN \xrightarrow[OH]{H_2O} CH_3CH_2COOH$

11.23 $CH_3CHO \xrightarrow{HCN} CH_3CHOHCN \xrightarrow[H]{H_2O} CH_3CHOHCOOH$

In the aromatic series, the nitriles may be obtained by fusion of the aromatic sulfonic acid salt with sodium cyanide:

11.24 $SO_2ONa + NaCN \xrightarrow{heat}$ $CN + Na_2SO_3$

Grignard reagents react with carbon dioxide to form the carboxylic acids. Since Grignard reagents are easily prepared from either aliphatic or aromatic compounds, this is a useful laboratory method for preparing acids (Eqs. 11.25 and 11.26).

11.25

$CH_3-CHBr \xrightarrow[ether]{Mg} (CH_3)_2CHMgBr$
$\qquad\ \ CH_3$

$\xrightarrow{CO_2} (CH_3)_2CHCOOMgBr \xrightarrow[H^+]{H_2O} (CH_3)_2CHCOOH$

11.26

CH_3 $Br \xrightarrow[ether]{Mg} CH_3$ $MgBr$

$\xrightarrow{CO_2} CH_3$ $COOMgBr \xrightarrow[H^+]{H_2O} CH_3$ $COOH$

Natural fats are important commercial sources of the higher-molecular-weight fatty acids. Fats consist of mixtures of triesters of glycerol with various fatty acids, but only those acids having an even number of carbon atoms in a continuous chain are found in quantity in fats. Fats may be hydrolyzed by superheated steam or by boiling with alkali in the saponification—or "soap-making"—reaction.

11.27

$CH_3(CH_2)_{10}COO-CH_2$
$CH_3(CH_2)_{10}COO-CH \xrightarrow{3\ NaOH} 3\ CH_3(CH_2)_{10}COO^-Na^+ + CHOH$
$CH_3(CH_2)_{10}COO-CH_2$

$\qquad\qquad$ trilaurin
$\qquad$ (a constituent of palm oil)

sodium laurate
(a soap)

CH_2OH
$CHOH$
CH_2OH

The most abundant aliphatic acids in fats are the 16- and 18-carbon acids palmitic and stearic acid, and certain unsaturated 18-carbon acids.

Unsaturated acids

Aliphatic carboxylic acids containing a double bond in the carbon chain are common in nature. The vegetable oils contain esters of oleic, linoleic, and linolenic acids (see Chapter 12). The lower-molecular-weight unsaturated acids or their esters are important industrially, particularly in the plastics industry. Table 11.03 lists some common unsaturated acids.

When the double bond is separated from the carboxylic acid, as in oleic acid, each function exhibits its usual reactions. The double bond may add hydrogen, halogens, be oxidized, or undergo any of the reactions described for olefins in Chapter 4. In the same way, the carboxyl group and its α-hydrogens undergo the usual reactions. When the double bond is between the second and third carbons, it is conjugated to the carbonyl group, and now addition occurs in the 1,4-manner (Chapter 4). Since the oxygen atom is always the most electronegative, nucleophilic reagents attack the β-carbon, giving β-substituted acids. For example, addition of hydrogen bromide to acrylic acid produces β-bromopropionic acid, even though this is apparently anti-Markovnikov.

11.28

$$B: + CH_2=CH-C=O \longrightarrow \left[B-CH_2-CH=C{\overset{O^-}{\underset{OH}{\bigg\langle}}} \right] \xrightarrow{H^+}$$

$$B-CH_2-CH_2C{\overset{O}{\underset{OH}{\bigg\langle}}}$$

11.29 $CH_2=CH-COOH + HBr \longrightarrow BrCH_2CH_2COOH$

Dicarboxylic acids

When two carboxyl groups are present in a molecule, they may have some influence on one another when located close together. When far apart, they react as ordinary carboxyl groups. The different dicarboxylic acids react differently when heated. When the carboxyl groups are close together, as in oxalic or malonic acid, they readily lose

11.30 $HOCO-COOH \xrightarrow{\Delta} HCOOH + CO_2$

11.31 $HOCOCH_2COOH \xrightarrow{\Delta} CH_3COOH + CO_2$

carbon dioxide. Succinic and glutaric acids react differently, losing water easily to form the cyclic anhydrides. These form more readily than do anhydrides from simple aliphatic acids, since the products are five- and six-membered rings which, because of the valence angles of carbon bonds, are most readily formed (see Chapter 3). The same situation can be found in the aromatic series. Phthalic acid is so readily

TABLE 11.03 SOME COMMON UNSATURATED ACIDS

Compound	Common name	I.U.C. name	M.P. °C	B.P. °C
$CH_2=CHCOOH$	acrylic acid	propenoic acid	12	142
$CH_3CH=CHCOOH$	crotonic acid	trans-2-butenoic acid	72	185
	isocrotonic acid	cis-2-butenoic acid	14.6	172
$CH_2=C(CH_3)COOH$	methacrylic acid	2-methylpropenoic acid	16	163
$CH_3(CH_2)_7CH=CH(CH_2)_7COOH$	oleic acid	cis-9-octadecenoic acid	13	286
$CH_3(CH_2)_4CH=CHCH_2CH=CH(CH_2)_7COOH$	linoleic acid	9,12-octadecadienoic acid	−11	230
$CH_3CH_2CH=CHCH_2CH=CHCH_2CH=CH(CH_2)_7COOH$	linolenic acid	9,12,15-octadecatrienoic acid	..	230
$HCCOOH$ $HCCOOH$	maleic acid	cis-butenedioic acid	130	..
$HCCOOH$ $HOOCCH$	fumaric acid	trans-butenedioic acid	287	..
$CH=CH-COOH$	cinnamic acid	trans-3-phenylpropenoic acid	133	300

11.32

$$\begin{array}{c} H_2C-COOH \\ | \\ H_2C-COOH \end{array} \xrightarrow{\Delta} \begin{array}{c} H_2C-C \diagup^{O} \\ | \qquad \diagdown O \\ H_2C-C \diagdown_{O} \end{array} + H_2O$$

succinic acid   succinic anhydride

11.33

$$H_2C \diagdown^{CH_2COOH}_{CH_2COOH} \xrightarrow{\Delta} H_2C \diagdown^{CH_2-C \diagup^{O}}_{CH_2-C \diagdown_{O}} \diagdown O + H_2O$$

glutaric acid   glutaric anhydride

dehydrated that phthalic anhydride is manufactured directly by
oxidation of naphthalene in the vapor state. On the other hand,

11.34

phthalic anhydride

11.35

$$HOOC-\bigcirc-COOH \xrightarrow{\Delta}$$

$$HOOC_6H_4COO(COC_6H_4COO)xCOC_6H_4COOH$$

strong heating is required to convert the *para*-acid, terephthalic acid,
to its polymeric anhydride. When adipic acid is heated, no seven-
membered cyclic anhydride is formed. Instead a poor yield of cyclopentanone is formed by loss of carbon dioxide, and the main product
is polymeric anhydride, formed by loss of water between molecules of

11.36

$$\begin{array}{c} CH_2CH_2COOH \\ | \\ CH_2CH_2COOH \end{array} \xrightarrow{\Delta} \begin{array}{c} CH_2-CH_2 \\ | \qquad \diagdown CO \\ CH_2-CH_2 \diagup \end{array} + \text{polymeric anhydride}$$

adipic acid   cyclopentanone

adipic acid. Heating the barium salt of adipic acid gives good yields
of cyclopentanone (p. 149).

The geometric isomers maleic and fumaric acids provide an excellent example of the influence of orientation of reacting groups on a
reaction. Maleic acid, the *cis*-isomer, is readily converted to its anhydride at temperatures slightly above the melting point, since the two
carboxyl groups lie close together and easily interact. Fumaric acid,
the *trans*-isomer, is much more difficult to dehydrate. This ease of
formation of a cyclic anhydride is useful in determining the structure
of geometric isomers. For example, *cis*-1,2-cyclopentanedicarboxylic
acid readily forms an anhydride, but the *trans*-isomer does not. There-

11.37

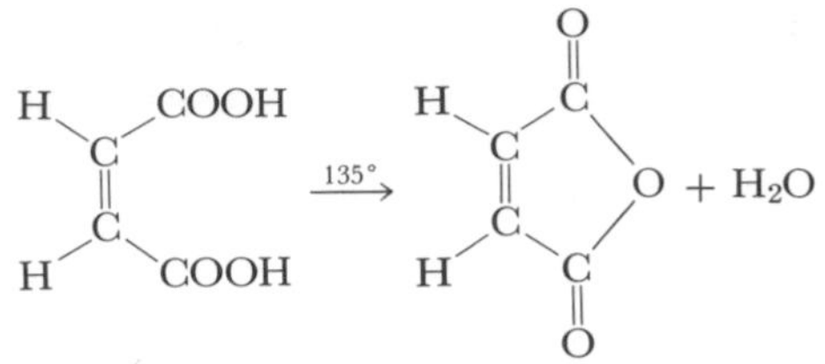

maleic anhydride

fore the ease of dehydration can be used to decide which isomer is which.

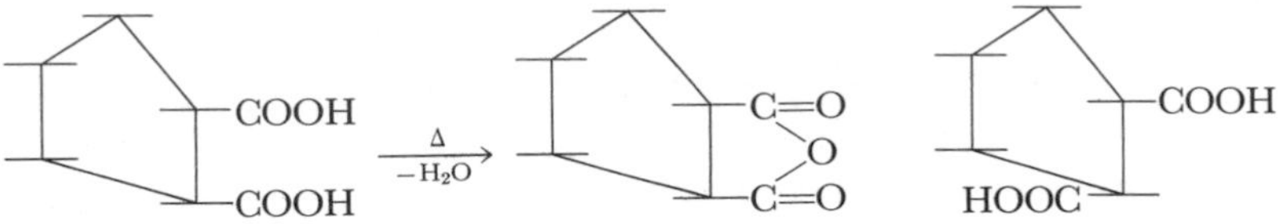

cis-   trans-

Malonic acid is of special interest because of the high reactivity of the *alpha*-hydrogen atoms, which are doubly activated because of the carboxyl group on either side. For example, malonic acid condenses directly with aldehydes in reactions of the Perkin type, using mild bases like ammonia as catalysts. This modification of the Perkin reaction is called the *Knoevenagel* reaction, and is especially useful for organic syntheses.

11.38

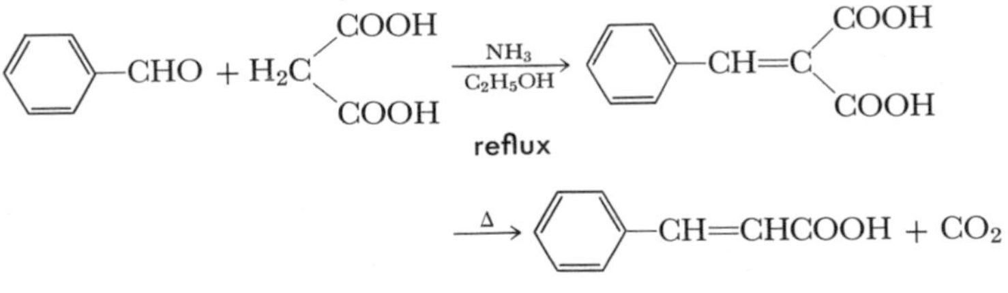

The *alpha*-hydrogen atoms of malonic esters may be replaced with metals, and the metal salts then reacted with alkyl halides to produce substituted malonic esters. Hydrolysis of the ester and decarboxylation produces a substituted acetic acid. The second *alpha*-hydrogen may be replaced to produce disubstituted malonic esters, which then yield the disubstituted acetic acids.

11.39

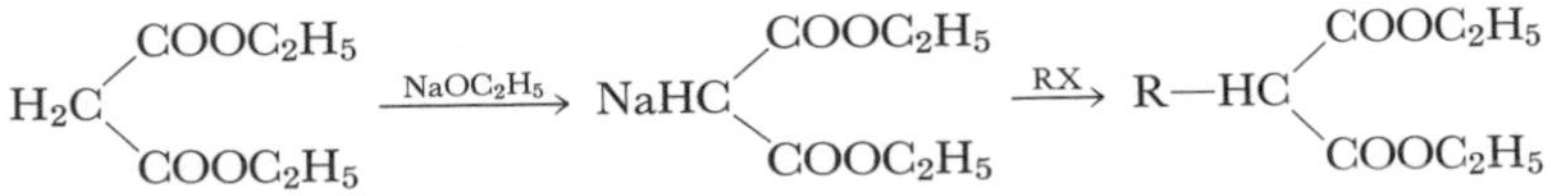

$$R-\underset{\underset{\displaystyle COOC_2H_5}{|}}{\overset{\overset{\displaystyle COOC_2H_5}{|}}{C}}-H \xrightarrow[\text{NaOH}]{H_2O} R-\underset{\underset{\displaystyle COOH}{}}{\overset{\overset{\displaystyle COOH}{}}{C}}H \xrightarrow{\Delta} RCH_2COOH + CO_2$$

11.40 $\Big\downarrow$ NaOC$_2$H$_5$

$$R-\underset{\underset{\displaystyle COOC_2H_5}{|}}{\overset{\overset{\displaystyle COOC_2H_5}{|}}{C}}-Na \xrightarrow{R'X} R-\underset{\underset{\displaystyle COOC_2H_5}{|}}{\overset{\overset{\displaystyle COOC_2H_5}{|}}{C}}-R' \xrightarrow[\text{2. H}_2{}^+-CO_2]{\text{1. H}_2O/OH^-} R-\underset{\underset{\displaystyle R'}{|}}{CH}-COOH$$

Some useful carboxylic acids

Formic acid, HCOOH, occurs free in the ant, in stinging nettles, and some other stinging insects and plants. It can be prepared industrially from carbon monoxide and sodium hydroxide under pressure.

11.41
$$NaOH + CO \longrightarrow NaO-\overset{\displaystyle O}{\overset{\displaystyle \|}{C}}-H$$

Formic acid contains the $H-\overset{\displaystyle O}{\overset{\displaystyle \|}{C}}-$ group present in aldehydes, and as such is a good reducing agent. It has been used as an irritant and tonic in medicine, particularly in ancient times, when the elixir was prepared by extracting macerated ants with alcohol.

Acetic acid is widely used in food chemistry as a weak acid, causing a tart taste. It is nontoxic, occurring naturally in the body in esters, and its salts are weak bases which can be used to counteract acidosis. As *vinegar,* a dilute solution of acetic acid which is obtained by fermentation of cider or other fruit juices, it was known to the ancients. Acetic acid is now more readily available from synthetic sources, such as acetylene (p. 150) or the reaction of methanol and carbon monoxide in the presence of a catalyst. Ordinary white vinegar is manufactured

11.42
$$CH_3-OH + CO \xrightarrow{\text{cat.}} CH_3-CO-OH$$

as a 5 per cent solution of synthetic acetic acid, although some vinegar is still prepared by fermentation and sold under the label "cider vinegar." Pure acetic acid, CH$_3$COOH, melts at 16°C and is called *glacial acetic acid,* because it resembles ice in the crystalline state. It is used as an industrial solvent, and in many manufacturing processes.

Propionic acid, CH$_3$CH$_2$COOH, has recently been found to reduce the tendency of bread dough to mold. This has led to many new developments in the baking industry, such as the partially pre-baked "brown and serve" rolls and bread, or frozen dough. Sodium propionate is added to the dough as the mold inhibitor. Propionic acid occurs naturally in some foods, such as strong cheese, but is conveniently manufactured from ethylene and carbon monoxide.

11.43 $$CH_2{=}CH_2 + CO + H_2O \xrightarrow{\text{cat.}} CH_3CH_2COOH$$

Butyric acid, $CH_3CH_2CH_2COOH$, is the simplest acid found esterified with glycerol in the natural fats, and comprises about 2 per cent of butter fat. It is remarkable for its powerful and penetrating odor, which is characteristic of rancid butter. It occurs free in minute amounts in sweat and feces. Indeed, all of the acids between butyric and decanoic have characteristic unpleasant odors. Valeric acid, C_4H_9COOH, is found in human sweat, together with caproic, $C_5H_{11}COOH$, caprylic, $C_7H_{15}COOH$, and capric, $C_9H_{19}COOH$, acids—all deriving their names from the Latin *caper,* or goat.

Stearic acid, $CH_3(CH_2)_{16}COOH$, is commonly found as a glyceryl ester in solid fats such as suet. It is used in candle-making and in soaps. The zinc salt is a mild antiseptic useful in baby powders and ointments. *Palmitic acid,* $CH_3(CH_2)_{14}COOH$, constitutes 40–45 per cent of the fatty acid found in palm oil, important in soap-making, and is also present in high concentration in beef tallow and hog lard. *Lauric acid,* $CH_3(CH_2)_{10}COOH$, is major constituent of coconut oil, also useful in manufacturing soaps and detergents.

Benzoic acid, C_6H_5COOH, is found in gum benzoin, and in cranberries. It is excreted in urine, particularly horse urine, conjugated with glycine by an amide linkage in hippuric acid, $C_6H_5CO{-}NHCH_2{-}COOH$. Benzoic acid is prepared commercially chiefly by hydrolysis of benzotrichloride, and is a mild antiseptic and germicide. As its salt,

11.44 $$C_6H_5{-}CCl_3 \xrightarrow{H_2O} C_6H_5{-}COOH + HCl$$

sodium benzoate, it is used as food preservative. Benzoic acid has been used as an expectorant in bronchitis, and is commonly used in this way in veterinary medicine. It has also found some use in rheumatic fever, but is not as effective as salicylic acid.

Oxalic acid, $(COOH)_2$, is the simplest dicarboxylic acid, and is found in many foods, particularly spinach and rhubarb. In the body it reacts to form insoluble calcium oxalate with the blood calcium, an excess causing the toxic symptoms of calcium deficiency. Certain forms of kidney stones are caused by crystallization of calcium oxalate in the kidneys. Oxalic acid can be made by oxidation of sugar, or by the pyrolysis of sodium formate. Oxalic acid is a good reducing agent, and as such is frequently used to bleach wood for blond furniture, straw for textile work, and leather. A dilute solution is effective in removing

11.45 　　　$2\,HCOONa \xrightarrow{\Delta} H_2 + Na^+O^-COCOO^-Na^+ \xrightarrow{H^+} (COOH)_2$

stains of potassium permanganate when this agent has been used for disinfection. In dentistry a 10 per cent solution is often used to harden plaster-of-Paris casts.

　　　Malonic acid, $CH_2(COOH)_2$, can be manufactured from chloroacetic acid *via* the cyanide. Its chief importance is as a chemical intermediate.

11.46 　　　$ClCH_2COOH \xrightarrow[OH^-]{NaCN} CNCH_2COONa \xrightarrow[H_2O]{NaOH} CH_2(COONa)_2 \xrightarrow{H^+}$

$$CH_2(COOH)_2$$

　　　Succinic acid, $(CH_2COOH)_2$, was known to the alchemists of the sixteenth century, who obtained it by the pyrolysis of amber. It can be manufactured from ethylene by way of the dinitrile, or by reduction of the unsaturated *fumaric acid,* available by fermentation of starch. Succinic acid is important in the manufacture of pharmaceu-

11.47 　　　$CH_2{=}CH_2 \xrightarrow{Cl_2} ClCH_2CH_2Cl \xrightarrow{2\,NaCN} CNCH_2CH_2CN \xrightarrow[OH^-]{H_2O}$

$$(CH_2COOH)_2$$

11.48 　　　　　　$HOCOCH{=}CHCOOH \xrightarrow[cat.]{H_2} HOCOCH_2CH_2COOH$

　　　　　　　　fumaric acid

ticals, and is widely used in the preparation of various kinds of plastics and electrical insulation. *Adipic acid,* $(CH_2CH_2COOH)_2$, is used in tonnage quantity in the manufacture of condensation polymers such as nylon. The synthesis of adipic acid from benzene through the intermediate cyclohexanol has been described (pp. 123 and 144). Adipic acid is also manufactured from tetramethylene dichloride by the sequence in Eq. 11.49.

11.49 　　　$Cl(CH_2)_4Cl \xrightarrow{NaCN} CN(CH_2)_4CN \xrightarrow[OH^-]{H_2O} HOCO(CH_2)_4COOH$

Tetramethylene dichloride is commercially available directly from tetrahydrofuran (p. 131), a product of corn cobs and oat hulls, or indirectly from acetylene and formaldehyde (p. 119).

　　　Phthalic acid, *o*-dicarboxybenzene, is used industrially in the manufacture of condensation polymers (Chapter 18), and as its dibutyl ester as a vehicle for insecticides. Its isomer, *terephthalic acid, p*-dicar-boxybenzene, is manufactured by air oxidation of *p*-xylene, and is also used in the manufacture of condensation polymers.

$$\text{COOC}_4\text{H}_9$$
$$\text{COOC}_4\text{H}_9$$

dibutyl phthalate

$$\text{HOOC} \quad \text{COOH}$$

terephthalic acid

Oleic acid is an unsaturated acid found in all animal and vegetable fats and oils. The mercury and lead salts are used as drugs. Oleic acid is usually found in nature associated with *linoleic* and *linolenic* acids, the dienoic and trienoic acids. The last two are especially abundant in the drying oils, such as linseed oil and tung oil, which are used in making paints. These unsaturated acids have been shown to have the proper-ties of vitamins, being essential in the diet of rats, and may be neces-sary for the prevention of skin disorders such as eczema in infants. Oxidation of oleic acid by ozone is a commercial source of pelargonic aldehyde (nonanal) and azelaic half aldehyde (9-oxononanoic acid).

$$\text{CH}_3(\text{CH}_2)_7\text{CH}{=}\text{CH}(\text{CH}_2)_7\text{COOH} \xrightarrow[\text{2. Zn/H}^+]{\text{1. O}_3}$$

11.50

$$\text{CH}_3(\text{CH}_2)_7\text{CHO} + \overset{\text{O}}{\overset{\|}{\text{HC}}}(\text{CH}_2)_7\text{COOH}$$

pelargonic   azelaic half-
aldehyde   aldehyde

Maleic acid may be obtained by heating malic acid, $\text{HOOCCH}_2\text{-CHOHCOOH}$, to form maleic anhydride, which is then hydrolyzed in water to maleic acid. Catalytic oxidation of benzene also produces maleic anhydride. Maleic acid is used in the manufacture of deter-gents, insecticides, and plastics.

Cinnamic acid is readily prepared by heating benzaldehyde with acetic anhydride and sodium acetate, in the Perkin reaction, or with malonic acid in the Knoevenagle reaction. The natural *trans*-acid occurs in balsam.

Study Questions

1. Write structural formulas for formic acid, acetic acid, butyric acid, lauric acid, oxalic acid, malonic acid, and phthalic anhydride.

2. Predict the melting points of tridecanoic acid and myrystic acid (tetradecanoic acid). What is the explanation of the fact that formic

acid melts approximately 40 degrees higher than valeric acid, even though its formula weight is less than half that of valeric acid?

3. Illustrate by an example the reactions of each of the *four* reactive sites of an aliphatic acid.

4. What explanation can you offer of the fact that carbonyl addition reactions occur more readily with acid derivatives, such as esters or acid chlorides, than they do with the acids themselves?

5. Write the structural formula of an example of each of the following:
   a) an anhydride;   b) a dicarboxylic acid;
   c) an amide;   d) a nitrile;
   e) an acyl chloride;   f) an aroyl bromide;
   g) a cyclic anhydride;   h) an ester.

6. Show by equations how you could convert: a) ethanol to acetic acid, b) ethanol to propionic acid, c) ethanol to malonic acid, d) ethanol to butyric acid, e) ethanol to 2-ethylbutanoic acid.

7. What chemical tests would distinguish between the following pairs of isomers?
   a) methylmalonic acid and succinic acid;
   b) ethyl acetate and methoxyacetone;
   c) *p*-toluic (*p*-methylbenzoic) acid and methyl benzoate;
   d) propionyl chloride and *beta*-chloropropionaldehyde.

8. Lauryl alcohol is an important commercial compound. What is its chief source?

9. Compound A, C_8H_8O, gave a silver mirror with Tollen's reagent. Upon mild oxidation, B, $C_8H_8O_2$, was formed. B is soluble in sodium bicarbonate solution. When A was oxidized vigorously, another substance, C, $C_8H_6O_4$, was formed which was also soluble in sodium bicarbonate solution. When C was gently heated, water was evolved, and substance D, $C_8H_4O_3$, was obtained. When D was stirred with sodium bicarbonate solution, it gradually dissolved, and when the solution was acidified, C was precipitated. Write structural formulas for A, B, C, and D, and show the reactions involved.

10. Show by equations what is meant by the Perkin reaction and the Knoevenagel reaction. How are they similar, and in what ways are they different?

11. What is the malonic ester synthesis? Using this reaction, show how 2-ethyl-butanoic acid could be synthesized.

12. Hydrolysis of an ester, $C_6H_{12}O_2$, gives an acid, X, and an alcohol, Y. Reduction of the acid, X, with lithium aluminum hydride yields the alcohol, Y. What is the structure and name of the original ester? Write equations for each reaction.

13. Give one commercial source, and one industrial use, of each of the following acids: a) formic acid, b) acetic acid, c) phthalic acid, d) adipic acid, e) benzoic acid, f) palmitic acid, g) oxalic acid, h) succinic acid.

Advanced Reading References

Organic Chemistry, R. Q. Brewster and W. E. McEwen, 3rd Ed., Prentice-Hall, Inc., Englewood Cliffs, N. J., 1961, Chapters 9, 10, and 30.

Chemistry of Organic Compounds, 2nd Ed., C. R. Noller, W. B. Saunders and Co., Philadelphia, 1957, Chapters 9, 26, and 37.

Organic Chemistry, 3rd Ed., L. F. Fieser and Mary Fieser, D. C. Heath and Co., Boston, 1957, Chapters 8 and 30.

Essential Principles of Organic Chemistry, James Cason, Prentice-Hall, Inc., Englewood Cliffs, N. J., 1956, Chapters 11, 12, and 26.

new terms & concepts

Esters occur widely in nature. The essential oils, waxes,
and fats have many industrial uses.
Reactions are hydrolysis (saponification), transesterification,
ammonolysis, and reduction.
Esters *can be prepared readily from acids, anhydrides, or acid chloride.*
Waxes *are high-molecular-weight esters which are naturally*
occurring protective substances.
Fats *are mixtures of mixed triglycerides, and important in foods, paints and soaps.*
The oils—which turn rancid easily—may be hydrogenated to solid fats.
Drying oils *are highly unsaturated, and form tough paint films.*
Hydrolysis of fats produces soaps, *the metal salts of fatty acids.*
Synthetic detergents resemble soaps in molecular structure and action.
Saponification number and iodine number are important
analytical figures for fat use.

12

Esters, fats, waxes, and detergents

Esters are the most important class of acid derivatives. They are generally lower-boiling than the acids, and have pleasant, fruity odors. The simple lower-molecular-weight esters are good solvents, and are manufactured for industrial use. Many of them are found in the essential oils (the essences) of flowers and fruits.

Naming esters

Esters are named as salts of the acids and the alcohol from which they are derived. The nomenclature was derived from the supposed analogy between esterification (Eq. 12.02) and neutralization (Eq. 12.01), in which a salt and water are produced from an acid and a

$$12.01 \qquad NaOH + HONO_2 \longrightarrow Na^+ONO_2^- + H_2O$$
$$\text{sodium nitrate}$$

$$12.02 \qquad CH_3CH_2OH + HOCOCH_3 \longrightarrow CH_3CH_2OCOCH_3 + H_2O$$
$$\text{ethyl acetate}$$

base. Even though this analogy is not valid, the names have continued. The name of any ester may then be formed by naming the radical of the alcohol, followed by a second word in which the -ic acid ending has been changed to -ate. For example:

$$CH_3-O-\overset{\overset{\textstyle O}{\|}}{C}-\bigodot$$

$$CH_3-\underset{\underset{\textstyle CH_3}{|}}{CH}-O-\overset{\overset{\textstyle O}{\|}}{C}-\underset{\underset{\textstyle CH_3}{|}}{CH}-CH_3$$

methyl benzoate   isopropyl isobutyrate

Other examples are given in Table 12.01.

Reactions of the esters

a) *Hydrolysis.* The saponification reaction has already been mentioned (pp. 115–167).

b) *Alcoholysis.* Just as alcohols will form hemiacetals with aldehydes (p. 139), so alcohols will add to the carbonyl group of esters, and the unstable intermediate hydroxyacetal may then decompose to produce either the original ester, or, if the alcohol was different, a new ester. By using an excess of an alcohol, one ester may be completely converted to another by this reaction, called *ester interchange* or *transesterification.*

12.03
$$R-\overset{\overset{\textstyle O}{\|}}{C}-OCH_3 + HOC_2H_5 \rightleftarrows \left[R-\overset{\overset{\textstyle O-C_2H_5}{|}}{\underset{\underset{\textstyle O-CH_3}{|}}{C}}-OH\right] \rightleftarrows$$

$$R-\overset{\overset{\textstyle O}{\|}}{C}-O-C_2H_5 + HOCH_3$$

c) *Ammonolysis.* Esters react readily with ammonia also, forming amides (p. 165). This reaction also involves addition of ammonia to the carbonyl group, followed by decomposition of the unstable intermediate. The fact that the reverse reaction of alcoholysis of the amide is much slower permits this reaction to go nearly to completion.

12.04 $$R-\overset{\overset{\textstyle O}{\|}}{C}-OCH_3 + HNH_2 \longrightarrow \left[R-\overset{\overset{\textstyle NH_2}{|}}{\underset{\underset{\textstyle OCH_3}{|}}{C}}-OH\right] \longrightarrow R-\overset{\overset{\textstyle O}{\|}}{C}NH_2 + CH_3OH$$

d) *Reduction and Grignard Addition.* These reactions have been described previously (pp. 118 and 162).

Preparation of esters

The common methods of preparing esters have already been presented (p. 165). They involve the reaction of acids or acid derivatives

TABLE 12.01   SOME ESTERS IN FLAVORING OILS AND WAXES

Formula	Name	Source
$CH_3CH_2CH_2COOC_2H_5$	Ethyl butyrate	Oil of pineapple
$CH_3CH_2CH_2COO(CH_2)_4CH_3$	Amyl butyrate	Apricots, strawberry
$CH_3COO(CH_2)_7CH_3$	Octyl acetate	Oil of orange
$CH_3COOCH_2CH_2CH(CH_3)_2$	Isoamyl acetate	Oil of pears, bananas
$(CH_3)_2CHCH_2COOCH_2CH_2CH(CH_3)_2$	Isoamyl isovalerate	Apple oil
COOCH$_3$ / OH	Methyl salicylate	Oil of wintergreen
COOCH$_2$CH(CH$_3$)$_2$ / OH	Isobutyl salicylate	Orchid perfume
COOCH$_3$ / NH$_2$	Methyl anthranilate	Oil of neroli, jasmine (synthetic grape)
COOCH$_2$CH$_3$ / NH$_2$	Ethyl anthranilate	Apple oil
$CH_3(CH_2)_{14}COOCH_2(CH_2)_{14}CH_3$	Cetyl palmitate	Spermaceti
$CH_3(CH_2)_{14}COO(CH_2)_{29}CH_3$	Myricyl palmitate	Beeswax
$CH_3(CH_2)_{24}COO(CH_2)_{29}CH_3$	Myricyl cerotate	Carnauba wax
$CH_3COOC_{27}H_{45}$	Cholesterol acetate	Brain wax

with alcohols or alcohol precursors, and are summarized in the following equations:

12.05 $$RCOOH + HOR' \rightleftharpoons RCOOR' + H_2O$$

12.06 $$RCOOCOR + HOR' \longrightarrow RCOOR' + RCOOH$$

12.07 $$RCOCl + HOR' \longrightarrow RCOOR' + HCl$$

12.08 $$RCOONa + XR' \longrightarrow RCOOR' + NaX$$

12.09 $$RCOOR'' + HOR' \longrightarrow RCOOR' + HOR''$$

Industrially, esters are usually prepared directly from acids and alcohols (Eq. 12.05) using solid catalysts and vapor phase reactions, although anhydrides (Eq. 12.06) may be used economically in esterification. The use of acid chlorides (Eq. 12.07) and metal carboxylates with alkyl halides (Eq. 12.08) is more expensive, and is usually limited to laboratory syntheses. Transesterification (Eq. 12.09) also has industrial applications. A wide variety of simple esters are prepared industrially for use as solvents for paints and lacquers in the protective-coating industries.

Naturally occurring esters

There are several important classes of esters which are found in nature. The *waxes,* which occur as protective substances in biological systems, are esters of high-molecular-weight alcohols, usually with high-molecular-weight acids. For example, the apple skin is coated with a thin film of wax, which prevents the fruit from becoming waterlogged and rotten during rainy periods. *Spermaceti* is a natural wax, cetyl palmitate, found in the head of the sperm whale, which is used in the cosmetics industry and in pharmaceutical preparations. *Beeswax* is a mixture of esters of high-molecular-weight aliphatic acids and alcohols, excreted by bees in building combs for storage of honey, and used to prepare ointments and creams for skin application. *Carnauba wax* is a very hard wax obtained from the leaves of the Brazilian wax palm, used in the manufacture of car, floor, and furniture polishes, and wherever a hard shiny surface is desired. The chief natural wax present in the human body is cholesterol acetate, present in nerve tissues and the bloodstream. Table 12.01 lists some of the perfume, flavoring, and wax esters by formula and source.

$$R^1-CO-O-CH_2$$
$$R^2-CO-O-CH$$
$$R^3-CO-O-CH_2$$

I

A second important group of naturally occurring esters are the triesters of glycerol, having the general formula I, where the alkyl groups may be the same or different. These substances, the triglycerides, are the fats and oils, such as butter or cottonseed oil. The acids found in these substances are chiefly the C_{18} and C_{16} acids, with a small amount of the lower even-numbered carbon acids, both saturated and unsaturated. The naturally occurring triglycerides are all mixtures of mixed esters, and therefore have no sharp melting points or specific chemical properties. The fats, such as lard or suet, are solids at room temperature, and tend to have more saturated fatty acids, such as palmitic and stearic acids, in the ester mixture. The oils, like corn oil, peanut oil and linseed oil, are liquids at room temperature, and will have a higher percentage of unsaturated fatty acids, such as oleic and linoleic acids, in the ester mixture. The average fatty acid compositions of several natural fats and oils are shown in Table 12.02. From this table can be seen the varying compositions of different fats. The important industrial uses of the various fats and oils depend on their composition.

TABLE 12.02   PER CENT ACID CONTENT OF SOME NATURAL FATS AND OILS

	Butter	Tallow, mutton	Palm oil	Corn oil	Linseed oil	Coconut oil
Saturated acids						
Butyric	3.2	..	..	..	..	..
Caproic	1.4	..	..	..	..	..
Caprylic	1.8	..	..	..	..	9.5
Capric	1.8	..	..	..	..	4.5
Lauric	6.9	..	..	..	3.1	51.0
Myristic	22.6	4.6	1.1	..	..	18.5
Palmitic	22.6	24.6	41.1	7.3	8.5	7.5
Stearic	11.4	30.5	4.2	3.3	..	3.0
Unsaturated acids						
Oleic	27.4	36.0	38.4	46.4	5.0	5.0
Linoleic	..	4.3	10.7	39.1	48.5	1.0
Linolenic	..	..	..	..	34.1	..
TOTAL:	99.1	100.0	95.5	96.1	99.2	100.0

Edible fats

The most important uses of fats are in foods, drying oils, and the manufacture of detergents. Both fats and oils are useful as foods. Corn oil and peanut oil are widely used as cooking oils, particularly for industrial baking and food processing. However, liquid fats have a greater tendency to turn *rancid,* and are therefore less desirable for home consumption, where longer storage of opened containers is necessary. When an unsaturated triglyceride is exposed to the oxygen of the air, it tends to decompose to form free acids, aldehydes, and ketones, all of which impart an unpleasant taste and odor to the fat. These reactions are catalyzed by contact with metal and by bacterial enzymes, and naturally occur more readily in liquids, where equilibrium is more rapidly obtained. By sterilizing, refrigerating, and sealing containers under nitrogen, fats can be safely stored for long periods, but once opened, they begin to turn rancid. Since this process is slower in the solid fats, the housewife prefers these, but the cheapest and most abundant fats are the vegetable oils of corn, peanut, soybean and cotton-

Fig. 12.01(a). Equipment for continuous hardening of natural oils for preparation of edible shortenings. (Courtesy of Procter & Gamble Company, Long Beach Plant.)

Fig. 12.01(b). In these tanks vegetable oils are hydrogenated or hardened by treating them with hydrogen in the presence of catalyst. Usually, the liquid vegetable oils are hardened sufficiently so that they are semi-solid at room temperatures. (Courtesy of Procter & Gamble Company, Long Beach Plant.)

seed. By hydrogenation (p. 55), the unsaturated esters are partially converted to saturated esters, and these vegetable oils become low-melting solids (compare corn oil to mutton tallow, Table 12.02, noting that reduction of oleic and linoleic esters will lead to stearic esters). These synthetic hardened fats are widely used in household cooking for shortening under such names as Crisco, Snowdrift, Spry, etc. Butter substitutes or oleomargarines are also made in this way, with flavoring, vitamins, and color being added if necessary. Some hydrogenated oils are naturally yellow, although they may be required by law to be bleached and then recolored.

Drying oils

When a thin film of a highly unsaturated oil, such as linseed oil, is exposed to the air it hardens to a glossy, tough, water-repellent film, useful as a protective coating for wood or metal. This hardening process is called "drying," but is actually an oxidation process, rather than evaporation of water. It depends on the presence of multiple double bonds in the fatty-acid chains. Oleic esters are not drying, but linolenic esters are good dryers. Drying can be speeded up by the addition of metal-oxide catalysts, and by heat-processing, which tends to produce conjugated double bonds in the esters. Boiled linseed oil drys quicker than raw linseed oil. Addition of suitable pigments, such as lead oxide (red lead) or titanium oxide, to drying oils makes *paint*. Tung oil is an important and useful drying oil, and growing the Asiatic tung tree has become an important part of the agriculture of the southern United States. Drying oils are also used in the manufacture of *linoleum* and *oil cloth*.

Soaps and detergents

When fats are saponified by boiling with sodium hydroxide, *soaps* are produced. Soaps are metal salts of fatty acids. Toilet soaps are

12.10
$$
\begin{array}{l}
\text{RCOO—CH}_2 \\
\text{RCOO—CH} + 3\,\text{NaOH} \longrightarrow 3\,\underset{\text{soap}}{\text{RCOONa}} + \underset{\substack{| \;\;\;\; | \;\;\;\; | \\ \text{OH} \;\; \text{OH} \;\; \text{OH} \\ \text{glycerol}}}{\text{CH}_2\text{—CH—CH}_2} \\
\underset{\text{fat}}{\text{RCOO—CH}_2}
\end{array}
$$

sodium or potassium salts of fatty acids, and are water-soluble. Calcium and magnesium salts of fatty acids are insoluble, and precipitate when soluble soaps are added to hard water, which contains calcium or magnesium ions. Aluminum soaps are used in cosmetics, and zinc soaps are mild antiseptics. Soluble soaps are useful *detergents*. Detergents are substances which cause oil or grease particles to form emulsions in water, so that soaps act as cleansing agents. Approximately 2 to 3 billion pounds of soap was sold last year in the United States. Soap is made from many different natural fats and oils, but coconut oil is an important source. Toilet soap is a complex mixture of sodium salts of various fatty acids, chiefly palmitic and stearic acids, with some glycerol and water added as softening agents, plus perfume and coloring. Scouring soaps have had sand, pumice, or other abrasives added.

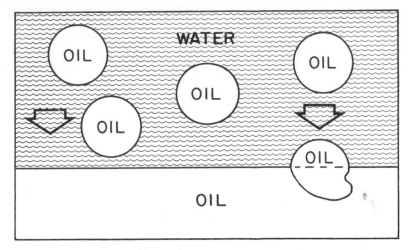

Fig. 12.02(a). Oil particles in water settle out.

Medicated soaps may have antiseptics added, while floating soaps have air beaten into the molten soap mixture before it is cast into bars.

Synthetic detergents have been one of the outstanding developments of modern chemistry. These substances resemble soaps in structure, but have the added advantage of not forming scummy precipitates in hard water, because the calcium and magnesium salts are soluble. In contrast to soaps, synthetic detergents are equally active as cleansing and foaming (sudsing) agents in hard or soft water. Sodium alkyl sulfates, such as sodium lauryl sulfate, were among the first of these

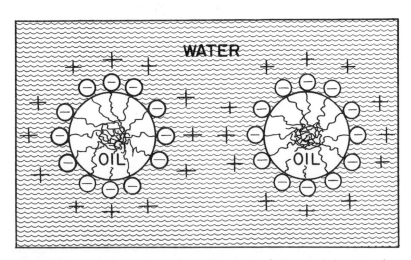

Fig. 12.02(b). Charged oil particles in detergent solution remain in suspension.

produced on a large scale. These substances resemble soaps, in that the molecules are composed of long aliphatic chains, which are fat-soluble, and ionic ends, which are water-soluble. This type of structure confers detergent action on the molecule, and most of the synthetic detergents have similar structures.

$$CH_3(CH_2)_{10}COO^-Na^+ \qquad CH_3(CH_2)_{11}\text{—}OSO_2O^-Na^+$$

soap   sodium alkyl sulfate

The cleansing action of soaps and synthetic detergents depends on two effects of these substances in solution: lowering of the surface tension, and emulsifying properties. The solution with lowered surface tension enters cracks and small holes more readily, thus loosening dirt and penetrating fibers of clothing more easily than plain water. The emulsifying properties of the soaps depend on the fact that colloidal solutions are stabilized by inducing an electrical charge on the particles. These charged particles then repel one another, and do not stick to surfaces. Oil particles then tend to absorb detergent molecules by dissolving the fat-soluble alkyl chains, leaving the negatively charged water-soluble heads on the surface of the globule (Figure 12.02). These negatively charged colloidal particles thus remain in suspension and are easily flushed away.

Analysis of fats

Since fats are mixtures of indefinite composition, the industries base their purchase of raw materials on batch analyses. A company manufacturing paint is interested in highly unsaturated drying oils. Food manufacturers prefer the oils containing less unsaturation, since these will not turn rancid as rapidly, and soap makers prefer the oils containing the lower-molecular-weight acids, such as lauric acid, since these make better soaps. A manufacturer can tell whether a given batch of oil will suit his needs by a laboratory report, which will contain, in addition to physical data, such as color, odor, taste, density, and viscosity, the results of quantitative chemical analysis. Two of the most informative figures are the *saponification number* and the *iodine number*.

Saponification Number. The saponification number is the number of milligrams of potassium hydroxide required to saponify 1 gram of fat. This is a measure of the average molecular weight of the alkyl (R) group in the fat, since the smaller the R groups, the more base required to hydrolyze 1 gram. Table 12.03 shows the saponification numbers of some common fats.

12.11 $(RCOO)_3C_3H_5 + 3\,KOH \longrightarrow 3\,RCOO^-K^+ + C_3H_5(OH)_3$

Iodine Number. The iodine number is the number of grams of iodine taken up by 100 grams of fat. This is a measure of the unsaturation of a fat, since the iodine is taken up by addition to the double bonds, and each mole of iodine consumed corresponds to one equivalent of double bond. The actual test procedure is complicated by the fact that iodine does not add to double bonds readily (p. 56), and more reactive halogens, such as iodine monochloride, must be used, and the data recalculated. The iodine numbers of some common fats are shown in Table 12.03.

TABLE 12.03   AVERAGE SAPONIFICATION AND IODINE NUMBERS OF SOME COMMON FATS AND OILS

Fat	Saponification number	Iodine number
Butter fat	210–230	26–28
Mutton tallow	190–200	18–25
Palm oil	200–205	45–59
Corn oil	187–193	111–128
Linseed oil	188–195	175–202
Coconut oil	253–262	6–10

Study Questions

1. Write structural formulas for the following: methyl acetate, propyl propionate, butyl valerate, glyceryl tripalmitate, ethyl benzoate.

2. Name the following esters:

$CH_3CH_2COOCH_3$, $CH_3COO(CH_2)_5CH_3$, $CH_3(CH_2)_{16}COOC_2H_5$,

$CH_3(CH_2)_7CH{=}CH(CH_2)_7COOCH_2$
$CH_3(CH_2)_7CH{=}CH(CH_2)_7COOCH$,
$CH_3(CH_2)_7CH{=}CH(CH_2)_7COOCH_2$

3. Using ethyl acetate as a model ester, illustrate the reactions of hydrolysis, alcoholysis, and ammonolysis. What is meant by transesterification? by saponification?

4. What products are produced by the high-pressure catalytic reduc- tion of coconut oil? (Consult Table 12.02 for the composition of coconut oil.)

5. If you wished to convert a very expensive rare alcohol, ROH, to an acetate, what reagent would you use? Why?

6. Write the structural formula, natural source, and one industrial use for each of the following natural esters: carnauba wax, sperm- aceti, methyl salicylate, methyl anthranilate, amyl acetate.

7. On the basis of the composition of the fats listed in Table 12.02, tell which is the best for soap-making and why? Which is the best drying oil, and why? Which is the best for use in hydrogenation for shortening and why?

8. What is meant by rancidity? a detergent? a drying oil? a soap? hydrogenation of an oil?

9. Define saponification number and iodine number. What does each measure? Of what significance are such numbers when they are applied to mixtures?

10. Show clearly your understanding of detergent action.

11. On the basis of the analysis of fats listed in Table 12.03, tell which is the best fat for soap-making and why? Which is the best drying oil and why? Which is the best fat for shortening production and why? Compare your answers to those on question 7.

Advanced Reading References

Organic Chemistry, R. Q. Brewster and W. E. McEwen, 3rd Ed., Pren- tice-Hall, Inc., Englewood Cliffs, N. J., 1961, Chapter 11.

Organic Chemistry, H. Harry Szmant, Prentice-Hall, Inc., Englewood Cliffs, N. J., 1957, Chapters 27 and 30.

Biochemistry of The Fatty Acids, W. R. Bloor, Reinhold Publishing Co., New York, 1943.

Introduction to the Chemistry of Fats and Fatty Acids, F. D. Gunstone, John Wiley and Sons, New York, 1958.

new terms & concepts

Nitrogen forms basic primary, secondary, and tertiary amines.
These react with acids to form salts or amides.
Primary, secondary, and tertiary amines can be distinguished by the
Hinsberg reaction with benzenesulfonyl chloride, or by the different
products formed with nitrous acid.
Aromatic amines form diazonium salts, which can be replaced or coupled to form dyes.
On the aromatic ring, the nitro group is a deactivating strong meta-*director,*
while the amine group is an activating strong para-*director.*
Amines are formed from ammonia and alkyl halides, or by reduction of
nitriles, amides, or nitro compounds.
The nitro group activates alpha-*hydrogen atoms.*
Nitro-paraffins are easily clorinated or condensed with aldehydes.
Many amine derivatives are useful drugs.
Nitro compounds are widely used as explosives.

13

Organic nitrogen compounds

Nitrogen commonly has three covalent bonds, and combines with carbon and hydrogen to form compounds having carbon-nitrogen single, double, or triple bonds. The simplest compounds may be thought of as derivatives of ammonia, in which one, two, or three hydrogens are replaced by organic groups to form the I°, II°, or III°

$$CH_3CH_2-NH_2 \qquad CH_3-\overset{\overset{\displaystyle CH_3}{|}}{N}-CH_3 \qquad \langle\!\!\!\!\bigcirc\!\!\!\!\rangle NH_2$$

ethylamine   trimethylamine   aminobenzene
(aniline)

amines. Like ammonia, the amines are bases, reacting rapidly with acids to form soluble salts. The ammonium ion, NH_4^+, has four replaceable hydrogens, and its organic analog, R_4N^+, is called the quaternary (IV°) ammonium salt—for example, tetramethylammonium chloride, $(CH_3)_4N^+Cl^-$. The lower-molecular-weight amines are water-soluble gases with characteristic unpleasant fishy odors. Indeed, trimethylamine is found in fish brines, and *putrescine*, H_2N-CH_2-$CH_2CH_2CH_2-NH_2$, and *cadaverine*, $H_2N-(CH_2)_5-NH_2$, are among the amines chiefly responsible for the unpleasant odor of decaying meat. Many of the more complex amines have physiological activity, and it is among this class of compounds that we find the widest variety of useful drugs.

193

THE AMINES

Naming the amines

The simple aliphatic amines are known by the I.U.C. names, but many of the more highly substituted amines have been given trivial names, especially in the aromatic series. The structures and names of a few amines are listed in Table 13.01. It will be recalled from Chapter 2 that the suffix *amine* is used only for the simple molecules, and that the prefix *amino-* is preferred when any other function is present. Even in simple amines it is sometimes preferable to use the prefix, i.e. CH_3—CH_2—CH_2—CH_2—CH_2—$CHNH_2$—CH_3, 2-aminoheptane, or $(CH_3)_2CHN(CH_3)_2$, 2-dimethylaminopropane. When there are substituents present on the nitrogen atom, their position must be indicated by the letter N—. For example, the two isomeric trimethyl-anilines:

2,4,6-trimethylaniline   N,3,5-trimethylaniline

Reaction of amines

The most important chemical property of the amines is their basic reaction with acids to form salts (Eq. 13.01), and the decomposition

13.01 $R_3N + HCl \longrightarrow R_3NH^+Cl^-$

13.02 $R_3NH^+Cl^- + OH^- \longrightarrow R_3N + H_2O + Cl^-$

of these salts by stronger bases (i.e. sodium hydroxide) to form the free amines again (Eq. 13.02). Because of this property, many of the amines which are useful drugs can be administered as their salts in aqueous solution. It should be noted that substitution of alkyl groups in ammonia increases the base strength, so that dimethylamine is a stronger base than methylamine, which is stronger than ammonia. However, substitution of positive groups such as benzene or acyl groups decreases the base strength, so that ammonia is a stronger base than aniline, and diphenylamine, $(C_6H_5)_2NH$, is not even soluble in acids. Acetamide, CH_3CONH_2, is a neutral substance, rather insoluble in water, and sulfonamides, R—SO_2—NH_2, which have an ammonia hydrogen substituted by the strongly positive RSO_2- group, are actually acids, being soluble in strong bases and ionizing according to the equation:

13.03 $\qquad R-SO_2-NH_2 + OH^- \longrightarrow R-SO_2-NH^- + H_2O$

TABLE 13.01   NAMES AND PROPERTIES OF SOME COMMON AMINES

Formula	I.U.C. name	Common name	B.P. °C
CH_3NH_2	Methylamine	Methylamine	-7
$(CH_3)_2NH$	Dimethylamine	Dimethylamine	7
$(CH_3)_3N$	Trimethylamine	Trimethylamine	4
$CH_3CH_2NH_2$	Ethylamine	Ethylamine	17
$CH_3CH_2CH_2NH_2$	Propylamine	n-Propylamine	49
$(CH_3)_2CHNH_2$	Isopropylamine	Isopropylamine	34
$CH_3(CH_2)_3NH_2$	Butylamine	n-Butylamine	76
$CH_3(CH_2)_4NH_2$	Pentylamine	n-Amylamine	104
$NH_2CH_2CH_2NH_2$	1,2-Ethanediamine	Ethylenediamine	117
$NH_2(CH_2)_4NH_2$	1,4-Butanediamine	Putrescine	158
$NH_2(CH_2)_5NH_2$	1,5-Pentanediamine	Cadaverine	178
(piperidine ring structure)	Azacyclohexane	Piperidine	106
(benzene ring)NH_2	Aminobenzene	Aniline	184
(benzene ring)$N(CH_3)_2$	Dimethylaminobenzene	Dimethylaniline	193
CH_3(benzene ring)NH_2	1-Methyl-4-aminobenzene	p-Toluidine	200

Amines are effective nucleophilic reagents and enter into many reactions of the nucleophilic type already described (Chapters 7, 10, 11). The following represent useful synthetic reactions of amines:

13.04 $\qquad RNH_2 + R'X \longrightarrow RR'NH_2^+X^- \xrightarrow{OH^-}$ II° amine
$\qquad\qquad\qquad\qquad\qquad\qquad\qquad RR'NH$

13.05 $\qquad R_2NH + R'X \longrightarrow R_2R'NH^+X^- \xrightarrow{OH^-}$ III° amine
$\qquad\qquad\qquad\qquad\qquad\qquad\qquad R_2R'N$

13.06 $\qquad R_3N + R'X \longrightarrow R_3R'N^+X^- \xrightarrow{Ag^+OH^-}$ IV° ammonium
$\qquad\qquad\qquad\qquad\qquad\qquad\qquad R_3R'N^+OH^-$ hydroxide

13.07 $\qquad R_2NH + R'OH \xrightarrow{\Delta} R_2NR' + H_2O$ III° amine

13.08 $R_2NH + H_2C\!-\!CH_2 \longrightarrow R_2NCH_2CH_2OH$ amino-alcohol
$\diagdown\!O\!\diagup$

13.09 $RNH_2 + R'CHO \longrightarrow RN\!=\!CHR'$ aldimine

13.10 $R_2NH + CH_2\!=\!CH\!-\!CN \longrightarrow R_2NCH_2CH_2CN$ amino-nitrile

13.11 $RNH_2 + R'COCl \longrightarrow R'CONHR + HCl$ amide

13.12 $R_2NH + R'COOR'' \longrightarrow R'CONR_2 + R''OH$ amide

The IV° ammonium hydroxides are strong bases, and some of the compounds of this class have found application as alkaline antiseptics, and basic catalysts.

The reaction of benzenesulfonyl chloride with amines is the basis of a method for distinguishing between I°, II°, and III° amines, called the *Hinsberg* test. A primary amine will react with benzene-sulfonyl chloride to produce a sulfonamide having one hydrogen on the nitrogen. As already mentioned, these substances are acidic, and dissolve in basic solution. A secondary amine produces a sulfonamide having no acidic hydrogens, while a III° amine does not react. There-

13.13 $\langle\!\!\bigcirc\!\!\rangle SO_2Cl + HNR_2 \longrightarrow \langle\!\!\bigcirc\!\!\rangle SO_2NR_2 + HCl$

N,N-diethylbenzenesulfonamide

fore, when an amine is shaken with benzenesulfonyl chloride, if the product dissolves in base, the amine was I°; if the product is un-soluble in acid or base, the amine was II°; but if the "product" dis-solves in acid (unreacted amine is isolated) the amine was III°.

13.14 $\langle\!\!\bigcirc\!\!\rangle SO_2Cl + H_2NR \longrightarrow \langle\!\!\bigcirc\!\!\rangle SO_2\overset{\overset{\text{H}}{|}}{N}\!-\!R \xrightarrow{\text{OH}^-} \langle\!\!\bigcirc\!\!\rangle SO_2N\!=\!R$

Amines react with nitrous acid to give several products, depend-ing on the nature of the amine. This reaction may also be used to dis-tinguish aliphatic I°, II°, and III° amines, since each of these gives a different product. The three reactions are illustrated by Eqs. 13.15–13.17. Both I° and II° amines react to form nitrosoamines by loss of

13.15   I° $R\!-\!\overset{\overset{\text{H}}{|}}{N}\!-\!H + HO\!-\!NO \longrightarrow \left[R\!-\!\overset{\overset{\text{H}}{|}}{N}\!-\!N\!=\!O \rightleftharpoons R\!-\!N\!=\!N\!-\!OH\right]$

$\longrightarrow R\!-\!OH + N_2$ (gas)

13.16   II° $R_2N\!-\!H + HO\!-\!NO \longrightarrow R_2N\!-\!NO$ (yellow insoluble nitrosoamine)

13.17   III° $R_3N + HO—NO \longrightarrow R_3NH^+NO_2^-$ (soluble trialkylammonium nitrite salt)

water, but in the first case, the nitrosoamine is unstable and undergoes an enol-like rearrangement to form the diazonium hydroxide. Alkyl diazonium hydroxides ($R—N{=}N—OH$) are also unstable, decomposing irreversibly to the alcohol and nitrogen (which bubbles out of the reaction as a gas). In the second case, the nitrosoamine cannot undergo rearrangement since there are no hydrogens available, and it is precipitated as a yellow solid. III° amines form salts with nitrous acid as with other acids, and simply go into solution. If an unknown amine is treated with nitrous acid, evolution of a gas indicates a I° amine, a yellow precipitate a II° amine, and a colorless solution a III° amine. When a I° aliphatic amine is treated with nitrous acid, the evolution of N_2 is quantitative. By measuring the volume of gas evolved, a quantitative method of analysis for I° amines—especially amino-acids and proteins—was developed by *Van Slyke,* and named after him.

Aromatic amines react with nitrous acid in essentially the same way, but the products are more stable. If a solution of aniline hydrochloride is cooled to 0°C in ice, and treated with nitrous acid, the diazonium salt, $ArN_2^+Cl^-$, is obtained in solution and is sufficiently stable to undergo reactions as long as the solution is kept cold. If the solution is allowed to warm up, the I° amine reaction occurs, and phenol is formed (Eq. 13.18). This is, in fact, a convenient way to

13.18   ⟨benzene⟩—NH_2 $\xrightarrow[\substack{HCl \\ 0°}]{HNO_2}$ ⟨benzene⟩—$N_2^+Cl^-$ $\xrightarrow{H_2O}$ ⟨benzene⟩—$OH + N_2 + HCl$

synthesize phenols from amines. The diazonium salts are difficult to isolate and are explosive when dry, but may be used in cold solutions. They are very reactive, and undergo a variety of replacement reactions in acid solution, accompanied by the evolution of nitrogen gas. These reactions are sometimes improved by catalytic amounts of cuprous salts, and are very useful in aromatic chemistry for replacing an amine group by some other function. The diazonium displacement reactions (Eqs. 13.19–13.23) illustrate the versatility of the reaction.

13.19 $Ar—N_2^+Cl^- + H_2O \xrightarrow{heat} Ar—OH + N_2 + HCl$

13.20 $Ar—N_2^+Cl^- + CN^- \xrightarrow{heat} Ar—CN + N_2 + Cl^-$

13.21 $Ar—N_2^+Cl^- + I^- \xrightarrow{heat} Ar—I + N_2 + Cl^-$

13.22 $Ar—N_2^+Br^- + Br^- \xrightarrow{Cu_2Br_2} Ar—Br + N_2 + Br^-$

13.23 $Ar-N_2^+Cl^- + H_2 \xrightarrow{H_3PO_2} Ar-H + N_2 + HCl$

Notice that by *diazotization* and *replacement,* the $-NH_2$ group in aromatic compounds may be changed to $-OH$, $-CN$, $-I$, $-Br$, or even removed by reduction. This reaction is especially useful in aromatic synthetic chemistry, since advantage may be taken of the directive effects of both the nitro and the amino groups, and then these groups may be replaced by other functions (p. 80).

All the above reactions take place in acid solutions. In neutral or basic solutions, aromatic diazonium salts will *couple* with reactive aromatic compounds such as phenols or aromatic III° amines to form *azo* compounds. The *azo* group, $-N=N-$, imparts color to the

13.24

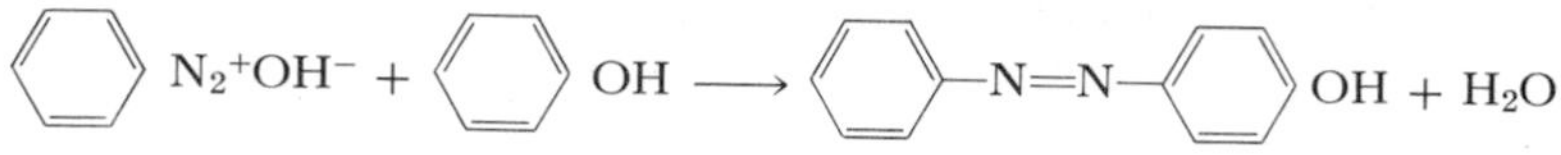

p-hydroxyazobenzene

molecule when coupled to an aromatic ring and is therefore said to be a *chromophoric* group. Many useful dyes are prepared by means of

13.25

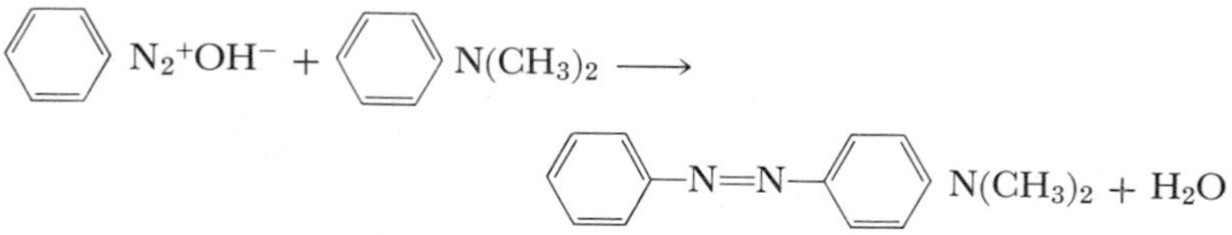

p-dimethylaminoazobenzene
(butter yellow)

13.26

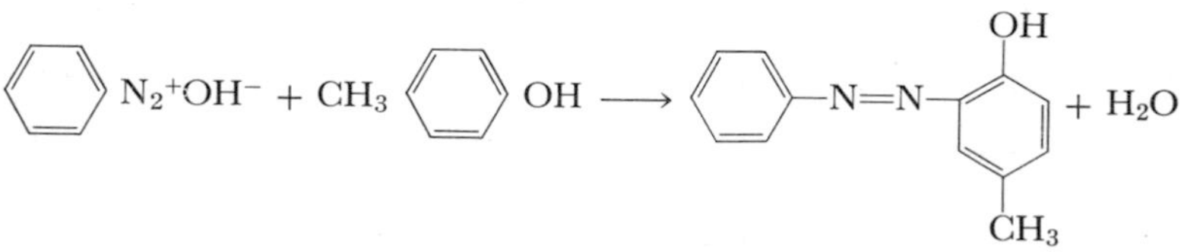

the azo coupling reaction. Coupling always occurs in the *para*-position unless it is blocked by some other group, in which case it can occur in the *ortho*-position. Many of the azo dyes have found use in medicine. For example, *scarlet red* is used to stimulate the growth of skin cells in burns and skin-grafts. *Pyridium* is used as a genito-urinary antiseptic.

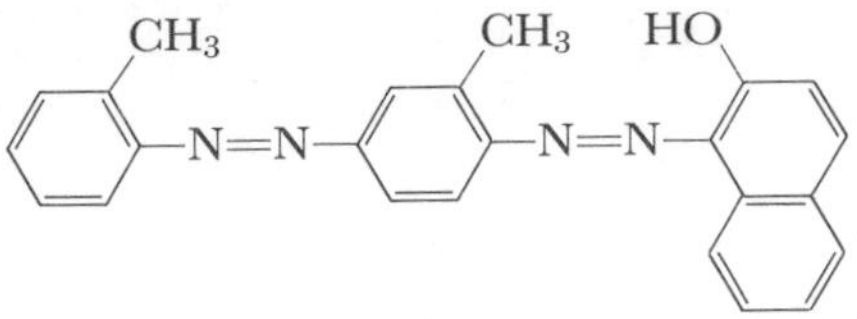
CH3
CH3
HO
N=N
N=N

scarlet red

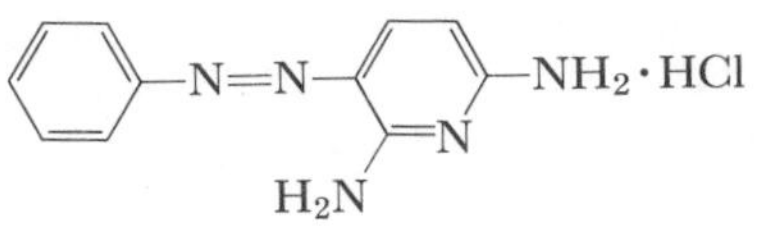
N=N
NH2 · HCl
N
H2N

pyridium

Substitution in aromatic nitrogen compounds

When an amine or substituted amine group is present in an aromatic ring, it increases the activity of the aromatic compound to substitution, and is a strong *para*-directing influence, comparable to the activating influence of the hydroxy group in phenols. Like phenol, when aniline is treated with bromine water, it reacts rapidly to form 2,4,6-tribromoaniline.

13.27

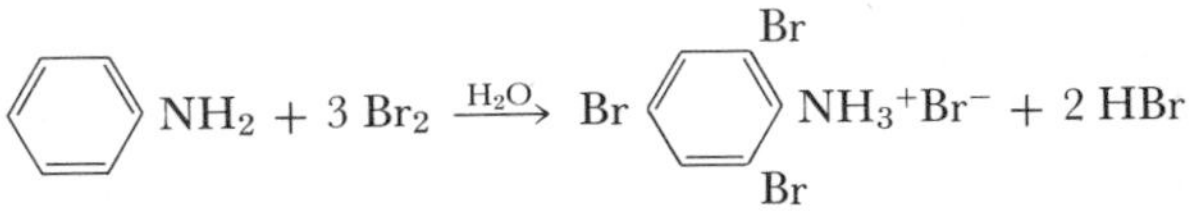
NH2 + 3 Br2
H2O
Br
Br
NH3+Br− + 2 HBr
Br

In order to carry out simple substitution reactions with aniline, it is usually necessary to deactivate the amine group by acetylation to form acetanilide, and then regenerate the amine by hydrolysis after carrying out the desired reactions. For example, in the manufacture of sulfanilamide from aniline, the first step is acetylation and the last step deacetylation to regenerate the free amino group.

13.28

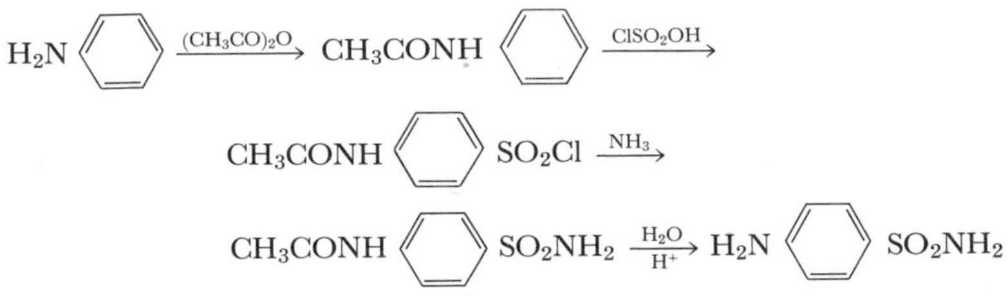
H2N
(CH3CO)2O
CH3CONH
ClSO2OH
CH3CONH
SO2Cl
NH3
CH3CONH
SO2NH2
H2O
H+
H2N
SO2NH2

sulfanilamide

Nitrobenzene, on the other hand, is not as easily substituted as benzene, and the nitro group is a strong *meta*-director (Table 5.02). Since the nitro group is easily reduced to the amine group, and amine groups are easily replaced, various combinations of the directive effects and diazonium replacement may be used in aromatic syntheses. For example, consider how benzene may be converted to *m*-bromophenol. Both the bromo- and -hydroxyl groups are *para*-directors (Chapter 5). However, the *meta*-directing influence of the nitro group may be used to introduce the bromine atom in the proper orientation, and the nitro group later replaced by reduction and diazotization (Eq. 13.29).

13.29

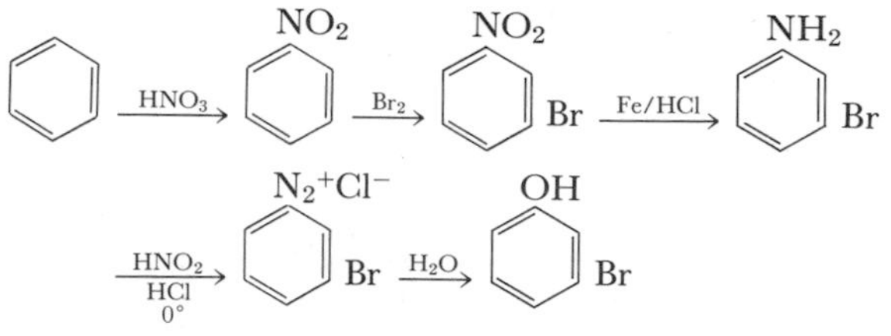

$$
\text{benzene} \xrightarrow{HNO_3} \text{NO}_2 \xrightarrow{Br_2} \text{NO}_2\text{-Br} \xrightarrow{Fe/HCl} \text{NH}_2\text{-Br}
$$

$$
\xrightarrow[HCl \ 0°]{HNO_2} \text{N}_2{}^+\text{Cl}^-\text{-Br} \xrightarrow{H_2O} \text{OH-Br}
$$

Preparation of amines

Amines may be made by the reaction of active halides with ammonia or amines (Eqs. 13.30–13.32). The reaction is somewhat complex for I° or II° amines but is quite useful in the III° series. The

13.30 $\qquad R{-}X + NH_3 \longrightarrow R{-}NH_2 + HX$

13.31 $\qquad R{-}X + R{-}NH_2 \longrightarrow R_2NH + HX$

13.32 $\qquad R{-}X + R_2NH \longrightarrow R_3N + HX$

yield of I° amines is greatly improved if a metal salt of ammonia is used. The preparation of I° amines from ammonia may also be

13.33 $\qquad R{-}X + K{-}NH_2 \xrightarrow{NH_3} R{-}NH_2 + K^+X^-$

accomplished by use of the *Gabriel synthesis*. The strong acidifying effect of two carbonyl groups on an *alpha*-hydrogen is illustrated by phthalimide, which is soluble in basic solution, forming salts. These salts are especially effective in replacement reactions of alkyl halides (Table 7.02, Chapter 7). The N-alkylphthalimides so formed may be hydrolyzed to produce I° amines in good yield.

13.34

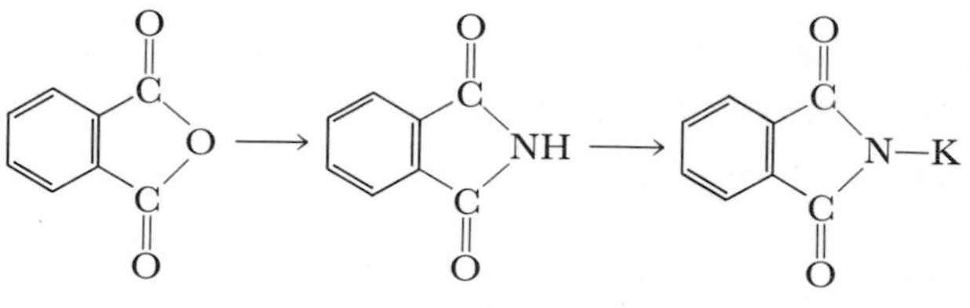

potassium phthalimide

13.35

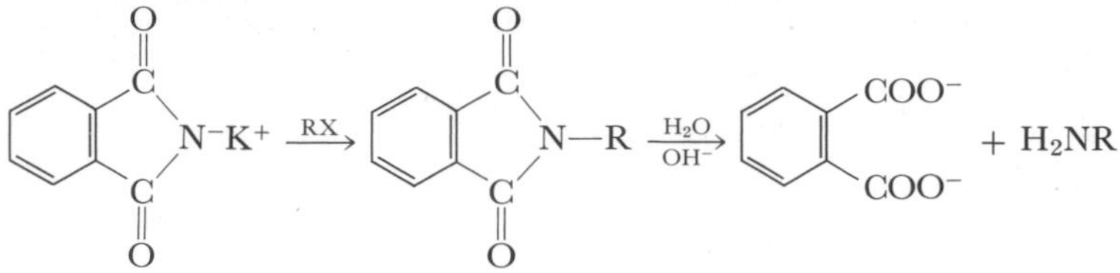

The reduction of nitrogen derivatives of acids or ketones provides a much more useful source of amines. For example, the reduction of oximes with sodium and alcohol, or the reduction of nitriles or amides with lithium aluminum hydride, provides amines in good yield. Nitro compounds are also reduced by a variety of chemical reagents, as well as catalytically, to produce amines. Since aromatic nitro compounds

13.36

$$CH_3{-}CO{-}CH_3 \xrightarrow{H_2NOH} CH_3{-}\overset{\overset{\displaystyle N{-}OH}{\|}}{C}{-}CH_3 \xrightarrow[\text{alc.}]{Na} CH_3{-}\overset{\overset{\displaystyle NH_2}{|}}{CH}{-}CH_3$$

13.37

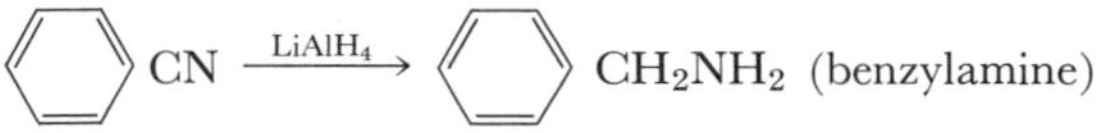

$CN \xrightarrow{LiAlH_4}$ CH_2NH_2 (benzylamine)

13.38 $CH_3CH_2CONHCH_3 \xrightarrow{LiAlH_4} CH_3CH_2CH_2{-}NH{-}CH_3$

13.39 $CH_3CH_2NO_2 \xrightarrow[\text{cat.}]{H_2} CH_3CH_2NH_2 + 2\,H_2O$

13.40 $NO_2 \xrightarrow[\text{Fe/HCl}]{H_2}$ $NH_2 + 2\,H_2O$

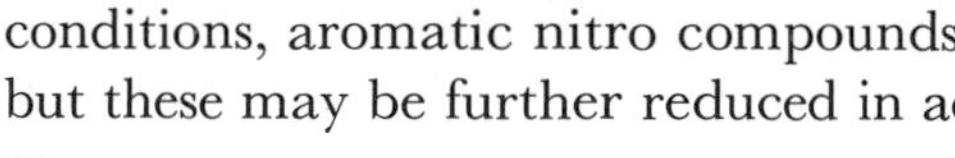

are more readily available than the aliphatic members, this method is especially useful for the preparation of aromatic amines. Industrially, nitrobenzene is converted to aniline by reduction with iron and steam. Under alkaline conditions, aromatic nitro compounds are reduced to azo derivatives, but these may be further reduced in acid or catalytically to the amines.

13.41 2 $NO_2 \xrightarrow[\text{NaOH}]{\text{tin}}$ $-N{=}N-$ $+ 4\,H_2O$

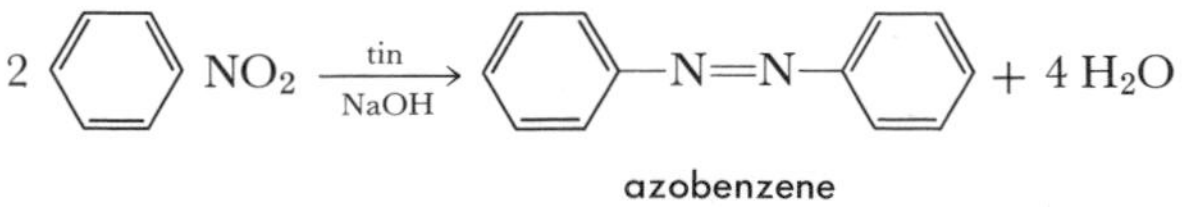

azobenzene

ORGANIC NITRO COMPOUNDS

The organic nitro compounds may be thought of as derivatives of nitric acid, $HO{-}NO_2$, in which the $HO{-}$ group has been replaced by an organic radical. They contain nitrogen in the oxidized state.

Organic nitro compounds are useful industrially as solvents, chemical intermediates, and in explosives.

Preparation of nitro compounds

The aliphatic nitro compounds are rather difficult to prepare. The most direct method is replacement of a halide, using silver nitrite. This reaction is called the *Victor Meyer* reaction. In addition to nitroalkanes, some alkyl nitrites are produced. The use of silver salts is not suitable to commercial application, and the commercially available aliphatic nitro compounds are prepared by high-temperature nitration of methane, ethane, and propane in the vapor phase (p. 39). Direct nitration of aromatic compounds with sulfuric and nitric acid mixture is satisfactory. Since the nitro group deactivates the ring to further substitution, the introduction of nitro groups may be carried out stepwise (p. 81). Nitrobenzene is manufactured in tonnage quantity by direct nitration of benzene.

Reactions of nitro compounds

The most important reaction of the nitro group itself is reduction. As has already been stated, the nitro group can be reduced chemically or catalytically to the amine group. Although some aliphatic amines are manufactured by reduction of nitroparaffins, the most important use of nitrobenzene is in the manufacture of aniline.

Since the nitro group is a strongly electron-attracting group, it exerts a powerful influence on adjacent atoms. *alpha*-Hydrogen atoms are strongly activated, as in aldehydes or *alpha*-dicarboxylic acids. Primary and secondary nitroparaffins are partially soluble in basic solution, since they exist in two tautomeric forms, the nitro and the acinitro (nitronic acid) forms. The latter is quite soluble in base. Like

$$13.42 \quad \underset{\text{nitro compound}}{R-CH_2-\overset{\overset{\textstyle O}{\uparrow}}{N}=O} \rightleftharpoons R-CH=\overset{\overset{\textstyle O}{\uparrow}}{N}-OH \xrightarrow{OH^-} \underset{\text{acinitro ion}}{RCH=\overset{\overset{\textstyle O}{\uparrow}}{N}-O^-} + H_2O$$

the aldehydes, aliphatic nitro compounds are readily halogenated in the *alpha*-position in alkaline solution. Chloropicrin, Cl_3CNO_2, is prepared commercially by this method for use as an agricultural insec-

$$13.43 \quad CH_3NO_2 + Cl_2 \xrightarrow{NaOH} Cl_3CNO_2 + 3 HCl$$

ticide. The *alpha*-hydrogens are available for condensations, and reactions similar to the aldol reaction occur in basic solution. Nitro-ethane, for example, condenses with formaldehyde in basic solution to produce 2-nitro-1-propanol, which in turn offers a source of the cor-

13.44
$$CH_3CH_2NO_2 + CH_2O \xrightarrow{OH^-} CH_3CHNO_2CH_2OH \xrightarrow{H_2}$$
$$CH_3CH_2NH_2CH_2OH$$

responding amino-alcohol. Benzedrine is manufactured commercially from nitroethane and benzaldehyde, as follows:

13.45

benzedrine

Some useful organic nitrogen compounds

Aniline ($C_6H_5NH_2$) is an important industrial substance used in the manufacture of drugs. It has powerful antipyretic and anti-neuralgic properties, but is toxic. Acetylation of the amino group de-creases the basicity, ease of substitution, and also the toxicity. *Acetanilide* (antifebrin, $CH_3CONHC_6H_5$), a crystalline, slightly water-soluble compound, is used in proprietary headache powders and febrifuges, as well as in chemical manufacturing. *Acetophenetidin* (phenacetin, $CH_3CH_2OC_6H_4NHCOCH_3$-*p*) *p*-ethoxyacetanilide, has similar action, and is somewhat less toxic, so that it is more widely used for the relief of pain and the reduction of body temperature.

Hexamethylene diamine ($NH_2(CH_2)_6NH_2$) is an important amine manufactured in quantity for use in making nylon (p. 290). One of the chief sources is reduction of adiponitrile (Eq. 13.46). *Hexam-*

13.46 $$Cl(CH_2)_4Cl \xrightarrow{CN^-} NC(CH_2)_4CN \xrightarrow[cat.]{H_2} NH_2(CH_2)_6NH_2$$

ethylene tetramine (urotropine, hexamine, $(CH_2)_6N_4$) is made from formaldehyde and ammonia (see p. 149) and is widely used com-mercially in making plastics, explosives, and other chemicals. *RDX,* or cyclonite, for example, is a new high explosive, more powerful than T.N.T. It is manufactured by nitration of hexamine in the presence of ammonium nitrate.

$$O_2N \diagdown \quad CH_2 \quad \diagup NO_2$$
$$N \qquad N$$
$$H_2C \diagdown \qquad \diagup CH_2$$
$$N$$
$$| $$
$$NO_2$$

RDX

$$CH_3$$
$$|$$
$$HOCH_2CH_2N-CH_3{}^+OH^-$$
$$|$$
$$CH_3$$

choline

Triethanolamine $(N(CH_2CH_2OH)_3)$ is used in the drug and cosmetic industry as an emulsifying agent. Kerosene solutions of insecticides or herbicides may be emulsified with water by adding triethanolamine or a fatty acid salt such as triethanolamine oleate. *Diethylaminoethanol* $((CH_3CH_2)_2NCH_2CH_2OH)$ finds use in the manufacture of drugs.

Choline (*beta*-hydroxyethyltrimethylammonium hydroxide) is a strong base found widely distributed in nature in brain and nerve tissues, egg yolk, hops, belladonna, etc. It has powerful physiological effects, causing a marked fall in blood pressure, slowing of the heart, stimulating gastric and intestinal peristalsis, and increasing salivary secretions. *Acetylcholine* is about 1000 times as potent as choline, but it is rapidly hydrolyzed to choline in the body. Acetylcholine is involved in the chemical transmission of the nerve impulse at the synapses of nerve cells, being liberated during the impulse, but is quickly hydro-

$$CH_3COOCH_2CH_2\overset{+}{N}(CH_3)_3$$

acetylcholine

$$CH_3COO-\underset{\underset{CH_3}{|}}{CH}-CH_2\overset{+}{N}(CH_3)_3Cl^-$$

mecholyl

lyzed by the enzyme, cholinesterase. A synthetic derivative, 2-acetoxy-propyl-1-trimethylammonium chloride, called *mecholyl,* has the same activity, counteracting the effects of the sympathomimetics, and is longer acting since it is not hydrolyzed so readily in the body. Aromatic esters of amino-alcohols related in structure to choline have proved effective as local anesthetics. These may be injected into the tissues at the site of the desired anesthesia, or simply applied topically as in eye surgery. There are many of these synthetic compounds used clinically, since small modifications in structure render them longer-acting, more readily absorbed at certain sites, and more compatible with other medication. Of these, *procaine,* (beta-diethylaminoethyl *p*-aminobenzoate, novocaine) is most widely used for injection as the *hydrochloride,* while *butacaine* (3-dibutylaminopropyl *p*-aminobenzoate, butyn) is used extensively as a surface anesthetic.

$$H_2N \underset{}{\bigcirc} COOCH_2CH_2N \overset{CH_2CH_3}{\underset{CH_2CH_3}{<}}$$

procaine

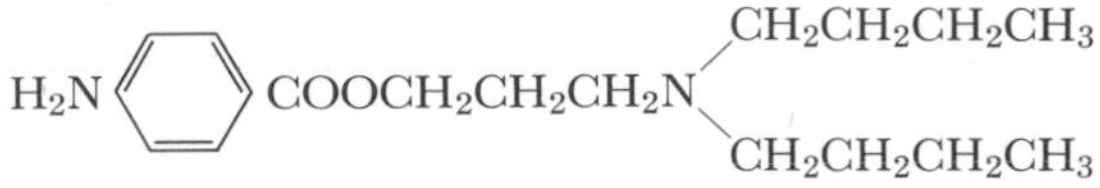

$$H_2N \underset{}{\bigcirc} COOCH_2CH_2CH_2N \overset{CH_2CH_2CH_2CH_3}{\underset{CH_2CH_2CH_2CH_3}{<}}$$

butacaine

Histamine is an amine found widely distributed in nature, present in nearly all tissues in a bound inactive form. On injection into animals, it causes shock and lowering of blood pressure; on inhalation in aerosol sprays it causes bronchospasm. It is believed to be the substance liberated in the tissues in anaphylactic shock, and to be responsible for various allergic reactions. A large number of dimethylaminoethyl derivatives attached to a large aromatic group $Ar—Z—Ar^1$ have been found to counteract the effects of histamine in the body, and are used clinically in the symptomatic treatment of allergies, hay fever, urti-

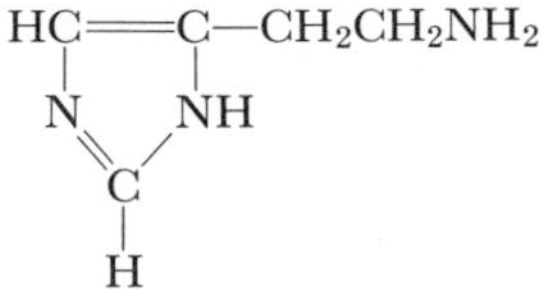

$$HC = C—CH_2CH_2NH_2$$
$$N \qquad NH$$
$$C$$
$$H$$

histamine

$$\overset{Ar}{\underset{Ar'}{>}}Z—CH_2CH_2N \overset{CH_3}{\underset{CH_3}{<}}$$

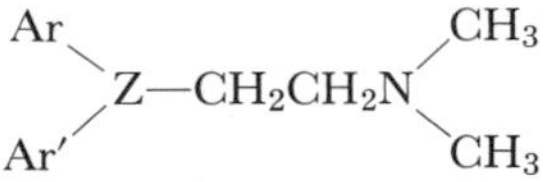

antihistamine

caria, etc. The groups Z may be nitrogen, carbon, or carbon-oxygen, but the most active members seem to be found in the dimethylamino-ethylamine series, $(CH_3)_2N\ CH_2CH_2N{<}$. *Diphenhydramine* (benadryl) and *tripelennamine* (pyrabenzamine) are two of the clinically useful antihistamines which illustrate the structural requirements of these compounds.

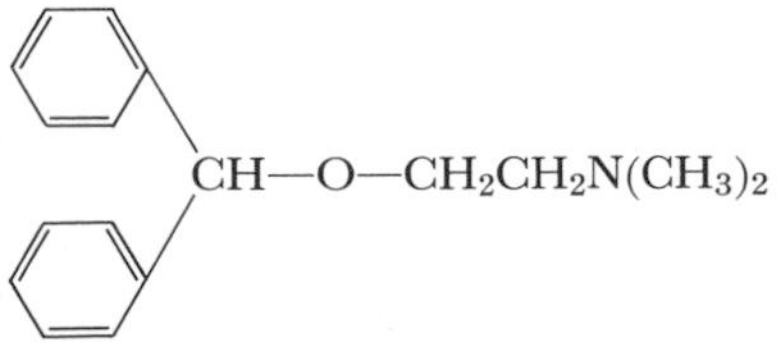

$$CH—O—CH_2CH_2N(CH_3)_2$$

diphenhydramine

$$\underset{}{\bigcirc} \overset{CH_2}{\underset{}{}} N—CH_2CH_2N(CH_3)_2$$

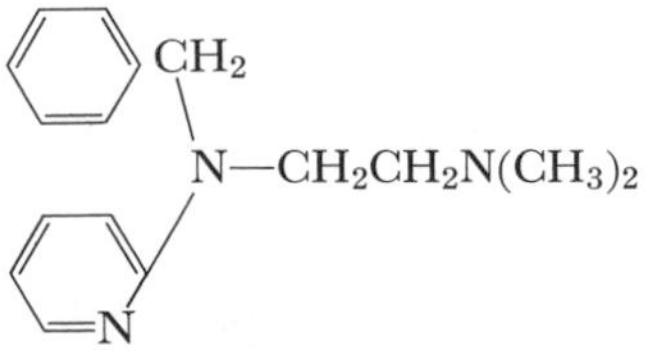

tripelennamine

Several simple IV° ammonium salts have found use as surface anti-septics—for example, hexadecyldimethylbenzylammonium chloride,

$$CH_3(CH_2)_{15}N(CH_3)_2CH_2C_6H_5)^+Cl^-$$

Nitrobenzene is used as an industrial solvent, although its chief use is in the manufacture of aniline. *Trinitrotoluene* (T.N.T.) is a widely used explosive, in bombs and warheads on shells and torpedoes. It is rather stable, and not easily detonated, so that it can stand the shock of being fired from a gun. The T.N.T. must be exploded by a detonator, such as lead azide, which explodes first, thus causing the T.N.T. to detonate. T.N.T. melts at 81°C, and can therefore be safely melted and cast into shells.

T.N.T.   picric acid

Picric acid (2,4,6-trinitrophenol) is used as an antiseptic in the treatment of burns and as the yellow dye for wool. Butesin picrate is the picric acid salt of the local anesthetic butesin (butyl *p*-aminobenzoate) which combines the surface anesthetic effect of butesin with the antiseptic action of picric acid. A 1 per cent ointment is used to treat burns. The aromatic nitro compounds are toxic, and should not be ingested or inhaled continuously. For this reason the use of 2,4-dinitrophenol, which stimulates fat metabolism, to control obesity is dangerous.

Study Questions

1. Write structural formulas for the following compounds: dimethylamine, 2-dimethylamino-1-propanol, methylaniline, 1,6-diaminohexane, picric acid, T.N.T., hexamethylenetetramine, cyclohexylamine, piperidine, 2-nitropropane.

2. What is meant by a I° amine? an amide? a sulfonamide? a quaternary ammonium salt? Write a structural formula to illustrate each.

3. Illustrate by equations four different reactions of amines.

4. How can primary, secondary and tertiary amines be distinguished by the Hinsberg test? Write equations illustrating these reactions.

5. Illustrate the reactions of nitrous acid with I°, II°, and III° amines.

6. What is meant by diazotization? Show how benzenediazonium chloride will react when heated with water, cyanide ion, and iodide ion.

7. Why is the azo group called a "chromophore"? How are azo compounds synthesized, and what are they used for?

8. Show by equations how benzene could be converted to 2,4,6-tribromoaniline; to *meta*-bromoaniline.

9. Write equations illustrating the synthesis of sulfanilamide; *p*-dimethylaminoazobenzene, benzedrine; aniline; trinitrotoluene.

10. Show by equations three different ways in which ethylamine might be prepared, starting with ethyl chloride, acetaldehyde, or nitroethane.

11. Compare the structure of acetylcholine, mecholyl, and procaine. Compare the physiological activities of these substances. Suggest a mechanism of action for these compounds.

12. Given the following pairs of compounds in unlabeled bottles, what simple chemical tests would distinguish one from the other?
    a) N-methylaniline and *p*-toluidine;
    b) *p*-aminobenzoic acid and *p*-nitrotoluene;
    c) triethylamine and di-*n*-propylamine;
    d) cyclohexylamine and benzamide.

Advanced Reading References

Organic Chemistry, H. H. Szmant, Prentice-Hall, Inc., Englewood Cliffs, N. J., 1957, Chapters 14 and 17.

Organic Chemistry, 3rd Ed., R. Q. Brewster and W. E. McEwen, Prentice-Hall, Inc., Englewood Cliffs, N. J., 1961, Chapters 13, 26, and 27.

Essential Principles of Organic Chemistry, James Cason, Prentice-Hall, Inc., Englewood Cliffs, N. J., 1956, Chapters 19 and 24.

new terms & concepts

Organic sulfur compounds are common in nature, since sulfur can replace oxygen in various functional groups.

Common types are thiols (RSH), sulfides (RSR), thiol acids (RCOSH), and disulfides (RSSR).

Oxidized sulfur is found in sulfinic (RSO_2H) and sulfonic (RSO_3H) acids, sulfoxides (RSOR), and sulfones (RSO_2R).

Thiols, or mercaptans, have unpleasant odors, precipitate heavy metals, are easily oxidized to disulfides, and act as effective addition reagents to carbonyl and olefin groups.

Organic sulfides resemble ethers, but may be oxidized to sulfoxides or sulfones.

Thiolacetic acid (CH_3COSH) is important in biological synthesis of fatty acids and related molecules by acetyl transfer in thioacetyl coenzyme A.

Carbon disulfide (CS_2) is useful in the preparation of industrially important xanthates, dithiocarbamates, and thiourea.

Disulfides are important biologically, are readily formed by reversible oxidation of thiols, and new disulfides are formed by exchange with thiols.

Thiokol rubber is a disulfide-containing polymer.

Sulfonic acids are strong organic acids, formed by oxidation of sulfur compounds, or by direct sulfonation.

Long-chain sulfonic acids are useful as detergents.

Some sulfonamides such as sulfanilamide are useful drugs, as are some sulfones.

14

Organic sulfur compounds

Organic sulfur compounds occur widely distributed in nature, and their importance in biochemical reactions has been increasingly recognized in recent years. Synthetic organic sulfur compounds are of great economic importance. They are used as insecticides, accelerators in the rubber vulcanization process, in the formation of polymers, and to improve the qualities of lubricating oils.

Like oxygen (Chapter 8) divalent sulfur, with its two valence bonds, can combine with carbon to form several functional groups. These form a series of functional groups similar to the oxygen derivatives, as for example the thiols, RSH, like alcohols, ROH. Table 14.01, part I, lists these compounds. In the sulfur series, however, many more classes of compounds exist because of the ability of sulfur to form chains of atoms, and to exist in several oxidation states. Table 14.01, part II, lists characteristic examples of compounds containing chains of two sulfur atoms (disulfides) and three sulfur atoms (trisulfides) and many sulfur atoms (polysulfides). Also listed are the oxidized sulfur compounds. These may be related to the inorganic oxidized sulfur compounds sulfurous acid (H_2SO_3) and sulfuric acid (H_2SO_4).

THIOLS

These compounds have long been known, and are infamous for their powerful unpleasant odors. Butyl mercaptan, n-C_4H_9SH, is a constituent of the odorous substance ejected by the skunk. Mercaptans are used as detection agents in gas lines, since slight leaks may be easily smelled out if the relatively odorless flammable gases are contaminated with traces of substances with powerful odors. One such agent is "Pentalarm," or 1-pentanethiol. The alchemists called these substances "mercaptans" because of their ability to form insoluble mercury salts, that is, to "capture mercury."

TABLE 14.01   CLASSES OF SULFUR COMPOUNDS

I. *Divalent Sulfur Compounds*		II. *Oxidized Sulfur Compounds*	
R—S—H	Thiol (mercaptan)	R—S—S—R	Disulfide
R—S—R	Sulfide (thioether)	R—S—S—S—R	Trisulfide
R—C—H (C=S)	Thial (thioaldehyde)	R—S—(S)$_n$—S—R	Polysulfide
		R—S—OH	Sulfenic acid
R—C—R (C=S)	Thione (thioketone)	R—S—OH (S=O)	Sulfinic acid
R—C—S—H (C=O)	Thiolacid	R—S—OH (O=, =O)	Sulfonic acid
R—C—OH (C=S)	Thionacid	R—S—R (S=O)	Sulfoxide
R—C—S—H (C=S)	Dithioacid	R—S—R (O=, =O)	Sulfone
S=C=S	Carbon disulfide		

Reactions of thiols

Just as hydrogen sulfide is a stronger acid than water, so thiols are stronger acids than alcohols, and both aliphatic and aromatic thiols dissolve in strong alkaline solution to form salts, called mercaptides (Eq. 14.01). Heavy-metal mercaptides are insoluble in water, but somewhat soluble in organic solvents. Lead mercaptides, $Pb(SR)_2$,

14.01 $RSH + Na^+OH^- \longrightarrow RS^-Na^+ + H_2O$

may be added to lubricating oils to improve their quality. The toxicity of arsenic is due to its ability to inactivate body enzymes having thiol groups. During the Second World War, it was discovered that 2,3-dimercaptopropanol, $CH_2SHCHSHCH_2OH$, would protect against several lethal doses of arsenic. This compound, now commonly called BAL (British Anti-Lewisite) is used as an antidote for heavy-metal (lead, mercury, arsenic) poisoning generally, and probably functions by forming stable nontoxic mercaptides.

14.02 $2\,RSH + (O) \rightleftharpoons R—S—S—R + H_2O$

The thiols are oxidized very easily to disulfides (Eq. 14.02). This is an easily reversible reaction in biochemical systems, and plays an important role in enzymatic oxidation and reduction. Thiols must be protected from air to prevent this reaction from contaminating the pure compounds with disulfide. Thiols may be oxidized further by suitable oxidizing agents, such as hydrogen peroxide, to sulfinic and sulfonic acids (Eq. 14.03).

14.03 $RSH \xrightarrow{(O)} RSSR \xrightarrow{(O)} RSO_2H \xrightarrow{(O)} RSO_3H$

Thiols are good addition reagents to unsaturated molecules. The addition of mercaptans to ketones and aldehydes to form mercaptals (Eq. 14.04) has already been mentioned (p. 139). Thiols add to olefins to form sulfides (Eq. 14.05) and especially easily under base catalysis, to α,β-unsaturated acids and their derivatives (Eq. 14.06).

14.04
$$R_2C{=}O + 2\,RSH \xrightarrow{H^+} \begin{array}{c} R \quad\ S{-}R \\ \diagdown \diagup \\ C \\ \diagup \diagdown \\ R \quad\ S{-}R \end{array}$$

14.05
$$RSH + CH_2{=}CHR \longrightarrow \begin{array}{c} RS{-}CHR \\ | \\ CH_3 \end{array}$$

14.06 $RSH + CH_2{=}CH{-}COOH \xrightarrow{OH^-} RSCH_2CH_2COOH$

Preparation of thiols

The thiols are most conveniently prepared by a nucleophilic displacement reaction on an active halide (Eq. 14.07) (Chapter 7). Either a hydrosulfide or thiourea may be used, but in the latter case, a stable odorless isothiuronium salt may be isolated (Eq. 14.08). This may be

14.07 $R{-}X + Na^+SH \longrightarrow RSH + Na^+X^-$

14.08
$$R{-}X + NH_2C{\overset{S}{\diagup}}NH_2 \longrightarrow R{-}S{-}C{\overset{NH}{\diagdown}}{\underset{NH_2}{}} \cdot HX$$

isothiuronium salt

stored until needed, and then hydrolyzed to form the mercaptan (Eq. 14.08a). In this synthesis, the readily oxidized evil-smelling mercaptans need not be stored, which is an advantage in laboratory work.

14.08a
$$R{-}S{-}C{\overset{NH}{\diagup}}{\underset{NH_2}{\diagdown}} \cdot HX \xrightarrow[OH^-]{H_2O} RSH + \text{polymers}$$

Another useful laboratory method involves the addition of thiolacetic acid to olefins (Eq. 14.09) followed by hydrolysis of the thiol ester obtained (Eq. 14.09a). This reaction proceeds by a free radical-chain mechanism (p. 60), and therefore yields the anti-Markovnikov primary thiol.

14.09 $RCH{=}CH_2 + CH_3COSH \longrightarrow RCH_2CH_2SCOCH_3$

                                                                 thiolester

14.09a $RCH_2CH_2SCOCH_3 + H_2O \longrightarrow RCH_2CH_2SH + CH_3COOH$

Aromatic thiols are usually formed by reduction of the aromatic sulfonyl chloride (Eq. 14.10).

14.10

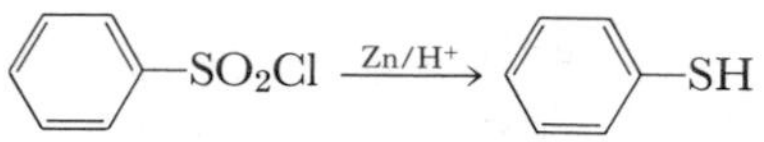

SULFIDES

The sulfides, R—S—R, are analogs of the ethers, R—O—R. They are, however, more reactive. Mustard gas (see p. 57), β,β'-dichloroethyl sulfide, produces skin blisters. Allyl sulfide, $(CH_2{=}CHCH_2)_2S$, is found in garlic, and certain phenolic sulfides, such as 4,4'-dihydroxy-5,5'-di-tert-butyl-2,2'-dimethylphenyl sulfide (Fig. 14.01) are used as anti-oxidants in rubber processing.

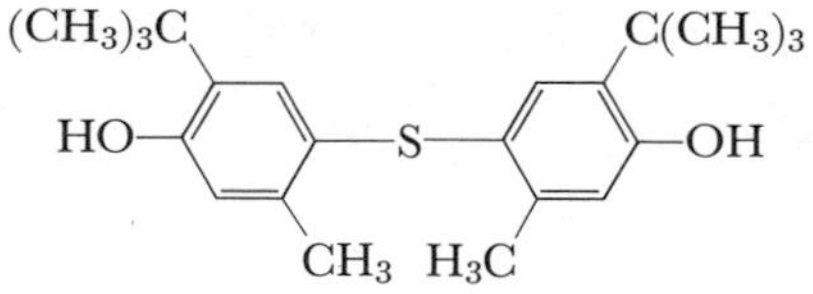

Fig. 14.01

Reactions of sulfides

Sulfides are readily oxidized to sulfoxides and sulfones (Eq. 14.11). Sulfides react with active halides to form crystalline water-soluble sulfonium salts (Eq. 14.12). These salts are analogs of the quaternary ammonium salts (p. 195).

14.11

$$R-S-R \xrightarrow{(O)} R-\overset{\overset{\displaystyle O}{\|}}{S}-R \xrightarrow{(O)} R-\overset{\overset{\displaystyle O}{\|}}{\underset{\underset{\displaystyle O}{\|}}{S}}-R$$

14.12

$$R-S-R + RX \longrightarrow R_3S^+X^-$$

Preparation of sulfides

Sulfides may be prepared by addition of thiols to olefins (Eqs. 14.05, 14.06) or by a reaction analogous to the Williamson synthesis of ethers (p. 130). In this synthesis, a mercaptide is allowed to react with an active halide to form the desired sulfide. For example, butyl phenyl sulfide may be prepared as in Eq. 14.13.

14.13 $\quad \langle\bigcirc\rangle\!-\!S^-Na^+ + BrCH_2CH_2CH_2CH_3 \longrightarrow \langle\bigcirc\rangle\!-\!S\!-\!C_4H_9 + Na^+Br^-$

THIOCARBONYL COMPOUNDS

Thioaldehydes and thioketones are known, but they are unstable compounds chiefly of theoretical interest. They exhibit a pronounced tendency to form rings and chains (Eq. 14.14).

14.14 $\quad HS\!-\!CH_2(SCH_2)_nSH \xleftarrow{-H_2O} H_2S + CH_2O \xrightarrow{-3 H_2O}$

$$\begin{array}{c} \text{CH}_2 \\ \text{S}\diagup\quad\diagdown\text{S} \\ |\qquad\quad| \\ \text{H}_2\text{C}\diagdown\quad\diagup\text{CH}_2 \\ \text{S} \end{array}$$

polythioformaldehyde   trithiane

This behavior is similar to that of some of the carbonyl compounds (p. 150) but is even more pronounced in the sulfur series.

Two monothio acids are shown in Table 14.01. However only one compound, the thiol acid, can be isolated. For example, all efforts to obtain acetothiolic and acetothionic acids give only one compound, b.p. 93°C, which is the thiolic acid as shown by the presence of —SH and C=O groups. The acid is a tautomeric mixture in which the one form predominates (Eq. 14.15). Esters of both acids can be isolated.

14.15
$$\begin{array}{cc} \text{S} & \text{O} \\ \| & \| \\ \text{CH}_3\!-\!\text{C}\!-\!\text{OH} \rightleftharpoons \text{CH}_3\!-\!\text{C}\!-\!\text{SH} \end{array}$$

Ethyl acetothionate, $\text{CH}_3\!-\!\overset{\text{S}}{\overset{\|}{\text{C}}}\!-\!\text{OC}_2\text{H}_5$, boils at 110°C, and is unstable. On prolonged heating or treatment with mild alkali it will rearrange to ethyl acetothiolate, $\text{CH}_3\!-\!\overset{\text{O}}{\overset{\|}{\text{C}}}\!-\!\text{S}\!-\!\text{C}_2\text{H}_5$, b.p. 116°C. The thiolacetate group, $\text{CH}_3\text{COS}\!-\!$, plays an important part in the biological synthesis of lipids. The CH_3CO group is transferred to larger molecules through the thiol ester $CH_3COSCoA$, or thioacetyl coenzyme A.

The dithioacids, RCSSH, are unstable compounds which are oxidized by air, and readily hydrolyzed. They may be easily prepared by the reaction of a Grignard reagent with carbon disulfide (Eq. 14.16).

$$14.16 \qquad RMgX \xrightarrow{CS_2} R-\overset{\overset{\displaystyle S}{\|}}{C}-S-MgX \xrightarrow{H^+} R-\overset{\overset{\displaystyle S}{\|}}{C}-SH + Mg^{++} + X^-$$

CARBON DISULFIDE AND RELATED COMPOUNDS

Carbon disulfide, CS_2, the sulfur analog of carbon dioxide, CO_2, can be cheaply prepared by heating coal and sulfur in the absence of air (Eq. 14.17) and is a useful industrial chemical. It is a low-boiling

$$14.17 \qquad C + 2S \xrightarrow{\Delta} CS_2$$

(46°C) liquid which is very flammable (flash point $-25°C$) and reactive. With alcohols in the presence of strong base, xanthates are formed (Eq. 14.18). This reaction is the basis of the viscose process

$$14.18 \qquad C_2H_5OH + CS_2 + KOH \longrightarrow C_2H_5-O-\overset{\overset{\displaystyle S}{\|}}{C}-S^-K^+ + H_2O$$

potassium ethyl xanthate

Secondary amines react with carbon disulfide to produce dithiocarbamates (Eq. 14.19). These compounds are useful in hasten-

$$14.19 \qquad R_2NH + CS_2 + NaOH \longrightarrow R_2N\overset{\overset{\displaystyle S}{\|}}{C}-S^-Na^+ + H_2O$$

ing the vulcanization process in rubber, and are known as the "thiurams." Dimethylthiuram is easily oxidized to tetramethylthiuram disulfide (TUADS) (Eq. 14.20) which is even more active as a rubber

$$14.20 \qquad (CH_3)_2N\overset{\overset{\displaystyle S}{\|}}{C}-S^-Na^+ + H_2O_2 \longrightarrow (CH_3)_2N-\overset{\overset{\displaystyle S}{\|}}{C}-S-S-\overset{\overset{\displaystyle S}{\|}}{C}-N(CH_3)_2$$

TUADS

accelerator. The observation that workers in the rubber industry in Sweden became violently ill after imbibing alcoholic beverages led to the discovery that ethyl tuads (tetraethylthiuram disulfide) inhibits normal metabolism of alcohol. This compound, under the name "Antabuse," has been used in treating chronic alcoholism. A number of valuable agricultural chemicals are derived from the thiurams. Ziram is a useful fungicide, and Vegtex is a useful pre-emergent herbicide for sandy soils.

$$((CH_3)_2N\overset{\overset{\displaystyle S}{\|}}{C}-S)_2Zn \qquad\qquad (C_2H_5)_2N\overset{\overset{\displaystyle S}{\|}}{C}-S-CH_2-\overset{\overset{\displaystyle Cl}{|}}{C}=CH_2$$

Ziram   Vegtex

Thiourea, NH_2CSNH_2, may be obtained by treating carbon disulfide with ammonia (Eq. 14.21) or by heating ammonium thiocyanate (Eq. 14.22). Thiourea is useful as a wood preservative, and has

14.21 $\qquad\qquad CS_2 + 2 NH_3 \longrightarrow NH_2CSNH_2 + H_2S$

14.22 $\qquad\qquad NH_4{}^+SCN^- \xrightarrow{\Delta} NH_2CSNH_2$

some application as a silver cleaner. It is useful in the synthesis of mercaptans (Eq. 14.08). α-Naphthylthiourea is a powerful specific rat poison, known as Antu.

$$\overset{\overset{\displaystyle S}{\|}}{NHCNH_2}$$

Antu

The alkyl isothiocyanates, $R-N=C=S$, are known as "mustard oils." They have a sharp, garliclike odor, and several isothiocyanates occur in nature. Allyl isothiocyanate, $CH_2=CH-CH_2-NCS$, is found in mustard seed and horse-radish. The isothiocyanates react with amines to form substituted thioureas (Eq. 14.23).

14.23 $$R-N=C=S + R'NH_2 \longrightarrow R-\overset{\overset{\displaystyle H}{|}}{N}-\overset{\overset{\displaystyle S}{\|}}{C}-\overset{\overset{\displaystyle H}{|}}{N}-R'$$

DISULFIDES AND POLYSULFIDES

Natural sulfur, S_8, exists as a ring of eight sulfur atoms. On heating it breaks open to form polymeric long chains of sulfur atoms which break down to gaseous S_2 only at very high temperatures. This tendency of sulfur atoms to form chains is reflected in the existence of a series of organic sulfur compounds, the disulfides, R—S—S—R, trisulfides, R—S—S—S—R, tetrasulfides, R—S—S—S—S—R, pentasulfides, and hexasulfides. The disulfides are easily formed by oxidation of thiols (Eq. 14.02) or by reaction of active halides with sodium disulfide (Eq. 14.24). Trisulfides may be obtained by oxidation of

14.24 $\qquad$ $2\,RX + Na_2S_2 \longrightarrow R—S—S—R + 2\,NaX$

disulfides with sulfur (sulfurizing, Eq. 14.25) or by the reaction of

14.25 $\qquad$ $R—S—S—R + S \rightleftharpoons R—S—S—S—R$

14.26 $\qquad$ $2\,RSH + SCl_2 \longrightarrow R—S—S—S—R + 2\,HCl$

sulfur dichloride with a thiol (Eq. 14.26). Similarly, tetrasulfides may be obtained by the reaction of sulfur monochloride with thiols (Eq. 14.27), or by reaction of sodium tetrathionate with active halides (Eq.

14.27 $\qquad$ $2\,RSH + S_2Cl_2 \longrightarrow R—S—S—S—S—R + 2\,HCl$

14.28 $\qquad$ $2\,RX + Na_2S_4 \longrightarrow R—S—S—S—S—R + 2\,Na^+X^-$

14.28). The compounds containing more than two sulfur atoms are less stable and may be "stripped" down to disulfides by heating in the presence of amines (Eq. 14.29). Disulfides undergo a reversible exchange reaction with thiols (Eq. 14.30) which is important in biological

14.29 $\qquad$ $R—S(S)_nSR \xrightarrow[\Delta]{RNH_2} RSSR + n\,S$

14.30 $\qquad$ $R—S—S—R + R'SH \rightleftharpoons R—S—S—R' + RSH$

systems. By this means complex changes in the nature of proteins having disulfide and thiol groups may be explained. Thioctic acid, or α-lipoic acid, is a substance occurring in nature containing a cyclic disulfide ring which may be easily opened.

$$
\begin{array}{c}
\text{CH}_2 \\
\diagup \quad \diagdown \\
\text{H}_2\text{C} \qquad \text{CH—CH}_2\text{CH}_2\text{CH}_2\text{CH}_2\text{COOH} \\
\diagdown \quad \diagup \\
\text{S—S}
\end{array}
$$

α-lipoic acid

Disulfides are less odorous than mercaptans, and "sour" gasoline, which contains mercaptans, is "sweetened" by conversion of these impurities to disulfides by the "doctor" process (Eq. 14.31). The Thiokol

14.31 $\qquad$ $2\,RSH + S + Na_2PbO_2 \longrightarrow R—S—S—R + PbS + 2\,NaOH$

rubbers are polymeric disulfides which are resistant to gasoline and lubricating oil, and remain pliable at very low temperatures. They are therefore useful in forming gasket seals in airplanes, protective covering around fuel tanks and in oil hose lines. The Thiokols are prepared by reaction of disulfide salts with reactive dihalides (Eq. 14.32).

14.32 $\qquad$ $n\ \text{ClCH}_2\text{CH}_2\text{Cl} + n\ \text{Na}_2\text{S}_2 \longrightarrow -(\text{SCH}_2\text{CH}_2\text{S}-)_n$

OXIDIZED SULFUR ACIDS

Three different oxidation states are represented by the three known classes of organic sulfur acids. Stability and acid strength increase with oxidation state. There is only one known sulfenic acid, although sulfenic acid derivatives are common. The sulfinic acids may be isolated,

$$\text{R—S—OH} \qquad \text{R—}\overset{\displaystyle \text{O}}{\underset{}{\overset{\|}{\text{S}}}}\text{—O—H} \qquad \text{R—}\overset{\displaystyle \text{O}}{\underset{\underset{\displaystyle \text{O}}{\|}}{\overset{\|}{\text{S}}}}\text{—OH}$$

sulfenic acid   sulfinic acid   sulfonic acid

but tend to be oxidized by air. Sulfonic acids are stable strong acids having industrial application. Methanesulfonic acid is manufactured from petroleum by-product methyl mercaptan (Eq. 14.33), but sulfonic acids are generally available by reaction of sodium sulfite with active halides (Strecker reaction—Eq. 14.34). Aromatic sulfonic acids are

14.33 $\qquad$ $\text{CH}_3\text{SH} + (\text{O}) \xrightarrow[\text{cat.}]{\text{air}} \text{CH}_3\text{SO}_3\text{H}$

14.34 $\qquad$ $\text{RX} + \text{Na}_2\text{SO}_3 \longrightarrow \text{RSO}_3^-\text{Na}^+ + \text{Na}^+\text{X}^-$

most commonly prepared by direct sulfonation, using fuming sulfuric acid (p. 78), but chlorosulfonic acid (Eq. 14.35) yields the more re-

14.35 $\quad$ $\text{CH}_3\!\!\left\langle\bigcirc\right\rangle + 2\ \text{ClSO}_3\text{H} \longrightarrow \text{CH}_3\!\!\left\langle\bigcirc\right\rangle\text{SO}_2\text{Cl} + \text{HCl} + \text{H}_2\text{SO}_4$

active sulfonyl chloride directly. The sulfonyl chloride may be hydrolyzed to the acid (Eq. 14.36), converted to the sulfonamide (Eq. 14.37) or sulfonate ester (Eq. 14.38), or reduced with zinc to the sulfinic acid salt (Eq. 14.39).

14.36 $\qquad$ $\text{ArSO}_2\text{Cl} + \text{H}_2\text{O} \longrightarrow \text{ArSO}_2\text{OH} + \text{HCl}$

14.37 $\qquad$ $\text{ArSO}_2\text{Cl} + 2\ \text{NH}_3 \longrightarrow \text{ArSO}_2\text{NH}_2 + \text{NH}_4^+\text{Cl}^-$

14.38 $ArSO_2Cl + HOC_2H_5 \longrightarrow ArSO_2OC_2H_5 + HCl$

14.39 $2\,ArSO_2Cl + 2\,Zn \longrightarrow Zn(SO_2Ar)_2 + ZnCl_2$

The salts of aromatic sulfonic acids having long alkyl side chains have detergent properties. Compounds of this class are used as household detergents (Chapter 12) in Europe, but are not as satisfactory as the alkyl sulfates. Barium or lead salts are used as detergents in lubri-

$$C_{12}H_{25} \langle \bigcirc \rangle SO_3{}^-M^+$$

cating oils or greases to improve lubricating properties in the presence of water. Sulfanilamide, or *p*-aminobenzenesulfonamide, is one of a series of useful drugs which inhibit the growth of bacteria. Saccharin, or *o*-sulfobenzimide, is a nondigestible sweetening agent useful in low-calorie or diabetic diets.

sulfanilamide   saccharin

SULFOXIDES AND SULFONES

Oxidation of sulfides with common oxidizing agents, such as hydrogen peroxide, forms first the intermediate sulfoxide, and further oxidation produces the sulfone (Eq. 14.11). Sulfones are also obtained by reaction of sulfinate salts with active halides (Eq. 14.40) or by Friedel-Crafts reactions of sulfonyl chlorides with aromatic compounds (Eq. 14.41).

14.40 $RSO_2{}^-Na^+ + XR' \longrightarrow RSO_2R'$

14.41 $RSO_2Cl + \langle \bigcirc \rangle \xrightarrow{AlCl_3} RSO_2 \langle \bigcirc \rangle + HCl$

A few sulfones have found use as drugs. Sulfonal was once used as a hypnotic, and *bis*-4-aminophenylsulfone is effective in the treatment of leprosy.

sulfonal   *bis*-4-aminophenylsulfone

Study Questions

1. Write structural formulas for the following: methyl mercaptan, dibutyl sulfide, acetothiolic acid, diethyl disulfide, p-toluenesulfonic acid, ethyl methyl sulfoxide, benzenesulfinic acid, diphenyl sulfone, thiourea, sulfanilamide.

2. A sample of thiophenol was allowed to stand exposed to the air. After several days, crystals began to form. What were they?

3. Show by equations three different ways to prepare n-butyl mercaptan in the laboratory.

4. What products are formed in the following reactions of n-butyl mercaptan?

    a) complete oxidation with hydrogen peroxide;

    b) reaction of an alkaline solution with ethyl bromide;

    c) treatment in acetone with acid.

5. Carbon disulfide and thiourea are important sulfur compounds. Show how each is made commercially, and name two uses for each.

6. Show by a formula what is meant by a xanthate, mustard oil, dithiocarbamate, sulfonium halide, dithioacid, Thiokol rubber.

7. Write the formulas of three different sulfur compounds useful as drugs, and tell how they are used.

8. The reaction of butyl mercaptan with butyl disulfide may be considered to be a chain reaction. Explain. When a small amount of methyl mercaptan is added to a large amount of α-lipoic acid, a polymer is formed. How can you account for this?

9. A compound C_7H_8S (I) bleached an iodine solution, and crystals of II, $C_{14}H_{14}S_2$, were formed. Further oxidation of II with hydrogen peroxide gave a strong water-soluble acid III, $C_7H_8O_3S$. When III was further oxidized with potassium permanganate, and the resulting acid heated under pressure with ammonia, saccharin was formed. Write structural formulas for I, II, and III, and show the reactions involved in these conversions.

Advanced Reading References

Organic Chemistry, H. Harry Szmant, Prentice-Hall, Inc., Englewood Cliffs, N. J., 1957, Chapter 19.

Organic Chemistry, 3rd Ed., R. Q. Brewster and W. E. McEwen, Prentice-Hall, Inc., Englewood Cliffs, N. J., 1961, Chapters 14 and 24.

"Organic Sulfur Compounds," R. Connors, Chapter 10 in *Organic Chemistry, An Advanced Treatise*, 2nd Ed., H. Gilman, Ed., John Wiley and Sons, Inc., New York, 1943, Vol. I.

new terms & concepts

The presence of two or more different functional groups in a molecule influences the reactivities of each group, and the properties of the whole molecule.
Halogenation increases the strength of acids, owing to the "inductive" electronegative effect.
Hydroxy-acids occur widely in nature, and are responsible for many flavors.
β-hydroxy-acids lose water easily to form α,β-unsaturated acids.
γ- and δ-hydroxy acids lose water easily, forming the γ- and δ-lactones.
α-hydroxy-acids form lactides by dehydration.
Salicylic acid is an important medicinal agent, convertible to aspirin and oil of wintergreen.
Keto-acids are important metabolic products.
Acetoacetic ester provides a useful synthetic intermediate.
Amino-acids occur widely in nature in proteins.
Since they have both acidic carboxyl and basic amino groups, they exist as salts (Zwitter-ions).
Some amino-acids form lactams, but α-amino-acids form the cyclic diamides, diketopiperazines.
Certain "essential" amino-acids must be present in the diet of humans for health.

15

Substituted acids

Previous chapters have discussed the chemistry of compounds having only one kind of functional group, and the influence of this group on the properties of the molecule. However, compounds of greatest importance both in nature and industrially usually have several different functional groups present on the same molecule. These groups impart special reactivity to the molecule, since the reactivity of each group will be present, but will be modified in a more or less subtle manner by the presence of other reactive functions. All possible combinations of the functional groups described in Chapter 2 are possible. However, the most important single class of polyfunctional compounds in nature are the substituted acids, and these will be discussed. Mention has already been made of unsaturated acids (Chapter 11) as a special case.

HALOGENATED ACIDS

Although the halogenated acids rarely occur naturally, the easy replacement of halogen by other functional groups (Chapter 7) makes these compounds important synthetic intermediates in the preparation of other substituted acids, such as hydroxy-acids, amino-acids, mercapto-acids, cyano-acids, etc. The halogen acids exist in various isomers having different reactivity, depending on the relative position of the halogen group to the carboxyl group.

Preparation of halogen acids

Direct replacement of α-hydrogens is made easy by the activation of the adjacent carboxyl group (p. 165), and α-chloro-acids can be made by reaction of the acid with chlorine in the presence of phosphorus trichloride as a catalyst (Eq. 15.01). Direct chlorination of acetic acid produces chloroacetic, dichloroacetic, and trichloroacetic acids, which may be separated by distillation (Eq. 15.02). Addition of

15.01 $\qquad R_2CHCOOH + Cl_2 \xrightarrow{PCl_3} R_2CClCOOH + HCl$

15.02 $\qquad CH_3COOH \xrightarrow{Cl_2} ClCH_2COOH + Cl_2CHCOOH + Cl_3CCOOH$

hydrohalides to a α,β-unsaturated acids produces the β-halo-acids (p. 168), and dihalo-acids are formed by addition of halogens (Eqs. 15.03 and 15.04).

15.03 $\qquad CH_2{=}CH{-}COOH + HBr \longrightarrow BrCH_2CH_2COOH$

15.04

Reactions of halogen acids

Because of the strong electronegativity of the halogens (Chapter 1), the α-halo acids are stronger than the unsubstituted acids. The strong attraction of the halogen atom for electrons tends to leave the weakest electronegative atom, hydrogen, most deficient in electrons, or most ready to ionize as a proton. This electronegative effect is called an "inductive" effect, since the higher tendency to ionize is induced on the ionizable hydrogen atom. This effect is illustrated in formulas showing direction of polarization of bonds, and may be transmitted

through several atoms. The more α-halogen atoms present, the stronger will be the effect, but the more atoms between the electronegative atom and the ionizable hydrogen, as in β-chloropropionic acid, the weaker will be the inductive effect. These effects are illustrated in Table 15.01, which compares the ionization constants of some unsubstituted and halogenated acids.

TABLE 15.01   IONIZATION CONSTANTS IN 0.1 M SOLUTION OF SOME ORGANIC ACIDS

Name	Formula	Ka $\times 10^5$
Acetic acid	CH_3COOH	1.8
Fluoroacetic acid	FCH_2COOH	210
Chloroacetic acid	$ClCH_2COOH$	155
Bromoacetic acid	$BrCH_2COOH$	138
Iodoacetic acid	ICH_2COOH	71
Dichloroacetic acid	$Cl_2CHCOOH$	5140
Trichloroacetic acid	Cl_3CCOOH	>10,000
Propionic acid	CH_3CH_2COOH	1.3
α-Chloropropionic acid	$CH_3CHClCOOH$	146
β-Chloropropionic acid	$ClCH_2CH_2COOH$	8

It can be seen from the table that the ionization constants of the halogen acids provide a measure of the electronegativity of the halogen atoms. Compare the ionization constants of the haloacetic acids (Table 15.01) with the assigned electronegativities of the halogen atoms (Table 1.01). Note also that propionic acid is a slightly weaker acid than acetic acid, which means that the electronegativity of a hydrogen atom is greater than that of a methyl group, or that the inductive effect of a methyl group should be illustrated thus:

$$CH_3 \rightarrow CH_2 - COOH$$

The halogen atoms in halo-acids may be easily replaced by various functional groups, as illustrated in Chapter 7. Equations 15.05–15.07 illustrate the synthesis of various substituted acids from halogen acids.

15.05 $\quad ClCH_2COOH + 2\,NaOH \longrightarrow HOCH_2COO^-Na^+ + NaCl + H_2O$

15.06 $\quad BrCH_2CH_2COOH + 2\,NaSH \longrightarrow$

$$HSCH_2CH_2COO^-Na^+ + NaCl + H_2S$$

15.07 $\quad CH_3CHClCOOH + 2\,NH_3 \longrightarrow CH_3\underset{\underset{NH_2}{|}}{CH}-COO^-NH_4^+$

HYDROXY-ACIDS

The names and structures of some common hydroxy-acids and their natural sources are given in Table 15.02.

Preparation of hydroxy-acids

The proper halo-acid can be converted to the analogous hydroxy-acid by treatment with alkali (Eq. 15.05). α-Hydroxy acids are conveniently prepared from aldehydes by hydrolysis of an intermediate cyanohydrin (p. 167). The synthesis of mandelic acid (α-hydroxyphenylacetic acid) from benzaldehyde by this method is shown in Eq. 15.08.

15.08

Reactions of hydroxy-acids

Both the hydroxy and carboxyl group of hydroxy-acids exhibit characteristic reactivity. The carboxyl group may be converted into salt, amide, or ester (Chapter 11) and the hydroxyl group esterified or oxidized (Chapter 8). When treated with phosphorus trichloride, both hydroxyl groups of a hydroxy acid are replaced by chloro groups. For example, glycollic acid yields chloroacetyl chloride under these conditions (Eq. 15.09). The hydroxy group may be oxidized to a carbonyl group (p. 115), and when the hydroxy group is secondary in hydroxy-acids, keto-acids are the initial products (Eqs. 15.10 and 15.11).

15.09 $3\ HOCH_2COOH + 2\ PCl_3 \longrightarrow 3\ ClCH_2COCl + 2\ H_3PO_3$

15.10 $CH_3CHOHCOOH \xrightarrow{(O)} CH_3\overset{O}{\overset{\|}{C}}COOH$

                           lactic acid   pyruvic acid

15.11 $CH_3CHOHCH_2COOH \xrightarrow{(O)} CH_3\overset{O}{\overset{\|}{C}}\text{---}CH_2COOH$

                   β-hydroxybutyric acid   acetoacetic acid

The position of the hydroxy group in relation to the carboxyl group has an influence on the reactivity of the molecule. Acids having a hydroxy group in the 3- (or β-) position are easily dehydrated to form

TABLE 15.02 SOME COMMON NATURALLY OCCURRING HYDROXY-ACIDS

Compound	Common name	I.U.C. name	Source
$HOCH_2COOH$	Glycolic acid	Hydroxyethanoic acid	Sugar-cane juice
$CH_3CHOHCOOH$	Lactic acid	2-Hydroxypropanoic acid	Sour milk, etc.
CHOHCOOH CH_2COOH	Malic acid	Hydroxybutanedioic acid	Sour apples
CHOHCOOH CHOHCOOH	Tartaric acid	2,3-Dihydroxybutanedioic acid	Fruits
CH_2COOH HOC—COOH CH_2COOH	Citric acid	3-Hydroxy-3-carboxy-pentanedioic acid	Citrus fruit
—CHOHCOOH	Mandelic acid	Phenylhydroxyethanoic acid	Almonds, peach pits
	Salicylic acid	2-Hydroxybenzoic acid	Oil of wintergreen
	Gallic acid	3,4,5-Trihydroxybenzoic acid	Tea leaves, oak bark, etc.

α,β-unsaturated acids (Eq. 15.12). This reaction is facilitated by the stabilization of conjugation energy in the product. Molecules which

15.12
$$CH_3\underset{\underset{\displaystyle OH}{|}}{CH}-CH_2-COOH \xrightarrow{\Delta} CH_3CH{=}CHCOOH + H_2O$$

are stabilized by conjugation or resonance are most easily formed. Acids having hydroxy groups in the 4- or 5-position spontaneously form cylic esters, called *lactones*. 4- (or γ-)hydroxyacids form 5-membered γ-lactones (Eq. 15.13), and 5- (or δ-)hydroxyacids form

15.13
$$HOCH_2CH_2CH_2COO^-Na^+ + H^+ \longrightarrow$$

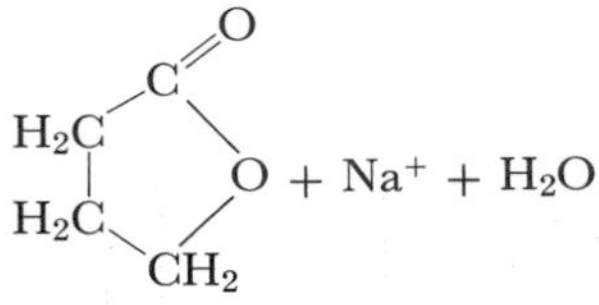

γ-butyrolactone

15.14
$$CH_3CHOHCH_2CH_2CH_2COO^-Na^+ + H^+ \longrightarrow$$

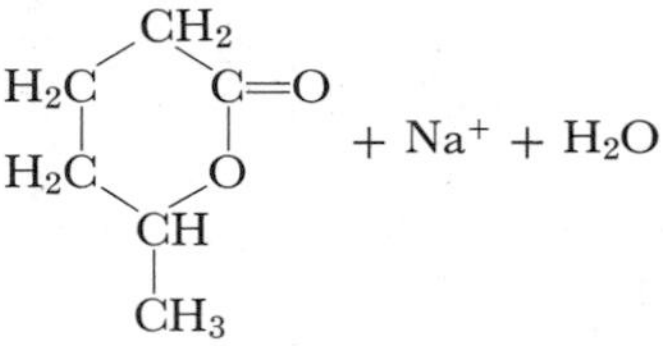

δ-caprolactone

6-membered δ-lactones (15.14). The ease of formation of these cyclic esters is illustrative of the natural tendency to form rings of five or six atoms, in which the bonds are not strained. The 3-membered α-lactones are not formed. Instead, efforts to force ester formation on an α-hydroxyacid result in the formation of a 6-membered di-ester (Eq. 15.15) called a lactide. The α-lactones have never been isolated.

15.15
$$2\ CH_3CHOHCOOH \xrightarrow{\Delta}$$

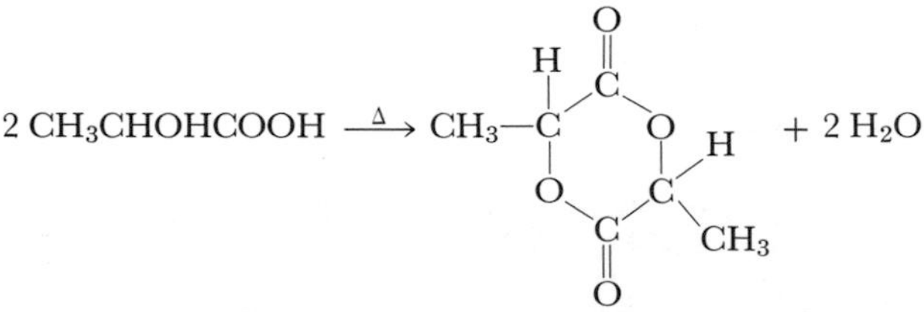

a lactide

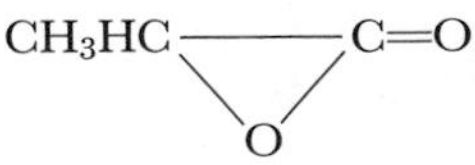

α-lactolactone

Some important hydroxy-acids

Lactic acid is formed when milk sours, by fermentation of the milk sugar. It is also present in sauerkraut, buttermilk, cheese, and other foods. Lactic acid increases in the muscle during work, as a breakdown product of glycogen (p. 285). During rest, it is partially reconverted to glycogen and partially excreted as carbon dioxide and water. Its salt, *calcium lactate,* is administered to increase the calcium intake in calcium deficiencies. Lactic acid is manufactured by fermentation and is used in the dyeing and leather-tanning industries. The tart taste of fruits, particularly unripe fruits, is due chiefly to the presence of hydroxy-acids. *Malic acid* is present in sour apples and pears, and its esters appear in the ripened fruit. *Tartaric acid* is present in many fruits but is especially rich in grapes. Several of its salts are used for medicinal purposes. *Sodium potassium tartrate* (Rochelle salt) is used as a saline cathartic. *Antimony potassium tartrate,* (tartar emetic) may be administered by mouth as an emetic, or injected intravenously in tropical diseases such as sleeping sickness, kala-azar, and leishmaniasis. *Acid potassium tartrate* (cream of tartar, $KOOC—CHOH—CHOH—COOH$) is a mild acid used in the manufacture of effervescent salts and baking powder to liberate carbon dioxide from sodium bicarbonate when the mixture of dry powders is moistened.

Citric acid is one of the most widely occurring of the natural acids. It is especially rich in the citrus fruits, lemon, lime, orange, etc., and is responsible for their desirable tart taste in fruit drinks. It can be manufactured by fermentation of sugar solutions, and is used as a synthetic citrus flavor in food products. Its salts are used as antacids and laxatives. For example, a solution of *magnesium citrate* is an effective, pleasant-tasting, saline laxative.

Mandelonitrile, $C_6H_5CHOHCN$, occurs in complexes in several fruits, such as almonds, peaches, and prunes. *Amygdalin,* one such complex from almonds, was once used in medicine as a sedative. Its action depended on the slow liberation of hydrogen cyanide! *Mandelic acid* itself is used as a urinary antiseptic, owing to the fact that it is not metabolized but is excreted in the urine, causing an antiseptic acidosis. *Salicylic acid* has many important medicinal uses. It is found in nature

15.16 $\langle\text{C}_6\text{H}_5\rangle$—$O^-Na^+ + CO_2 \xrightarrow[200°]{heat}$ ring—OH $\xrightarrow{H^+}$ ring with COOH and OH

                                         COO^-Na^+

                                                     salicylic acid

chiefly as the methyl ester in oil of wintergreen, but is prepared commercially by the *Kolbe synthesis* which involves a reaction between
sodium phenoxide and carbon dioxide under pressure. Salicylic acid
and its derivatives have definite analgetic and antipyretic effects, and
give marked relief owing to a specific action in acute articular rheu-
matism. The free acid is an antiseptic and corrosive irritant. It is used
in corn-removing agents because it has a softening effect on keratin,
the principal protein of hair and skin. *Methyl salicylate* (oil of wintergreen) is used chiefly as a counterirritant in liniments and ointments
for topical application, and as a flavoring oil. Although sometimes used
internally, salicylic acid derivatives with a free phenolic group are
gastric irritants. Esterification leads to the formation of *acetylsalicylic
acid* (aspirin) which today is one of the most commonly used antipy-
retics and analgetics. Aspirin is usually administered in the form of
tablets. When mixed with sodium bicarbonate in water it forms a
foaming carbonated solution which is more pleasant to the taste than
the rather bitter free acid. Soluble aspirin is the calcium or sodium salt
of the acid.

acetylsalicylic
acid (aspirin)

methyl salicylate
(oil of wintergreen)

KETO-ACIDS

Keto-acids may be formed by oxidation of the corresponding
hydroxy-acids (Eq. 15.10). They are important intermediate compounds in the metabolism of carbohydrates, fats, and proteins. *Pyruvic
acid* (2-ketopropanoic acid, $CH_3COCOOH$) is an intermediate step
in the fermentation of glucose (p. 268). *Acetoacetic acid* (3-ketobutanoic
acid, *beta*-ketobutyric acid, CH_3COCH_2COOH) is formed in the
metabolism of fats. When acetoacetic acid is heated, carbon dioxide

$$CH_3COCH_2COOH \xrightarrow{\text{heat}} CH_3COCH_3 + CO_2$$

is evolved, and acetone is formed. This is a characteristic reaction of
beta-keto-acids. It occurs in certain pathological conditions in the
human body, such as diabetes, so that acetone is excreted in the urine
and from the lungs. The characteristic "sweet breath" of diabetics is
due to acetone excretion. The ester, ethyl acetoacetate, is an important industrial chemical, and is made by condensation of ethyl acetate
by strong base (Eq. 15.17). This *acetoacetic ester condensation* is similar to

15.17

$$CH_3\overset{O}{\overset{\|}{C}}-OC_2H_5 + CH_3\overset{O}{\overset{\|}{C}}-OC_2H_5 \xrightarrow{C_2H_5O^-Na^+} \left[CH_3-\overset{OH}{\underset{OC_2H_5}{\overset{|}{\underset{|}{C}}}}-CH_2COOC_2H_5 \right]$$

$$\longrightarrow CH_3\overset{O}{\overset{\|}{C}}-CH_2COOC_2H_5 + C_2H_5OH$$

the aldol (p. 142) and Perkin (p. 166) condensations. Acetoacetic ester has highly activated α-hydrogens between two carbonyl groups. Like malonic ester (p. 171), acetoacetic ester readily undergoes the Perkin condensation (Eq. 15.18) or forms sodium salts which may then be alkylated (Eq. 15.19). This latter reaction, coupled with the ease of decarboxylation of β-keto-acids, provides a convenient synthesis of methyl ketones (Eq. 15.20).

15.18 $\quad RCHO + H_2C\overset{\overset{O}{\overset{\|}{C}}-CH_3}{\underset{\underset{O}{\overset{\|}{C}}-OC_2H_5}{}} \xrightarrow{base} RCH=C\overset{\overset{O}{\overset{\|}{C}}-CH_3}{\underset{COOC_2H_5}{}} + H_2O$

15.19 $\quad H_2C\overset{COCH_3}{\underset{COOC_2H_5}{}} \xrightarrow{C_2H_5O^-Na^+} NaHC\overset{COCH_3}{\underset{COOC_2H_5}{}} \xrightarrow{RX}$

$$RHC\overset{COCH_3}{\underset{COOC_2H_5}{}}$$

15.20 $\quad RHC\overset{COCH_3}{\underset{COOC_2H_5}{}} \xrightarrow[OH^-]{H_2O} RCHCOCH_3\overset{COO^-}{\underset{}{|}} \xrightarrow[H^+]{\Delta}$

$$RCH_2COCH_3 + CO_2$$

AMINO-ACIDS

Compounds containing both an amine group and a carboxyl group are especially important in biochemistry, since they are the building blocks from which *proteins* are made (see Chapter 18). There are about twenty-six different amino-acids found in natural proteins. Most of these are *alpha*-amino-acids, $R-CHNH_2-COOH$, where R— may be an aliphatic, substituted aliphatic, aromatic, or heterocyclic radical. Table 15.03 gives the formulas and names of a few representative amino-acids.

TABLE 15.03   SOME NATURALLY OCCURRING AMINO-ACIDS

Formula	Name
NH_2CH_2COOH	Glycine
CH_3CHNH_2COOH	Alanine
$NH_2CH_2CH_2COOH$	*beta*-Alanine
$(CH_3)_2CHCHNH_2COOH$	Valine*
$(CH_3)_2CHCH_2CHNH_2COOH$	Leucine*
$CH_3CH_2CH(CH_3)CHNH_2COOH$	Isoleucine*
$C_6H_5CH_2CHNH_2COOH$	Phenylalanine*

$$\overset{\displaystyle NH}{\underset{\displaystyle \parallel}{}}$$
$NH_2CNHCH_2CH_2CH_2CHNH_2COOH$ — Arginine*

Formula	Name
$H_2NCH_2CH_2CH_2CH_2CHNH_2COOH$	Lysine*
$HOOCCH_2CH_2CHNH_2COOH$	Glutamic acid
$CH_3CHOHCHNH_2COOH$	Threonine*
$CH_3SCH_2CH_2CHNH_2COOH$	Methionine*
SCH_2CHNH_2COOH	
$\overset{|}{S}CH_2CHNH_2COOH$	Cystine
$HSCH_2CHNH_2COOH$	Cysteine
$H_2NCOCH_2CHNH_2COOH$	Asparagine
HO—⟨benzene⟩—CH_2CHNH_2COOH	Tyrosine
(diiodo)HO—⟨ring⟩—O—⟨ring⟩(diiodo)—CH_2CHNH_2COOH	Thyroxine
⟨indole⟩—CH_2CHNH_2COOH	Tryptophan*
⟨imidazole⟩—CH_2CHNH_2COOH	Histidine*
H_2N—⟨benzene⟩—$COOH$	*para*-Aminobenzoic acid

* The essential amino-acids.

Reactions of amino-acids

Since the amino-acids contain both a basic amino group and an acidic carboxyl group, they exhibit some unusual properties, owing to their amphoteric character. They are all soluble in water, and have high melting points, indicating that they are actually salts, and should be written with the formula,

$$\underset{H}{\overset{R}{\diagdown}}C\underset{NH_3^+}{\overset{COO^-}{\diagup}}$$

This *Zwitter* ion (in-between ion) formula accounts for the behavior of amino-acids and proteins in solution. Amino-acids may be acetylated to form an acidic amide or esterified to form a basic ester (Eq. 15.21). Like the hydroxy-acids, the γ- and δ-amino-acids spontaneously form the 5- and 6-membered rings. The cyclic amides are called *lactams*

15.21
$$CH_3CONHCHCOOH \xleftarrow{CH_3COCl} + H_3N-\overset{R}{\underset{|}{CH}}-COO^- \xrightarrow[H^+]{C_2H_5OH}$$

$$H_2NCHCOOC_2H_5$$

15.22
$$H_2N(CH_2)_3COOH \longrightarrow \begin{array}{c} H_2C-\!\!\!-\!\!\!-CH_2 \\ H_2C \quad\quad C=O \\ \diagdown N \diagup \\ | \\ H \end{array} + H_2O$$

γ-butyrolactam

(Eq. 15.22). When α-amino acids are heated, they form 6-membered cyclic di-amides, called diketopiperazines (Eq. 15.23). Amino-acids react like any I° aliphatic amine with nitrous acid, evolving nitrogen quantitatively. This is the basis of the Van Slyke method of analysis for amino-acids (p. 197). Under the proper conditions, amino-acids condense with themselves by forming amide linkages (Eq. 15.24). Such compounds are called *peptides* (Chapter 18).

15.23
$$\begin{array}{c} O \quad\quad H \\ \| \quad\quad | \\ RHC \overset{C+OH\ H+N}{\diagdown \quad\quad \diagup} H-C-R \\ \overset{N+H\ HO+C}{\diagup \quad\quad \diagdown} \\ | \quad\quad O \\ H \end{array} \xrightarrow{\Delta} \begin{array}{c} O\ H \\ \| \ | \\ R \quad C-N \quad H \\ \diagup \quad\quad \diagdown \\ H \quad N-C \quad R \\ | \quad \| \\ H \quad O \end{array} + \underline{2\,H_2O}$$

a diketopiperazine

15.24
$$2\,H_2NCH_2COOH \longrightarrow H_2NCH_2CONHCH_2COOH$$

glycine   glycylglycine,
                                  a peptide

Preparation of amino-acids

Amino-acids may be prepared by hydrolyzing proteins. Proteins consist of long chains of amino-acids held together by amide (peptide) linkages. These bonds are broken by boiling in acid solution, and the various amino-acids making up the protein can be liberated and separated by special techniques. When a protein is rich in a single amino-acid it can be used as a source of that acid. For example, after hair (keratin) has been boiled in hydrochloric acid for 12 hours, cystine may be isolated in about 15 per cent yield. Similarly, silk may be hydrolyzed to produce glycine in 35–40 per cent yield.

Most of the pure amino-acids are more conveniently synthesized in the laboratory. α-Halo-acids are convenient starting compounds (Eq. 15.07). The Strecker synthesis of α-amino-acids (Eq. 15.25) depends on the availability of the necessary aldehyde, which readily forms an amino-nitrile hydrolyzable to the amino-acid. Recently acetamidomalonic ester has become commercially available, providing a convenient source of amino-acids by way of the malonic ester alkylation (p. 171). The synthesis of phenylalanine shown is characteristic of this method (Eq. 15.26).

$$\textbf{15.25} \qquad CH_3CHO \xrightarrow{NH_4CN} CH_3\underset{\underset{NH_2}{|}}{C}HCN \xrightarrow[H^+]{H_2O} CH_3\underset{\underset{NH_2}{|}}{C}HCOOH$$

$$\textbf{15.26}$$

$$\underset{\underset{COOC_2H_5}{|}}{\overset{\overset{COOC_2H_5}{|}}{H}}CNHCOCH_3 \xrightarrow{NaOC_2H_5} Na^+\underset{\underset{COOC_2H_5}{|}}{\overset{\overset{COOC_2H_5}{|}}{C}}NHCOCH \xrightarrow{C_6H_5CH_2Cl}$$

acetamidomalonic ester

$$C_6H_5CH_2\underset{\underset{COOC_2H_5}{|}}{\overset{\overset{COOC_2H_5}{|}}{C}}NHCOCH_3$$

$$\xrightarrow{H_2O} C_6H_5CH_2\underset{\underset{NH_2}{|}}{\overset{\overset{COOH}{|}}{C}}{-}COOH \xrightarrow[-CO_2]{\Delta} C_6H_5CH_2\underset{\underset{NH_2}{|}}{C}HCOOH$$

phenylalanine

Some important amino-acids

Since they are the building blocks of proteins, amino-acids are important to life processes. Man can synthesize from other food sources some of the amino-acids needed for the building of muscle, blood, and similar protein materials. However, certain others must be present in the human diet, and are essential for normal growth and development. These "essential amino-acids" are *threonine, valine, phenylalanine, arginine, lysine, methionine, leucine, isoleucine, tryptophan* and *histidine* (see Table 15.03). Not all of these are present in every protein food. Therefore a diet limited to one kind of protein will result in malnutrition, and a wide variety of proteins should be included in a healthful diet. For example, it was found that rats fed a diet in which casein (milk protein) was the only protein source soon died, unless a supplement of tryptophan was added.

β-Alanine is important as part of the vitamin pantothenic acid, an amide of pantoic acid (2,4-dihydroxy-3,3-dimethylbutyric acid)

$$\underset{\underset{CH_3}{|}}{\overset{\overset{CH_3}{|}}{HOCH_2C}}-CHOHCONHCH_2CH_2COOH$$

pantothenic acid

p-Aminobenzoic acid is considered to be a vitamin for certain bacteria. Although it is not an essential amino-acid, a derivative occurs in folic acid, the anti-pernicious anemia factor.

folic acid

Study Questions

1. Write structural formulas for the following: lactic acid, chloroacetic acid, tartaric acid, alanine, malic acid, *p*-aminobenzoic acid, α-bromobutyric acid, salicylic acid, γ-butyrolactone, citric acid.

2. Show by equations a good method for the preparation of the following substituted acids:
   a) chloroacetic acid;   b) 2,3-dibromopropanoic acid;
   c) phenylalanine;   d) β-hydroxybutyric acid;
   e) chloroacetyl chloride;   f) ethyl acetoacetate.

3. Which is the stronger acid, chloroacetic or trichloroacetic? Why?

4. Predict the ionization constant of dibromoacetic acid. Compare your prediction to the actual constant. (See a chemical handbook.) Will glycollic acid be stronger or a weaker acid than acetic acid?

5. Show how lactic acid can be converted to:
    a) pyruvic acid;   b) a lactide;
    c) acrylic acid;   d) β-mercaptopropionic acid;
    e) ethyl α-chloropropionate.

6. Show by equations how phenol may be converted into salicylic acid, aspirin, and oil of wintergreen. Name a specific medicinal use for each of the compounds mentioned.

7. A compound A, C_7H_7O, smells like almonds, and gives a silver mirror with Tollens' reagent. A on treatment with hydrogen cyanide gives B, C_8H_7NO, and after B is boiled in hydrochloric acid solution, crystals of C, $C_8H_8O_3$, appear on cooling. C is soluble in ammonia. Write possible structures for A, B, and C, and show the reactions involved.

8. In what ways are the acetoacetic ester condensation and the aldol and Perkin condensations alike?

9. What products would be expected when glycine is treated in the following ways:
    a) with acetyl chloride;
    b) with methanol and dry hydrogen chloride;
    c) with aqueous nitrous acid;
    d) heated above its melting point.

10. What are the essential amino-acids? How do they differ from the nonessential amino-acids?

11. Define the following terms:
    a) lactone;   b) inductive effect;
    c) Zwitter ion;   d) lactide;
    e) lactam;   f) keto-acid;
    g) cyanohydrin;   h) peptide.

13. An acid, I, $C_4H_8O_3$, on distillation yielded a second acid, II, $C_4H_6O_2$, which reacted readily with bromine in glacial acetic acid to yield a crystalline acid, III, $C_4H_6O_2Br_2$. I on mild oxidation and heating evolved carbon dioxide and produced acetone. Give the structures of I, II, and III, and show the reactions involved.

Advanced Reading References

Organic Chemistry, 3rd Ed., R. Q. Brewster and W. E. McEwen, Prentice-Hall, Inc., Englewood Cliffs, N. J., 1961, Chapters 18, 19, and 20.

Chemistry of Organic Compounds, 2nd Ed., C. R. Noller, W. B. Saunders and Co., Philadelphia, 1957, Chapters 35, 36, and 38.

Essential Principles of Organic Chemistry, James Cason, Prentice-Hall, Inc., Englewood Cliffs, N. J., 1956, Chapters 15 and 20.

new terms & concepts

*Stereoisomers have different arrangement of the atoms in space.
Plane-polarized monochromatic light is rotated by optically
active substances in a levorotatory (−) or dextrorotatory (+) direction.
This rotation may be measured quantitatively by a polarimeter.
A tetrahedral carbon atom with four different substituents is asymmetric,
and can be arranged in two different isomeric structures—mirror
images—called enantiomorphs.
Pasteur resolved the tartaric acids.
Both d- and l-lactic acids are found in nature from different sources.
Racemic mixtures of equimolar amounts of d- and l-enantiomorphs, formed in chemical synthesis,
are optically inactive.
Molecules with two or more different asymmetric centers have 2^n isomers, consisting of pairs
of enantiomorphs and non-mirror image diastereoisomers.
Enantiomorphs are identical in all physical and chemical properties
except effect on polarized light.
Diastereoisomers have different physical and chemical properties.
Molecules with like asymmetric centers have optically inactive meso-forms
as well as optically active forms.
Rotomers are the configurations around carbon-carbon single bonds
in equilibrium with each other.
They can be illustrated by Newman projections.
Resolution of racemic mixtures may be accomplished by mechanical separation,
reactions catalyzed by enzymes, or through conversion to diastereoisomers.
Racemization is the process of converting an optical isomer into an
equimolar mixture of enantiomorphs.
Epimerization is the process of racemizing only one of several asymmetric
centers in a molecule—the diastereoisomeric products are epimers.*

16

Optical isomers

Isomers are compounds which have the same numbers and kinds of atoms (same formulas) but differ in the arrangement of these atoms—that is, they differ in molecular structure. Several kinds of isomers have already been described. *Position isomers* differ in the position of a functional group in the molecule. For example, there are two propyl alcohols (Table 8.01) having quite different physical properties. These isomers differ in that the hydroxy group is attached to a primary carbon

$$CH_3CH_2CH_2OH \qquad CH_2CHOHCH_3$$
1-propanol 2-propanol

in one case, and to a secondary carbon in the other. *Chain isomers* are a special case of position isomer, in which an alkyl group may be attached at various positions, as in butane and isobutane, in which a

$$CH_3CH_2CH_2CH_3 \qquad CH_3CH(CH_3)CH_3$$
butane isobutane

methyl group is attached to a primary chain or a secondary carbon. *Functional isomers* (p. 19) exist when the atoms can combine in different ways to form different functional groups. For example, hydroxyacetone

$$CH_3COCH_2OH \qquad CH_3CH_2COOH$$
hydroxyacetone propionic acid

and propionic acid are functional isomers of formula $C_3H_6O_2$. *Tautomers* (p. 141) are a special case of functional isomers, which are in equilibrium with one another, as in the case of the *keto* and *enol* forms of acetoacetic ester.

$$CH_3\overset{\overset{\displaystyle O}{\|}}{C}-CH_2COOC_2H_5 \rightleftharpoons CH_3-\overset{\overset{\displaystyle OH}{|}}{C}=CHCOOC_2H_5$$

ethyl acetoacetate

Stereoisomers

Isomeric molecules may have the same atoms and groups attached to the same carbon atoms, but have different properties because these atoms have different arrangement in space. Such isomers are called *stereoisomers,* or space isomers. *Geometric isomers* (p. 51) are one class of stereoisomer, which exist because of restricted rotation around double bonds or in ring structures. For example, maleic and fumaric acids (p. 169) both have the formula $C_4H_4O_4$, but have quite different physical and chemical properties.

Stereoisomers of a second, more subtle type, known as optical isomers, occur in nature. *Optical isomers* have similar physical and chemical properties, but differ in their effect on polarized light. For example, lactic acid ($CH_3CHOHCOOH$) isolated from sour milk rotates the plane of polarized light counterclockwise (to the left— levorotatory). Lactic acid isolated from muscle tissue is identical in every respect, except that it rotates the plane of polarized light clockwise (to the right—dextrorotatory). Lactic acid synthesized in the laboratory is identical in chemical properties to the two natural isomers, but has no effect on polarized light.

PLANE-POLARIZED LIGHT

Light is composed of rays moving in waves. White light consists of rays of different wavelengths, vibrating in all possible planes perpendicular to the direction of propagation (Figure 16.01). *Monochromatic light* is light of a single wavelength (Figure 16.02), and may be obtained by passing a beam of white light through a filter which absorbs all but light of one color. Also light from a special source, such as incandescent sodium, may be monochromatic. *Plane-polarized light* is obtained when a beam of light is passed through special filters which allow only the wavelengths vibrating in one plane to pass (Figure 16.03).

Certain mineral crystals, such as tourmaline, have the property of transmitting only one plane of light when a beam is shown through

Fig. 16.01. White light beam, all wavelengths of light vibrating in all possible planes —lengthwise and cross-sectional diagrams.

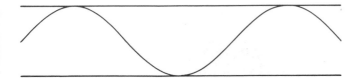

Fig. 16.02. Monochromatic light—light of a single wavelength vibrating in all possible planes—lengthwise and cross-sectional diagrams.

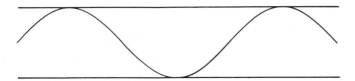

Fig. 16.03. Plane-polarized monochromatic light—light of a single wavelength vibrating in single plane—lengthwise and cross-sectional diagrams.

them. Iceland spar, which transmits two perpendicular planes, may be used to construct a Nicol prism, which is an effective filter for the production of plane-polarized light. Polaroid film is produced by depositing tiny crystals of an optically active substance, such as quinine, on a film. All crystals must be oriented in the same way, so that light from each crystal is polarized in the same plane. This polarization may be demonstrated by superimposing the lenses of two pairs of Polaroid sunglasses, and observing that the intensity of the transmitted light is greatly reduced when the lateral axes of the lenses are at right angles (Figure 16.04). Light reflected from a flat surface at a long angle will be partially polarized in the direction perpendicular to the plane of the surface. Sunlight reflected from the surface of a lake or a highway in the early morning or at sundown will produce a bright glare of polarized light because those rays which are perpendicular to the surface are reflected strongly. Polaroid sunglasses are therefore constructed so that the plane of polarization is horizontal.

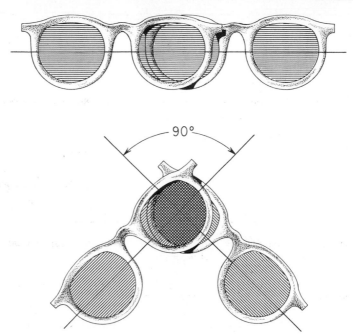

Fig. 16.04. Light transmitted through two Polaroid lenses at right angles is greatly reduced.

They are most effective against the glare of polarized light. Substances which transmit only one plane of light are called *polarizers.* A beam of light will pass through two polarizers only if the axes (planes of polarization) are parallel (Figure 16.04). When the axes are perpendicular, no light passes the second polarizer.

Optically active substances

When a beam of polarized light is passed through a quartz crystal, the plane of polarization is rotated. Substances which rotate the plane of polarized light are said to be *optically active.* Quartz crystals have right- and left-handed (mirror-image) shapes. Crystals of one form are dextrorotatory (clockwise rotation of the plane of polarization) while the mirror-image crystals are levorotatory (counterclockwise.)

When monochromatic light is used, in each case the plane of polarization is rotated exactly the same number of degrees, but in opposite direction. The ability of such right- and left-handed crystals to rotate plane-polarized light is attributed to the asymmetry of the crystals, and is lost when the crystals are dissolved.

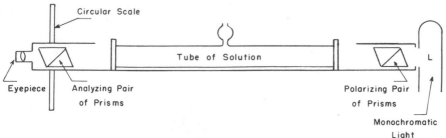

Fig. 16.05. Diagram of a polarimeter.

Many organic substances found in nature are optically active, rotating the polarized beam when it is passed through them, either in the pure state (solid or liquid) or in solution. Rotation in such cases must be caused by asymmetry of the molecules themselves, rather than by an asymmetric arrangement in crystals.

The polarimeter

Optical activity may be measured quantitatively by a polarimeter. Monochromatic light must be used, since optically active substances have different effects on different wavelengths of light. An efficient polarizer, such as a Nicol prism, is fixed permanently, to provide a fixed plane of polarization. A tube of accurately known length contains the solution or liquid sample. The plane-polarized light emerging from the tube passes through a second movable polarizer, which is set in a circular scale calibrated in 360°. When this polarizer is oriented to the plane of light emerging from the solution, the degree of orientation may be measured on the scale (Figure 16.05). A simple model of a polarimeter may be demonstrated by using a cardboard strip and two books (Figure 16.06). The first book, perpendicular to the table, rep-

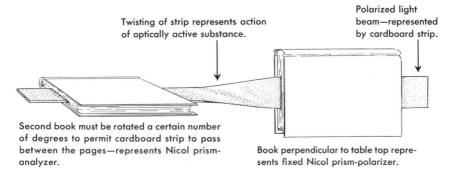

Fig. 16.06. Model of polarimeter system.

resents the fixed polarizer, which allows the cardboard (light) to pass in only one plane. The emerging cardboard may be twisted by hand, representing the action of an optically active substance. The second book must then be rotated to permit the cardboard to pass through its pages.

ASYMMETRY OF THE TETRAHEDRAL CARBON

Following the discovery by Biot in 1815 that organic substances in solution are optically active, many organic substances were tested for this property. By 1870 only a relatively few examples had been found, however, and these were always from natural sources. Tartar, a sludge produced in the fermentation of wine, yielded two organic acids, each having the formula $C_4H_6O_6$. One of these, tartaric acid, was dextrorotatory. The other, called racemic acid, was optically inactive. Pasteur studied these compounds, and found that all tartrate salts crystallized in an unsymmetrical shape (hemihedral crystal). Racemate salts, surprisingly, also crystallized in hemihedral crystals. Pasteur observed that crystal faces which were all turned the same way in the tartrate, were sometimes turned right and sometimes turned left in the racemate. He separated from a collection of large racemate crystals those having right-handed faces from those having left-handed faces. Those salt crystals having right-handed faces rotated plane-polarized light to the right, and the acid proved to be identical to dextrorotatory (+) tartaric acid. Those having left-handed faces rotated the light to the left an equal number of degrees, and the acid, identical in every respect except that it had an opposite effect on polarized light, was the previously unknown optical isomer, levorotatory (−) tartaric acid. When equal weights of the two kinds of crystals were dissolved in water, an optically inactive solution was obtained, which yielded racemic acid on acidification. Pasteur had thus for the first time resolved an optically inactive compound, racemic acid, into its optically active components, (+) and (−) tartaric acid.

In 1873, Wislicenus completed a study of the lactic acids. The substance isolated from sour milk which had the formula $C_3H_6O_3$, rotated plane-polarized light to the left, and melted at 26°C, was shown to be α-hydroxypropionic acid. Muscle tissue provided the optical isomer having identical properties except that it affected plane-polarized light in equal but opposite direction. Chemical degradation proved this compound also to be α-hydroxypropionic acid. Synthesis of α-hydroxypropionic acid yielded a substance melting at 18°C which was optically inactive. These reactions are summarized in the reaction scheme (Figure 16.07). Wislicenus concluded that molecules which were identical in structure but had different properties must differ in their arrangement of the atoms in space.

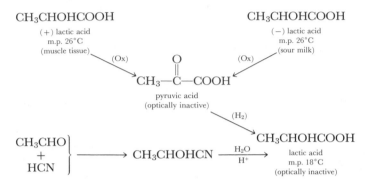

Fig. 16.07. Relationship of lactic acid isomers.

In 1874, two young chemists, van't Hoff in Holland and Le Bel in France, independently announced the structural theory which explained optical activity. They suggested that the four valencies of carbon were arranged in a regular tetrahedron (Figure 16.08). A carbon atom which had four different substituents would therefore be asymmetric, and could exist in two different isomeric structures, which would differ from one another as do mirror images (Figure 16.09). The two stereoisomeric mirror-image structures of lactic acid are shown in Figure 16.10. Right- and left-handed mirror-image isomers are called *enantiomorphs*. Enantiomorphs have identical physical and chemical properties, except for their effect on polarized light, which they rotate an 'equal amount but in opposite direction. Enantiomorphs cannot be separated by ordinary physical or chemical methods.

A mixture containing equal amounts of enantiomorphs will be

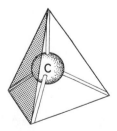

Fig. 16.08. Valencies of carbon directed to corners of a regular tetrahedron.

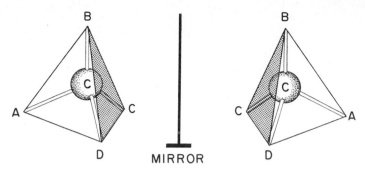

Fig. 16.09. Asymmetrically substituted carbon atoms may exist in isomeric mirror-image forms.

optically inactive because any rotation of plane-polarized light by one form will be cancelled by the opposite rotation of its enantiomorph. Such mixtures are called *racemic* mixtures, after the original racemic acid. Synthetic formation of asymmetric carbon atoms always results in racemic mixtures. This is because any chemical reaction which creates an asymmetric center may do so in either a left- or right-handed manner. In ordinary chemical reactions, the statistical probability that one or the other form will result prevails, and an equal amount of each isomer is formed. For example, a racemic mixture of (+) and (−) α-bromopropionic acid may be made by bromination of the α-carbon atom of propionic acid (Eq. 16.01). The reaction in-

16.01 $$CH_3CH_2COOH \xrightarrow[PBr_3]{Br_2} CH_3CHBrCOOH$$

volves replacement of one of two equivalent hydrogen atoms on the α-carbon atom, and the probability of replacing either is equal. Therefore a racemic mixture is obtained. For the same reason, reduction of

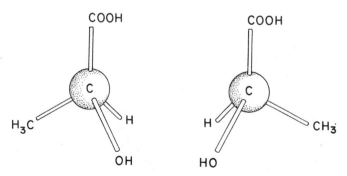

Fig. 16.10. Lactic acid is a typical example of an asymmetrically substituted carbon atom, having two isomeric structures.

the carbonyl group in pyruvic acid results in racemic lactic acid (Figure 16.07). The reaction involves addition of a hydrogen atom to the carbonyl carbon, which can occur on either side with equal probability.

It is remarkable that while laboratory syntheses of asymmetric centers always results in racemic mixtures, similar reactions in living systems frequently result in a single optically active form. Such reactions are catalyzed by optically active enzymes, which can direct the reaction exclusively in a right- or left-handed manner owing to their own asymmetry.

Two-dimensional notation

It is inconvenient to attempt to draw three-dimensional structural formulas to illustrate optical isomers, such as those shown for the enantiomorphs of lactic acid in Figure 16.10. Several conventions have been adopted for writing about such isomers. Attention is called to an asymmetric atom by marking it with an asterisk, thus: CH_3C^*HOH-$COOH$ or $CH_3C^*HOHCH_2CH_3$. Tetrahedral structures, written as squares in the plane of the paper, can show the relative configuration.

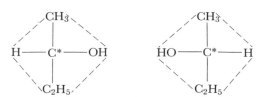

Fig. 16.11. Enantiomorphic 2-butanols.

The right and left-handed two-dimensional structures, such as those shown in Figure 16.11, are not superimposable so long as they are kept in two dimensions. They must not be lifted out of the plane of the paper, as this would be equivalent to transporting an actual molecule through the fourth dimension, which is impossible.

The direction of optical rotation of different molecules is not related to their relative configuration. For example, when $(+)$ α-hydroxy-propionaldehyde is oxidized, $(-)$ lactic acid is obtained, although the

16.02

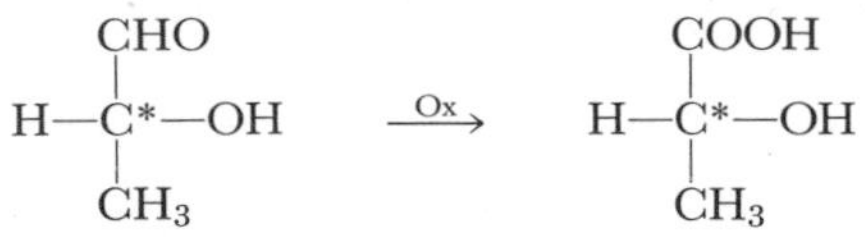

$$\underset{(+)\ \alpha\text{-hydroxypropionaldehyde}}{\overset{\displaystyle CHO}{\underset{\displaystyle CH_3}{\mid}}}\ \overset{Ox}{\longrightarrow}\ \underset{(-)\ \text{lactic acid}}{\overset{\displaystyle COOH}{\underset{\displaystyle CH_3}{\mid}}}$$

configuration at the asymmetric center is unchanged. It is important to indicate configurational relationships between different molecules. This has been done by calling the structure written with the hydroxy group on the right of the asymmetric carbon the D-configuration (after dextrorotatory glyceraldehyde) and indicating direction of optical rotation by (+) and (−) signs. Note that a small capital letter (D- or L-) signifies configuration while a lower-case letter (d- or l-) or plus (+) and minus (−) signs indicate direction of rotation.

16.03

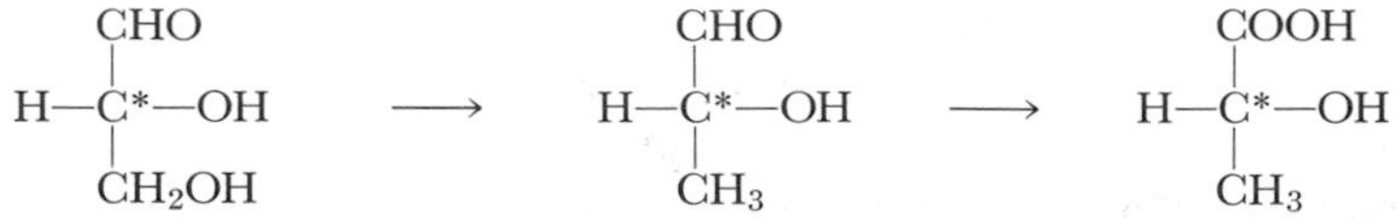

$$
\begin{array}{ccc}
\text{CHO} & \text{CHO} & \text{COOH} \\
| & | & | \\
\text{H—C*—OH} & \text{H—C*—OH} & \text{H—C*—OH} \\
| & | & | \\
\text{CH}_2\text{OH} & \text{CH}_3 & \text{CH}_3 \\
\end{array}
$$

D(+) glyceraldehyde   D(+) α-hydroxypropionaldehyde   D(−) lactic acid

Molecules having more than one asymmetric center

Molecules may have an unlimited number of asymmetric carbon atoms. For example, 2,3-dihydroxybutyric acid contains two different asymmetric centers (Figure 16.12). By writing structures in which

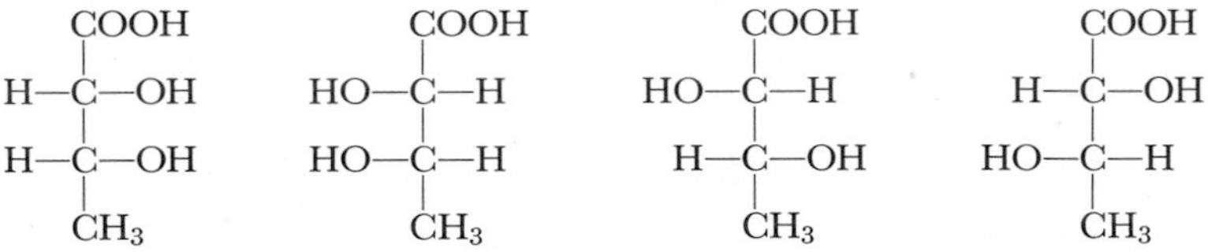

$$
\begin{array}{cccc}
\text{COOH} & \text{COOH} & \text{COOH} & \text{COOH} \\
| & | & | & | \\
\text{H—C—OH} & \text{HO—C—H} & \text{HO—C—H} & \text{H—C—OH} \\
| & | & | & | \\
\text{H—C—OH} & \text{HO—C—H} & \text{H—C—OH} & \text{HO—C—H} \\
| & | & | & | \\
\text{CH}_3 & \text{CH}_3 & \text{CH}_3 & \text{CH}_3 \\
(A) & (B) & (C) & (D) \\
\end{array}
$$

Fig. 16.12. Structures of the optical isomers of 2,3-dihydroxybutyric acids.

each center has either the D- or L-configuration, we find stereoisomers exist. It is apparent from the structures written in Figure 16.12 that (A) and (B) are a pair of enantiomorphs, which would form a racemic mixture. Likewise (C) and (D) are mirror images, and would form a racemic mixture. However, although (A) is a stereoisomer of (C) and (D), it is not a mirror image of either. Such non-mirror image stereoisomers are called *diastereoisomers*. Any given asymmetric molecule will have one enantiomorph, but may have several diastereoisomers, depending on the number of asymmetric centers in the molecule. Diastereoisomers differ in optical rotation and in physical and chemical properties, such as boiling point, melting point, solubility, and rate of reaction. They may therefore be separated from one another by ordinary means, such as crystallization.

A molecule with three different asymmetric centers will have four pairs of enantiomorphs or eight isomers in all. In this case each isomer will have one mirror image but six diastereoisomers. A molecule with four different asymmetric centers will have eight pairs of enantiomorphs, or sixteen stereoisomers in all. The *van't Hoff* rule states that *if a molecule has n different asymmetric centers, it will have 2^n possible isomers.*

Compounds having identical asymmetric centers

When a molecule has asymmetric centers which are alike, the number of possible stereoisomers will be less than that predicted by the van't Hoff rule. Tartaric acid represents the case of a molecule having two identical asymmetric centers. It has only three stereoisomers: one pair of enantiomorphs, (E) and (F), and one optically inactive symmetrical structure, (G), called a *meso* form. Note that the *meso* configuration shown by (G) is identical to (G'), and can be superimposed on (G') by rotating the structure in the plane of the paper by 180°. It is also apparent that (G) has a plane of symmetry which divides the molecule into two mirror-image halves.

$$
\begin{array}{cccc}
\text{COOH} & \text{COOH} & \text{COOH} & \left[\text{COOH}\right. \\
| & | & | & | \\
\text{HO--C--H} & \text{H--C--OH} & \text{plane of H--C--OH} & \text{HO--C--H} \\
| & | & | & | \\
\text{H--C--OH} & \text{HO--C--H} & \text{symmetry: H--C--OH} & \text{HO--C--H} \\
| & | & | & | \\
\text{COOH} & \text{COOH} & \text{COOH} & \left.\text{COOH}\right] \\
(E) & (F) & (G) & (G')
\end{array}
$$

$=$

Rotomers

Formulas such as (E), (F), and (G) represent configurations of molecules which have been frozen in one position. However, there is free rotation around single bonds. Therefore each type of molecule must exist in many shapes. Since like atoms repel one another, a structure with free rotation around a carbon-carbon single bond tends to fall naturally into three different structures, much like the operation of a ratchet. For example, 1,2-dichloroethane actually exists principally in three different configurations. These are shown in the three-dimensional models (Figure 16.13). These stereoisomeric structures which are interconvertible and in equilibrium are called *rotomers*. They can be illustrated in two dimensions by *Newman projections*. If the structure is viewed along the carbon-carbon axis, the first carbon may be

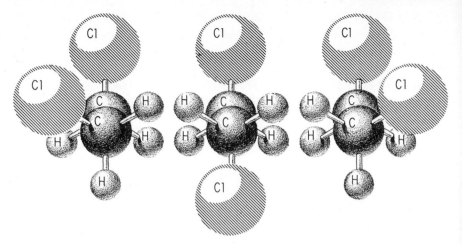

Fig. 16.13. Models of rotomeric configurations of 1,2-dichloroethane.

shown by ⅄ and the second by ⅄ . The three rotomers of 1,2-
dichloroethane are then illustrated by Figure 16.14.

Notice that H_1 and H_2 in Figure 16.14 are a mirror-image pair
which are interconvertible. 1,2-Dichloroethane is not optically active,
since (H_1) and (H_2) must exist in exactly equal amounts. (H_1) cannot be isolated, since it would immediately equilibrate to a mixture of
(H_1), (H_2), and (H_3). (H_3) may be considered a *meso* form, since it has
a plane of symmetry.

Similar three-dimensional considerations must also be applied to
free rotation in optical isomers. Each structure must exist in a set of
interconvertible rotomers. Figure 16.15 illustrates the case of tartaric
acid in Newman projections. *meso*-Tartaric acid is shown by (G_1), (G_2),
and (G_3). Like 1,2-dichloroethane, a mirror-image pair of interconvertible rotomers, (G_1) and (G_2), must exist in equal amounts, thus

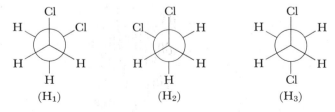

Fig. 16.14. Newman projections of rotomers of 1,2-dichloroethane.

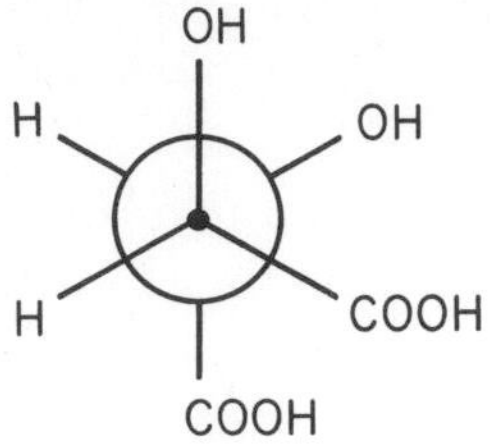

G_1

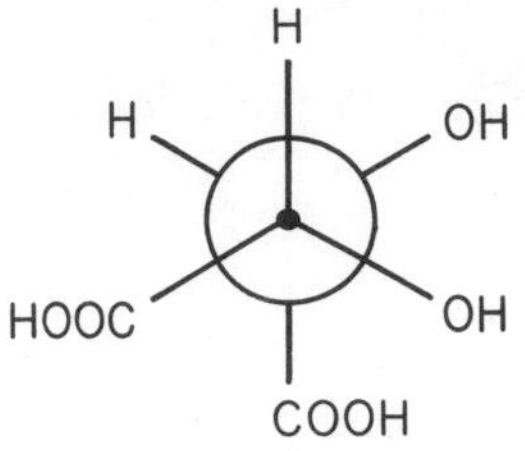

G_2

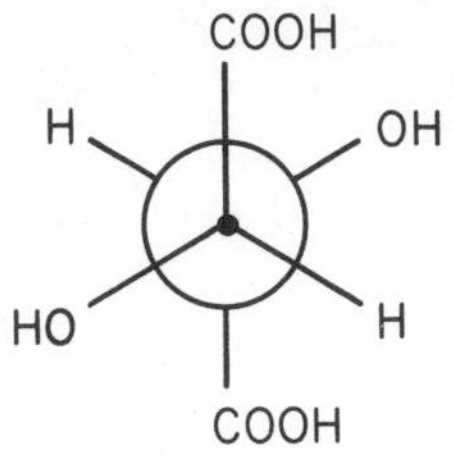

G_3

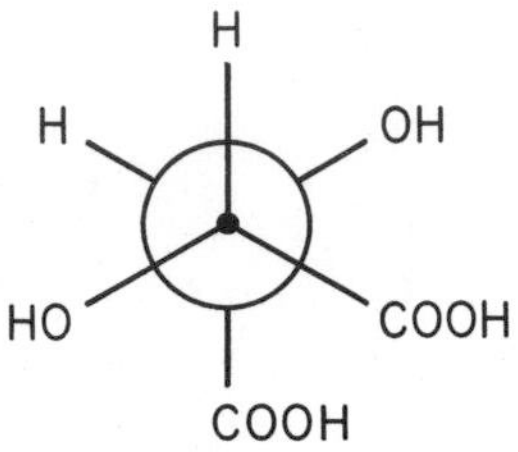

E_1

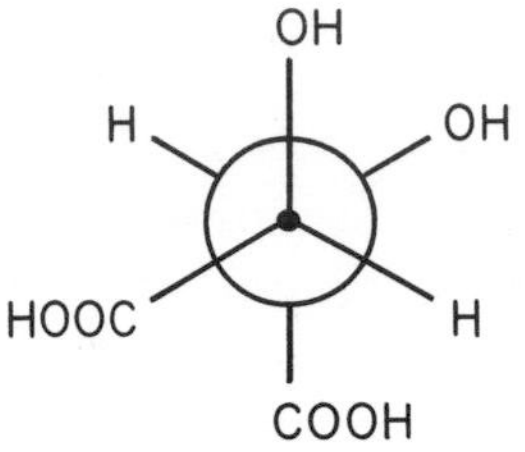

E_2

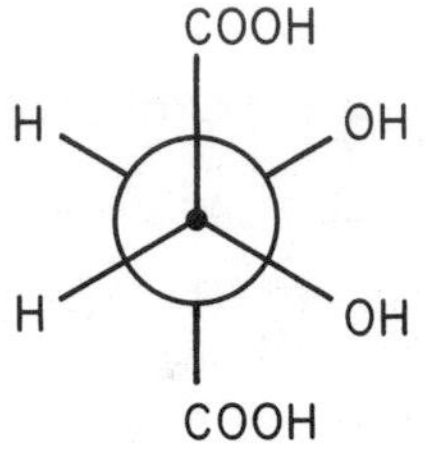

E_3

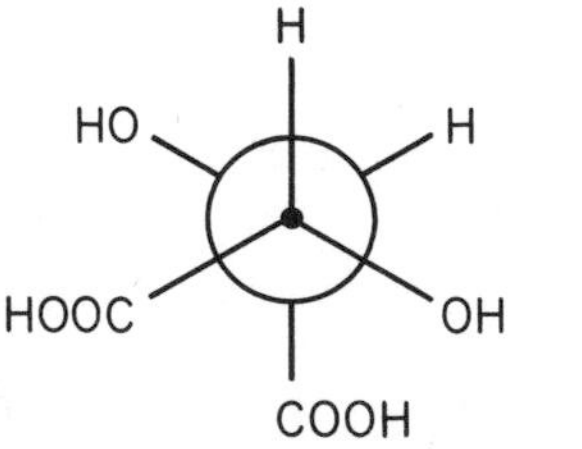

F_1

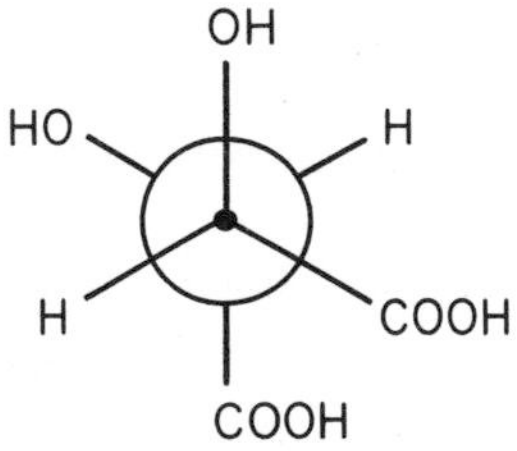

F_2

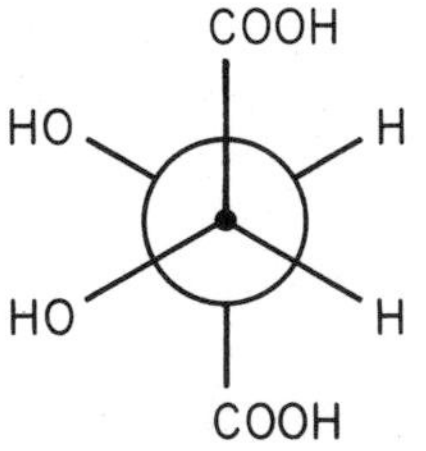

F_3

Fig. 16.15. Newman projections of rotomers of *meso, d-* and *l-tartaric* acids.

cancelling optical activity contributed by these forms. (G_3) is optically inactive since it possesses a center of symmetry, from which a line extended an equal distance in opposite directions will always meet an identical structure. Each of the rotomers of (E) is asymmetric and therefore optically active. The optical activity of a quantity of (E) will therefore be the sum of the activities of structures (E_1), (E_2), and (E_3). For each rotomer of (E), a mirror-image rotomer occurs in (F). Since the energy of these forms is identical to their enantiomorphs in (E), they will exist to exactly the same extent. The optical activity of a quantity of (F), the sum of the activities of (F_1), (F_2), and (F_3), will be exactly equal to that of an equal quantity of (E), but of opposite sign.

SEPARATION OF RACEMIC MIXTURES

Enantiomorphs have identical chemical and physical properties, and cannot be separated by ordinary means, such as distillation or crystallization. Since racemic mixtures are produced when asymmetric compounds are synthesized, it is important to resolve these mixtures to obtain their dextro- and levorotatory isomers. Such separation is called *resolution*.

Mechanical resolution

Pasteur accomplished the first optical resolution by picking apart the right- and left-handed hemihedral crystals of tartaric acid. This method is of historical interest, but is rarely useful, since it is laborious and depends on formation of mirror-image crystals, which rarely occurs.

The use of enzymes in optical resolution

Enzymes, which are themselves asymmetric, may catalyze a reaction with one enantiomorph without influencing the other. This phenomenon may be used to effect resolution. For example, certain microorganisms, when grown upon a medium containing a racemic mixture, will destroy one form, and leave the other. When rabbits are fed racemic malic acid, they metabolize the *d*-form, and excrete *l*-malic acid in the urine, from which it can be recovered. Such resolution methods are unsatisfactory, since one form is destroyed in the process, and they are only applicable to metabolic substances.

In certain cases, isolated enzymes may be used to effect resolution, and in this way both isomers may be obtained. For example, an enzyme isolated from hog kidney catalyzes the hydrolysis of amides, and is known as an *amidase*. If a racemic mixture of the amide of alanine is treated with this amidase (Eq. 16.04), the levorotatory

$$CH_3C^*HNH_2CONH_2 + H_2O \xrightarrow{\text{amidase}}$$

dl-alanylamide

16.04

$$CH_3C^*HNH_2COOH + NH_3 + CH_3C^*HNH_2CONH_2$$

l-alanine   *d*-alanylamide

amide is hydrolyzed to *l*-alanine, while the dextrorotatory amide is unchanged. The *l*-acid may be easily separated from the *d*-amide, which may then be hydrolyzed by ordinary chemical means to the *d*-acid. By this means complete resolution is affected. This method is very useful in the special cases where enzymes which will accomplish the desired action are available.

Use of diastereoisomers in optical resolution

The most important and general method of optical resolution depends on the fact that diastereoisomers do have different physical and chemical properties, and may be separated by solubility differences, boiling points, or rates of reaction. If a racemic substance can be converted into diastereoisomers by reaction with an optically active reagent, the products may be separated and the original optically active enantiomorphs recovered separately by reversal of the reaction.

For example, consider the resolution of the racemic *dl*-mandelic acid. If the *dl*-acid reacts with an optically active base, such as the alkaloid *l*-brucine, diastereoisomeric salts are formed (Eq. 16.05). These salts may be separated by recrystallization from alcohol or chloroform. After separation, the salts may be decomposed by strong acid, and the *d*- and *l*-mandelic acids obtained in optically active form. The resolving reagent may be recovered unchanged.

This method depends on the availability of an optically active reagent, usually some natural product, such as an alkaloid, or a derivative thereof. Optically active acids, once resolved, may be used in the same way to resolve racemic bases. Racemic alcohols are usually resolved by conversion to half-esters with dibasic acids (Eq. 16.08). The resulting racemic acids are then resolved and recovered in the usual way, after which they can be hydrolyzed to the optically active alcohols. By similar combinations of reactions and a careful choice of reagents, most classes of racemic substances can be resolved into their component enantiomorphs.

16.05   *dl*-mandelic acid + 2 *l*-brucine $\longrightarrow$ *l*-brucine *d*-mandelate + *l*-brucine *l*-mandelate

16.06   *l*-brucine *d*-mandelate + HCl $\longrightarrow$ *d*-mandelic acid + *l*-brucine hydrochloride

16.07   *l*-brucine *l*-mandelate + HCl $\longrightarrow$ *l*-mandelic acid + *l*-brucine hydrochloride

16.08

$$CH_3C^*HOHC_2H_5 \; +$$

dl-2-butanol   phthalic anhydride   dl-2-butyl monophthalate

RACEMIZATION

Racemization is the opposite of resolution. In some cases an optical isomer may be converted to its enantiomorph. If this is an equilibrium reaction, the result is a racemic mixture, and the process is called racemization. Racemization occurs most easily when the asymmetric center bears a hydrogen atom α to a carbonyl group. Racemization then proceeds by a process of enolization, which involves a symmetrical enolate. Ketolization then becomes a synthesis of an unsymmetrical center from a symmetrical center, and results in a racemic mixture (Eq. 16.09). Racemization is promoted by the reagents which catalyze enolization, such as strong bases.

16.09

$$\begin{array}{ccc} \underset{b}{\overset{a}{\diagdown}}\overset{\overset{\displaystyle H}{|}}{\underset{*}{C}}-\overset{\overset{\displaystyle O}{\|}}{C}-R & \rightleftharpoons & \underset{b}{\overset{a}{\diagdown}}C=C\underset{\diagdown R}{\overset{\diagup OH}{}} \rightleftharpoons & \underset{a}{\overset{b}{\diagdown}}\overset{\overset{\displaystyle H}{|}}{\underset{*}{C}}-\overset{\overset{\displaystyle O}{\|}}{C}-R \\ (+) & \begin{array}{c}\text{inactive}\\\text{(symmetrical)}\end{array} & (-) \end{array}$$

Racemization is an important industrial process where an optical isomer is being manufactured from inactive compounds. In this case the *dl*-compound is always formed and resolved to obtain the desired isomer. The enantiomorph is wasted by-product unless it can be racemized, and the racemate again resolved. By a combination of resolution and racemization, an optically inactive substance can essentially be converted into one optically active form in 100 per cent yield. For example, in the synthesis of the vitamin pantothenic acid, *d*-pantoic acid is required. *dl*-Pantoic acid is synthesized from optically inactive β-hydroxypivaldehyde (Eq. 16.10). This product is then resolved, and

16.10

$$\underset{\text{β-hydroxypivaldehyde}}{\overset{\overset{\displaystyle CH_3}{|}}{\underset{\underset{\displaystyle CH_3}{|}}{HOCH_2C}}-CHO} \xrightarrow{HCN} \underset{\text{dl-pantoylnitrile}}{\overset{\overset{\displaystyle CH_3}{|}}{\underset{\underset{\displaystyle CH_3}{|}}{HOCH_2C}}-CH^*OHCN} \xrightarrow[H^+]{H_2O}$$

$$\underset{\text{dl-pantoic acid}}{\overset{\overset{\displaystyle CH_3}{|}}{\underset{\underset{\displaystyle CH_3}{|}}{HOCH_2C}}-C^*HOHCOOH}$$

the *d*-acid used in synthesis of the vitamin. The *l*-acid is racemized by being heated with caustic solution, and *dl*-pantoic acid is formed. This material is then added to the next synthetic batch of *dl*-acid, and the whole again resolved. These processes are carried on alternately, and by this means optically inactive β-hydroxypivaldehyde is converted nearly quantitatively into *d*-pantoic acid.

Epimerization

When a compound has more than one asymmetric carbon atom, selective racemization of one asymmetric center (usually one next to a carbonyl group) may occur without affecting the other asymmetric centers. The result is transformation of the original substance into one of its diastereoisomers. For example, 2,3,4-trihydroxypentanal (I) is partially converted to its diastereoisomer (J) when allowed to stand in alkaline solution. Diastereoisomers which have opposite configurations at one center and all other centers of identical configuration, such as (I) and (J), are called *epimers,* and the transformation of one into the other is called *epimerization.*

$$\begin{array}{ccc}
\text{CHO} & \text{H} \quad \text{OH} & \text{CHO} \\
\text{H—C—OH} & \text{C} & \text{HOCH} \\
\text{H—C—OH} \rightleftharpoons & \text{C—OH} \rightleftharpoons & \text{HCOH} \\
\text{H—C—OH} & \text{HC—OH} & \text{HCOH} \\
\text{CH}_3 & \text{HC—OH} & \text{CH}_3 \\
& \text{CH}_3 & \\
\text{(I)} & & \text{(J)}
\end{array}$$

Study Questions

1. What is meant by stereoisomer? What is the difference between geometric and optical isomers? Why are not *cis*- and *trans*-2-butenes optically active?

2. Explain why reduction of ethyl methyl ketone gives *dl*-2-butanol.

3. Define the following terms:

   a) monochromatic light; *b*) polarizer;
   c) optical rotation; *d*) enantiomorph;
   e) racemic mixture; *f*) diastereoisomer;
   g) configuration; *h*) *meso*-form;
   i) rotamer; *j*) resolution.

4. Draw two-dimensional structural formulas illustrating the configuration of all possible isomers of 2,3-dibromobutyric acid. Point out which of these structures are enantiomorphs, which diastereoisomers, which *meso*-forms.

5. How are D(+)-glyceraldehyde and D(−)-lactic acid related? Explain the symbols used.

6. Which of the following compounds can exist in optical isomers? Write a structural formula for each and indicate any asymmetric carbons by asterisks.

   a) 3-hydroxybutyric acid;   *b*) 2-chloropropane;
   c) β-alanine;   *d*) alanine;
   e) glycine;   *f*) malic acid;
   g) citric acid;   *h*) 3-chloro-2-butanone;
   i) cyclohexanol;   *j*) 1,2-dihydroxycyclopentane.

7. When optically active 2-iodohexane is treated with potassium iodide in acetone solution, the optical rotation of the solution rapidly falls to zero. How can you account for this phenomenon? What is it called?

8. When an optically active 2,3-dibromobutyric acid is dissolved in dilute base, the initial rotation slowly changes to another rotation, at which it stabilizes. Can you explain this phenomenon?

Advanced Reading References

Essential Principles of Organic Chemistry, James Cason, Prentice-Hall, Inc., Englewood Cliffs, N. J., 1956, Chapter 16.

Organic Chemistry, 2nd Ed., L. F. Fieser and Mary Fieser, D. C. Heath and Co., Boston, 1950, Chapter 11.

"Stereoisomerism," by R. L. Shriner, Roger Adams, and C. S. Marvel, Chapter 4 in *Organic Chemistry, An Advanced Treatise,* 2nd Ed., ed. Vol. I, H. Gilman, John Wiley and Sons, Inc., New York, 1943.

Steric Effects in Organic Chemistry, ed. M. S. Newman, John Wiley and Sons, Inc., New York, 1956.

new terms & concepts

*Carbohydrates, $C_mH_{2n}O_n$, common constituents of living tissue, are
the main source of energy for mammals.
Sugars, the monosaccharides and disaccharides, are simple carbohydrates.
Glucose, the most abundant monosaccharide, is an aldohexose, or six-carbon
pentahydroxy aldehyde, which exists as a cyclic hemi-acetal.
Galactose and mannose are naturally occurring diastereoisomers of glucose.
Fructose, or fruit sugar, is a ketohexose.
Mutarotation occurs when crystalline glucose is dissolved in water, and
is a change in rotation due to equilibrium between
hemi-acetal and open-chain structures.
Reducing sugars are those with free aldehyde or ketone groups
which reduce Benedict's or Fehling's solution.
They form osazones with phenylhydrazine, and glycosides by forming ether
linkages through the hemi-acetal structure.
Sucrose, common table sugar, is a nonreducing disaccharide
made up of glucose and fructose.
Lactose, milk sugar, is an important food made up of galactose and glucose.
Maltose and cellobiose are disaccharides which are the building blocks
of starch and cellulose, respectively.
They are both glucose dimers, one having an α-glucoside linkage,
the other a β-glucoside linkage.
Glucose is synthesized in nature from carbon dioxide and water by a process
of photosynthesis, which is catalyzed by chlorophyll.
Intermediates in this synthesis are phosphoglyceric acids.
These substances are also intermediates in the degradation
of glucose to lactic acid or alcohol.
The most powerful sweetening agents are synthetic organic compounds,
such as saccharin or sucaryl, which have no food value.
Among the natural sugars, fruit sugar is ten times as sweet as milk sugar.*

17

Sugars

One of the most important classes of naturally occurring organic compounds is the *carbohydrates*. They are composed of carbon, hydrogen, and oxygen, the last two usually in the ratio of $2:1$, as in water, H_2O. They have the general formula $C_m(H_2O)_n$. Treatment of a carbohydrate with a strong dehydrating agent like sulfuric acid, or heating, will remove water from the molecule and leave carbon, hence the name, "hydrate of carbon" or carbohydrate. Water is not actually present as such in these molecules, and the term "carbohydrate" is misleading. The general formula $C_mH_{2n}O_n$ is preferred.

Carbohydrates are the main source of energy for mammals, and are a common constituent of all living plants and animals. They make up the main portion of all plant tissues—stems, roots, and leaves. Common examples of carbohydrate include table sugar, flour, cotton, and wood. The carbohydrates consist of simple low-molecular-weight molecules, called the sugars, and complex high-molecular-weight polymers. This chapter will be concerned only with the sugars. The polymeric materials will be described in Chapter 18.

GLUCOSE

Glucose was the first simple sugar isolated, and is by far the most common sugar. Many different polymeric carbohydrates, such as starch, wood fiber, or cotton, on boiling with concentrated hydrochloric acid are converted to glucose. Blood sugar, the carbohydrate circulating in blood, is glucose. "Dextrose" is the commercial name for glucose, usually prepared by hydrolysis of starch. When table sugar (sucrose) is boiled with dilute acid, a mixture of two sugars, glucose and fructose, is obtained. Glucose, or "dextrose," is not as sweet as sucrose, and is used in the manufacture of "semi-sweet" confections.

Structure of glucose

Much of the chemical work which has been done to determine the structure of the sugars depends on pioneering work on the structure of glucose, and can be attributed to the great German organic chemist Emil Fischer (1852–1919). The outline (Table 17.01) of experimental evidence will serve not only to elucidate the structure of glucose, but to illustrate the deductive reasoning used in the determination of the molecular structure of any natural product.

TABLE 17.01   EXPERIMENTS WITH GLUCOSE

Hydrolysis of starch yields a white solid, which may be crystallized from water or alcohol to yield glucose, m.p. 146° C.

Result	Conclusion
1. Anal: C, 40%; H, 6.6%; O, 53.4%.	1. Empirical formula = CH_2O.
2. A solution of 18 g of glucose in 20 g of water freezes at $-9.3°$ C.	2. Molecular weight = 180. Formula is $C_6H_{12}O_6$.
3. Reduction with hydrogen iodide yields 2-iodohexane, $CH_3CHICH_2CH_2CH_2CH_3$.	3. Carbon skeleton of glucose is 6 carbons in a continuous chain: $$-C-C-C-C-C-C-$$

4. An aqueous solution on treatment with:
    a) Tollens' reagent $\longrightarrow$ silver mirror.
    b) Benedict's solution $\longrightarrow$ red ppt.
    c) phenylhydrazine $\longrightarrow$ yellow ppt.
	4. Glucose contains an aldehyde group: $$-C-C-C-C-C-CHO$$

5. Reaction with acetic anhydride yields $C_{16}H_{22}O_{11}$.	5. A penta-acetate: $$C_6H_7O_6(CH_3CO)_5$$ 5 OH groups on 5 different carbon atoms: $$CH_2OH\overset{*}{C}HOH\overset{*}{C}HOH\overset{*}{C}HOH\overset{*}{C}HOHCHO$$
6. A solution of glucose shows a specific rotation of $+52°$ in a polarimeter.	6. Since formula above has 4 different asymmetric carbons, 2^4 or 16 stereoisomers possible. Glucose must be one of these.

Glucose is called an *aldohexose,* since it contains an aldehyde (*aldo*), six carbons (*hex*), and is a sugar (*ose* suffix). All of the possible 16 optical isomers of the aldohexoses are known. The methods used to determine the configuration of each isomer, and the relationship, are complex but have been determined. The eight structures with D-configuration (that is, related to the configuration of D-glyceraldehyde) are shown in Figure 17.01. The other eight isomers are mirror-image enantiomorphs of these. The three structures enclosed in boxes have been found in nature; the others were synthesized.

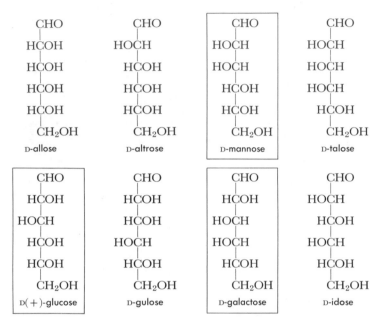

Fig. 17.01. Stereoisomeric aldohexoses (D-configuration only) showing naturally occurring compounds in boxes.

Mutarotation and the cyclic forms of glucose

Early studies on the optical rotation of glucose revealed a remarkable phenomenon. A fresh aqueous solution of pure glucose which had been recrystallized from alcohol had a specific rotation of $+111°$, but on standing the rotation gradually dropped to $+52°$. Later, Tanret discovered that a fresh solution of pure glucose which had been recrystallized from a saturated hot aqueous solution by evaporation had a rotation of $+19°$, but this rotation gradually increased to $+52°$ on standing. This phenomenon was called *mutarotation,* the changing rotation of an aging solution of an optically active substance. If the glucose in the solution of $+52°$ rotation was recovered in the crystalline state, fresh solutions again showed a rotation of $+111°$ (α-D-glucose) or $+19°$ (β-D-glucose), depending on the method of recrystallization, and mutarotated to the equilibrium solution, rotation $+52°$, on standing.

The explanation for the existence of two optical isomers, α- and β-D-glucose, was discovered when Fischer attempted to convert glucose into its methyl acetal. A characteristic reaction of aldehydes is the formation of acetals by addition of alcohols (p. 139, and Eq. 17.01).

$$
\textbf{17.01} \quad R\!-\!\overset{\overset{\textstyle H}{|}}{C}\!\!=\!\!O + R'OH \rightleftharpoons R\!-\!\overset{\overset{\textstyle H}{|}}{\underset{\underset{\textstyle OH}{|}}{C}}\!-\!OR' \xrightarrow[H^+]{HOR'} R\!-\!\overset{\overset{\textstyle H}{|}}{\underset{\underset{\textstyle OR'}{|}}{C}}\!-\!OR' + H_2O
$$

hemi-acetal   acetal

When Fischer treated glucose in methanol with dry hydrogen chloride, only *one* mole of methanol per mole of glucose was added, but the product (*methyl glucoside*) had characteristic acetal properties, rather than those of a hemiacetal. From Eq. 17.01, this result must mean that glucose itself is actually a hemi-acetal. Since the molecule contains hydroxy groups, it is highly likely that intramolecular hemiacetal formation could occur, much as lactones are formed (Chapter 15). By analogy with lactone formation, one would expect that 5- and 6-membered rings would be most likely. Actually both rings are possible in glucose, but the 6-membered hemi-acetal ring predominates. Conversion of the aldehyde group in the open-chain structure of glucose to a hemi-acetal creates a new asymmetric center. The two new optical isomers are diastereoisomers, separable by crystallization, but in aqueous solution they are in equilibrium with one another and the open-chain structure. The optical rotation of the equilibrium mixture is $+52°$.

β-D-glucose   D-glucose   α-D-glucose
optical rotation +19°   optical rotation +111°

The actual three-dimensional ring structure of glucose resembles cyclohexane in that it forms a puckered "chair" structure with axial and equatorial bonds. β-D-glucose is then best represented as having all of the bulky hydroxy groups in the least hindered equatorial positions (Figure 17.02), and it is not surprising that this is the more stable of the two structures.

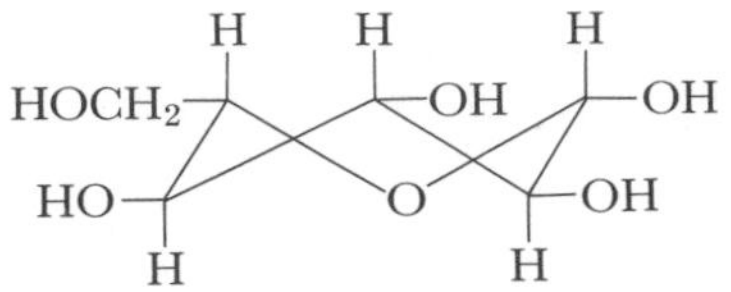

Fig. 17.02. β-D-glucose.

CLASSIFICATION OF CARBOHYDRATES

Carbohydrates are *polyhydroxyaldehydes* or *polyhydroxyketones,* or more complex compounds composed of polyhydroxycarbonyl compounds coupled together to form higher-molecular-weight substances. Since many kinds of carbohydrates occur in nature, they have been classified into categories.

A. Monosaccharides: Simple sugars, $C_nH_{2n}O_n$.
   1. Aldoses—contain an aldehyde group.
   2. Ketoses—contain a ketone group.
B. Disaccharides: Two monosaccharides linked together by acetal or ether linkages.
C. Trisaccharides: Three monosaccharides linked together by acetal or ether linkages.
D. Polysaccharides: An indefinite large number of monosaccharides, linked together by acetal or ether linkages.

Monosaccharides

Among the monosaccharides, only the 5- and 6-carbon compounds have been isolated from natural sources, although synthetic monosaccharides containing up to 10 carbon atoms (an aldodecose) have been obtained. Much of the configurational relationship of the simple sugars and other optical isomers, such as the hydroxyacids, have been worked out from studies of the two synthetic aldotetroses, *erythrose* and *threose*. When D(+)-glyceraldehyde is treated with hydrogen cyanide, and the resulting cyanohydrin hydrolyzed, diastereoisomeric lactones are obtained. These can be reduced to the two diastereoisomeric D-aldotetroses. The sequence for converting an aldose into its next higher homologs is known as the *Kiliani* synthesis. Oxidation of erythrose with nitric acid converts it to *meso*-tartaric acid, thus proving that the two hydroxy-groups should be written on the same side of the formula. D(+)-threose must then have the diastereoisomeric structure shown, and oxidation converts it to D(−)-tartaric acid, which establishes the configurational relationship of the tartaric acids. By further Kiliani syntheses, the configurational relationships of all the sugars have been established. The reactions described are shown in Figure 17.03.

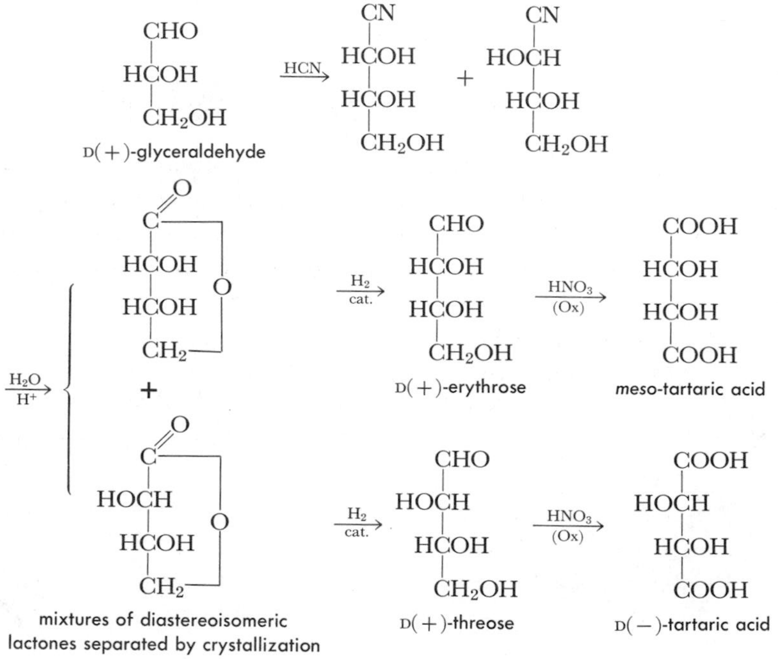

Fig. 17.03. Configurations of D-erythrose, D-threose, and tartaric acids are related chemically to D(+)-glyceraldehyde.

All isomeric *aldopentoses* are known. Several of these occur in nature. D(+)-ribose is an important constituent of certain mammalian enzymes and related substances. Arabinose and xylose are found in the pithy centers of many plants. The four D-configurations of the aldopentose are shown in Figure 17.04. They have been related to the configurations of the aldotetroses by chemical synthesis.

Other important hexoses

In addition to glucose, some other hexoses occur rather commonly. D(+)-mannose is an epimer of D(+)-glucose, and may have its origin

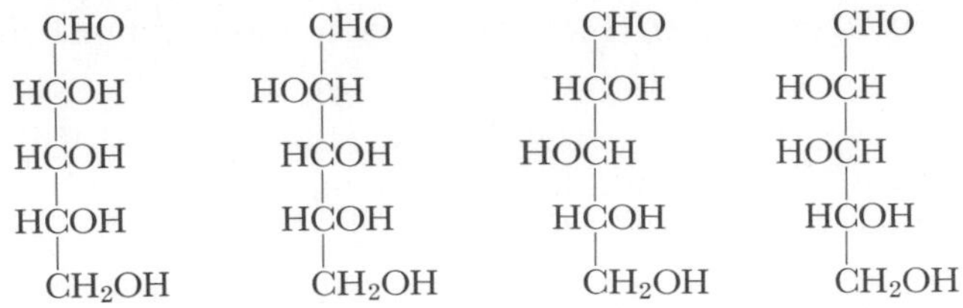

$$
\begin{array}{llll}
\text{CHO} & \text{CHO} & \text{CHO} & \text{CHO} \\
\text{HCOH} & \text{HOCH} & \text{HCOH} & \text{HOCH} \\
\text{HCOH} & \text{HCOH} & \text{HOCH} & \text{HOCH} \\
\text{HCOH} & \text{HCOH} & \text{HCOH} & \text{HCOH} \\
\text{CH}_2\text{OH} & \text{CH}_2\text{OH} & \text{CH}_2\text{OH} & \text{CH}_2\text{OH} \\
\text{D}(-)\text{-ribose} & \text{D}(-)\text{-arabinose} & \text{D}(+)\text{-xylose} & \text{D}(+)\text{-lyxose}
\end{array}
$$

Fig. 17.04. Configurations of D-aldopentoses.

by epimerization of glucose in nature. Mannose occurs in certain polysaccharides, called "mannans" (ivory nut mannan, for example). D(+)-*galactose* commonly occurs in milk sugar (lactose). It is also found in brain and nerve tissue. The only important ketoses are ketohexoses. D(−)-*fructose* is the most common ketose. It occurs in table sugar (sucrose), honey, and fruits, and is closely related to glucose in structure (Figure 17.05). Fructose most commonly occurs in its compounds in a five-membered hemi-ketal ring structure. It can be produced by hydrolysis of inulin, a polysaccharide found in dahlia bulbs. Fructose is the only commonly occurring monosaccharide which is levorotatory, and it is known commercially as levulose.

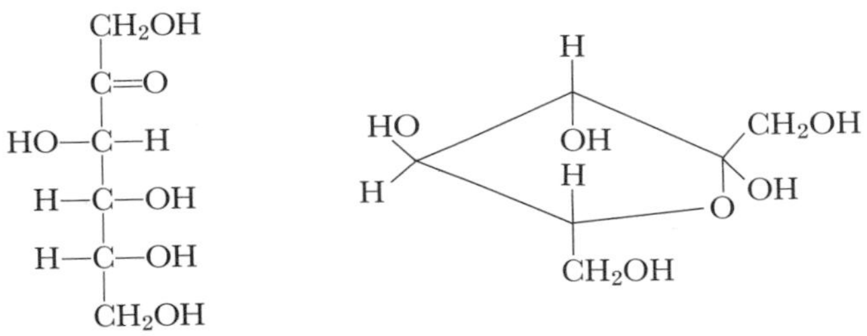

Fig. 17.05. Open-chain and ring structures of D(−)-fructose.

Reactions of monosaccharides

All monosaccharides are hydroxycarbonyl compounds, and give the characteristic reactions of such functional groups. The most important reactions, which distinguish the simple sugars, depend on the presence of both groups in the same molecule.

A. Benedict's and Fehling's Tests. All monosaccharides, and some disaccharides, are oxidized by the alkaline copper ion of Benedict's or Fehling's solutions (Chapter 10). This reaction occurs even with ketoses, since they are easily oxidized. Sugars which give a red, yellow, or orange precipitate with the blue cupric ion solutions are called *reducing sugars*.

    B. Formation of Osazones. Reaction of simple sugars with phenylhydrazine leads to the formation of osazones. These substances are beautiful yellow compounds, which can be identified by their characteristic crystal structures. They are therefore of great value in the identification of certain sugars. The initial step in the reaction involves formation of the expected phenylhydrazone of the aldehyde or ketone (see Chapter 10). This compound, having an α-hydroxy group, undergoes enolization, and further reaction with phenylhydrazine is then possible. Three moles of phenylhydrazine are used up, and the osazone formed is a di-hydrazone. The over-all balanced equation is shown in Eq. 17.02, but the reaction sequence is as shown in Figure 17.06.

17.02

$$RCHOHCHO + 3\,C_6H_5NHNH_2 \longrightarrow$$

$$\begin{array}{l} H\!-\!\overset{|}{C}\!=\!NNHC_6H_5 \\ R\overset{|}{C}\!=\!NNHC_6H_5 + 2\,H_2O + C_6H_5NH_2 + NH_3 \end{array}$$

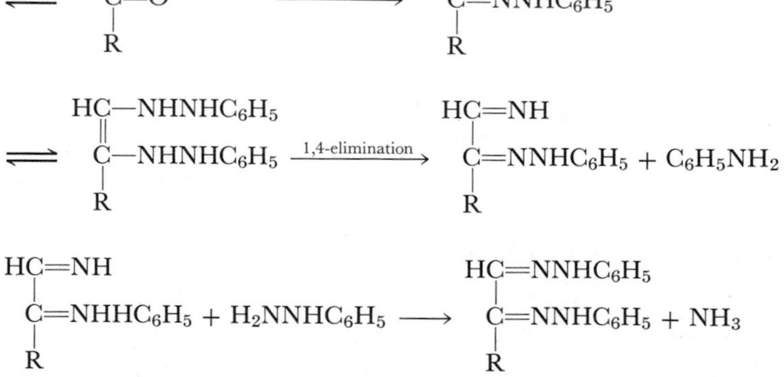

$$\begin{array}{c} CHO \\ | \\ CHOH \\ | \\ R \end{array} \xrightarrow{C_6H_5NHNH_2} \begin{array}{c} H\!-\!C\!=\!NNHC_6H_5 \\ | \\ CHOH \\ | \\ R \end{array} \rightleftharpoons \begin{array}{c} HCNHNHC_6H_5 \\ \| \\ C\!-\!OH \\ | \\ R \end{array}$$

$$\rightleftharpoons \begin{array}{c} H_2CNHNHC_6H_5 \\ | \\ C\!=\!O \\ | \\ R \end{array} \xrightarrow{C_6H_5NHNH_2} \begin{array}{c} H_2C\!-\!NHNHC_6H_5 \\ | \\ C\!=\!NNHC_6H_5 \\ | \\ R \end{array}$$

$$\rightleftharpoons \begin{array}{c} HC\!-\!NHNHC_6H_5 \\ \| \\ C\!-\!NHNHC_6H_5 \\ | \\ R \end{array} \xrightarrow{1,4\text{-elimination}} \begin{array}{c} HC\!=\!NH \\ | \\ C\!=\!NNHC_6H_5 + C_6H_5NH_2 \\ | \\ R \end{array}$$

$$\begin{array}{c} HC\!=\!NH \\ | \\ C\!=\!NHHC_6H_5 + H_2NNHC_6H_5 \longrightarrow \\ | \\ R \end{array} \begin{array}{c} HC\!=\!NNHC_6H_5 \\ | \\ C\!=\!NNHC_6H_5 + NH_3 \\ | \\ R \end{array}$$

Fig. 17.06. Enolization reactions in formation of osazones.

Sugars which have the same configuration of all but the first two carbon atoms will give the same osazone. For example, note that glucose, fructose, and mannose all yield glucosazone.

C. Formation of Glycosides. The monosaccharides all exist in nature as cyclic hemi-acetals or hemi-ketals. These substances react easily with alcohols to form acetal or ketal derivatives, called *glycosides.* For example, treatment of glucose in methanol with dry hydrogen chloride leads to the formation of β-D-methyl glucoside (Eq. 17.03).

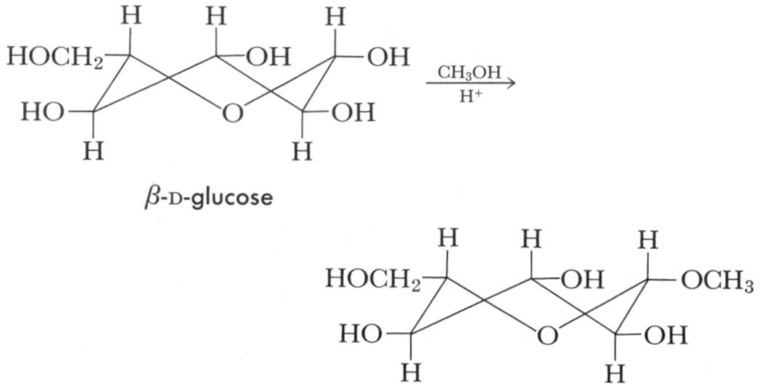

β-D-glucose

17.03

β-D-methyl glucoside

The glycosides are stable substances, and occur frequently in nature. Coupling high-molecular-weight alcohols with sugars to form the glycosides is nature's way of confering water-solubility on these substances, which is essential if they are to be metabolized in aqueous systems. For example, *prunasin* is the glucoside of D-mandelonitrile, found in prunes.

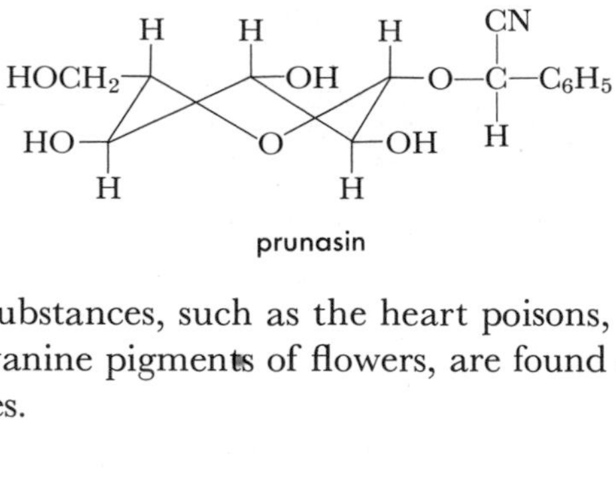

prunasin

Many natural substances, such as the heart poisons, curare, steroids, and the anthocyanine pigments of flowers, are found as stable, water-soluble glycosides.

Disaccharides

The disaccharides contain two hexose units. *Sucrose* is common table sugar, obtained from sugar cane or sugar beets. Other important disaccharides are *maltose,* from starch, *lactose,* or milk sugar, and *cellobiose,* from cellulose hydrolysis. They all have the formula $C_{12}H_{22}O_{11}$.

Sucrose is a nonreducing sugar, and therefore does not have a free aldehyde or ketone group. Hydrolysis of sucrose produces equal amounts of D-glucose and D-fructose. Since sucrose is dextrorotatory, but the mixture of sugars produced is levorotatory, this mixture is called *invert sugar,* and does not readily crystallize. Honey is largely invert sugar. Candy makers boil sucrose with a trace of acid to form invert sugar and thus inhibit crystallization of the candy. Since sucrose does not reduce Benedict's solution nor react with phenylhydrazine, the two hexoses must be linked through the free hydroxyl groups of the hemi-acetal and hemiketal functions (Figure 17.07).

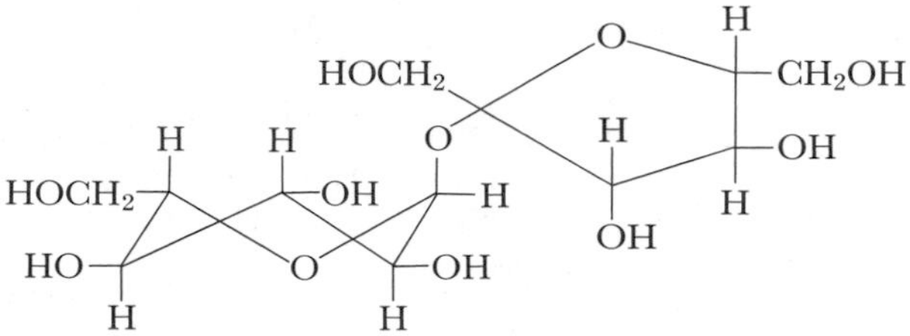

β-D-fructofuranosyl α-D-glucopyranoside
sucrose

Fig. 17.07

Lactose is the disaccharide formed in milk. Human milk contains 5 to 8 per cent, while cow's milk has a somewhat lower concentration. Since lactose is present in high concentration in the nerve tissues (brain and spinal chord), infant food should have a high concentration of lactose during the time nerve tissue is being formed at a high rate. On hydrolysis, lactose gives equal amounts of glucose and galactose. Lactose is a reducing sugar, and forms an osazone with phenylhydrazine. It is also easily fermented to produce lactic acid.

Maltose is obtained by enzymatic hydrolysis of starch. It contains two glucose units, joined together by an α-glucoside linkage of one unit to the hydroxyl group of carbon atom number *four* in the second unit. Maltose is a reducing sugar, since the second glucose unit must contain a free aldehyde or hemi-acetal group. Starch is composed of many maltose units coupled together.

Cellobiose is obtained by the careful hydrolysis of cotton fibers or wood (cellulose). It consists of two units of glucose, like maltose, but differs in that the first unit is joined by a β-glucoside linkage to carbon number four of the second. Cellobiose is also a reducing sugar, having a free aldehyde or hemi-acetal group.

Trisaccharides and polysaccharides

Only a few trisaccharides occur in nature, and these are rare. The polysaccharides are very important, and will be discussed in the chapter on polymers.

FORMATION AND DEGRADATION OF GLUCOSE

Formation. Glucose is synthesized by plants from simple precursors by a process known as *photosynthesis.* This is an important reaction, since it not only provides food for the plant itself, but the plant serves as food for both animal and man. Photosynthesis takes place by the following process: Carbon dioxide from the air and water from the soil combine in the leaves of plants to form glucose. The reaction is catalyzed by chlorophyll, an organic substance present in the plant. The energy necessary for the reaction is secured from the sunlight. The sunlight must furnish approximately 700 calories of energy per mole of sugar formed. This energy is subsequently stored in the plant, and becomes available to animals and man when the carbohydrate is eaten and metabolized (oxidized) in the body.

17.04
$$6\,CO_2 + 6\,H_2O + Energy \longrightarrow C_6H_{12}O_6 + 6\,O_2$$
$$C_6H_{12}O_6 + 6\,O_2 \longrightarrow 6\,CO_2 + 6\,H_2O + Energy$$

Evidence gained through the use of radioactive tracer elements has done much to improve our knowledge concerning the chemical reactions involved in photosynthesis. The pioneering work centered around the use of radioactive carbon, ^{11}C, but recent workers, such as Professor Calvin at the University of California, have used ^{14}C in their studies because of the long half-life of the latter element. Much of the experimental work has centered around phosphoglyceric acid as an important intermediate. In photosynthesis by algae cells in the presence of $^{14}CO_2$, it has been shown that about 85 per cent of the ^{14}C appears in the 2- and 3-phosphoglyceric acids.

Degradation. The reverse process involves degradation of glucose and other hexoses to these same phosphoglyceric acids. This process takes place in the metabolism of carbohydrate and in the fermentation of sugar to alcohol. The hexoses are converted to their phosphate esters by enzymes, and by further enzymatic reactions these are converted to metabolic products, such as lactic acid or ethanol. Some of the intermediate products of carbohydrate metabolism are shown in Figure 17.08. It is probable that most of these reactions are reversible, and this scheme can generally account for the reformation of glucose in the body from pyruvic acid, an important key intermediate. Some of the intermediates shown in the scheme may also be converted into or obtained from amino-acids or fatty acids, so that conversion of carbohydrate into fat or protein may be accounted for.

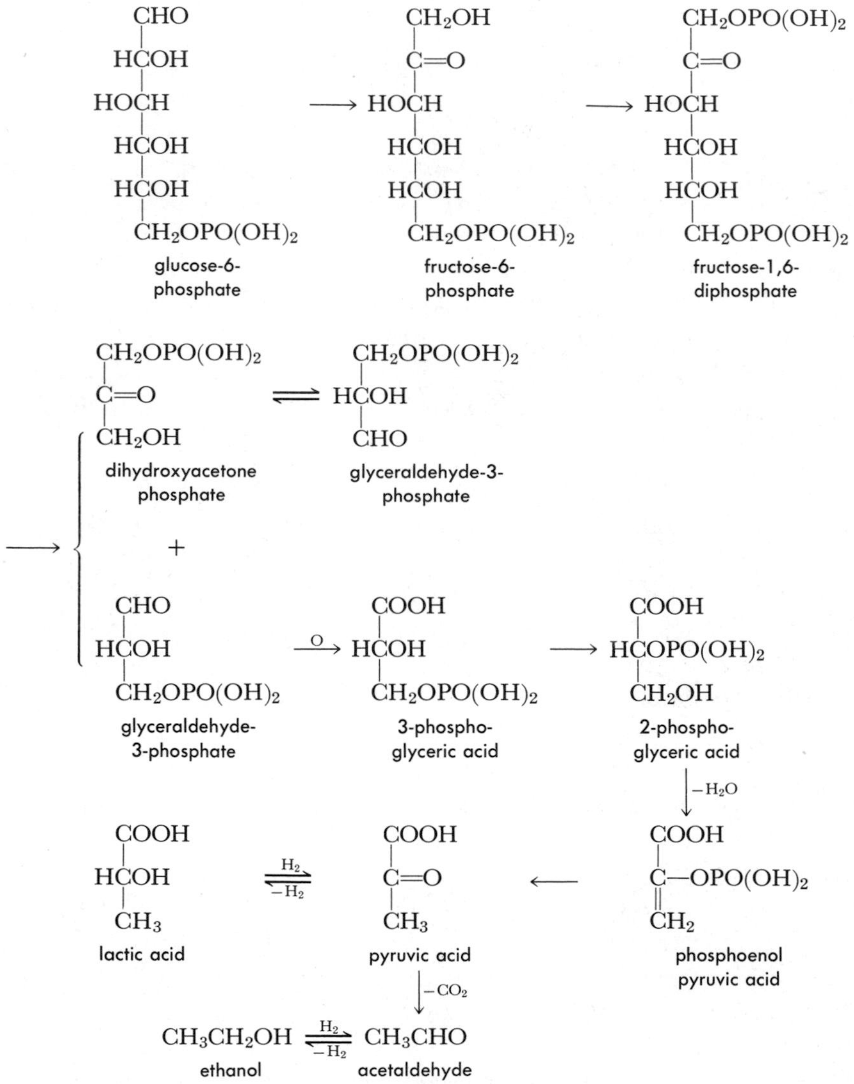

$$
\begin{array}{ccc}
\text{CHO} & \text{CH}_2\text{OH} & \text{CH}_2\text{OPO(OH)}_2 \\
\text{HCOH} & \text{C=O} & \text{C=O} \\
\text{HOCH} \longrightarrow & \text{HOCH} \longrightarrow & \text{HOCH} \\
\text{HCOH} & \text{HCOH} & \text{HCOH} \\
\text{HCOH} & \text{HCOH} & \text{HCOH} \\
\text{CH}_2\text{OPO(OH)}_2 & \text{CH}_2\text{OPO(OH)}_2 & \text{CH}_2\text{OPO(OH)}_2 \\
\text{glucose-6-} & \text{fructose-6-} & \text{fructose-1,6-} \\
\text{phosphate} & \text{phosphate} & \text{diphosphate}
\end{array}
$$

$$
\begin{array}{cc}
\text{CH}_2\text{OPO(OH)}_2 & \text{CH}_2\text{OPO(OH)}_2 \\
\text{C=O} \rightleftharpoons & \text{HCOH} \\
\text{CH}_2\text{OH} & \text{CHO} \\
\text{dihydroxyacetone} & \text{glyceraldehyde-3-} \\
\text{phosphate} & \text{phosphate}
\end{array}
$$

+

$$
\begin{array}{ccc}
\text{CHO} & \text{COOH} & \text{COOH} \\
\text{HCOH} \xrightarrow{\text{O}} & \text{HCOH} \longrightarrow & \text{HCOPO(OH)}_2 \\
\text{CH}_2\text{OPO(OH)}_2 & \text{CH}_2\text{OPO(OH)}_2 & \text{CH}_2\text{OH} \\
\text{glyceraldehyde-} & \text{3-phospho-} & \text{2-phospho-} \\
\text{3-phosphate} & \text{glyceric acid} & \text{glyceric acid}
\end{array}
$$

$$\downarrow -\text{H}_2\text{O}$$

$$
\begin{array}{ccc}
\text{COOH} & \text{COOH} & \text{COOH} \\
\text{HCOH} \underset{-\text{H}_2}{\overset{\text{H}_2}{\rightleftharpoons}} & \text{C=O} \longleftarrow & \text{C—OPO(OH)}_2 \\
\text{CH}_3 & \text{CH}_3 & \text{CH}_2 \\
\text{lactic acid} & \text{pyruvic acid} & \text{phosphoenol} \\
& & \text{pyruvic acid}
\end{array}
$$

$$\downarrow -\text{CO}_2$$

$$\text{CH}_3\text{CH}_2\text{OH} \underset{-\text{H}_2}{\overset{\text{H}_2}{\rightleftharpoons}} \text{CH}_3\text{CHO}$$
ethanol   acetaldehyde

Fig. 17.08. Intermediates in degradation of hexose to lactic acid or ethanol in fermentation processes.

SWEETNESS

A sweet taste is a physiological property commonly associated with sugars. It is not a property of carbohydrates specifically, however, and several synthetic organic compounds have been made which are much sweeter than any known sugars. Three of these have actually been sold commercially as sweetening agents. They are o-sulfobenzimide (saccharin), sodium N-cyclohexylsulfamate (sucaryl), and 2-amino-4-nitropropoxybenzene (nectarin).

| saccharin | Sucaryl | Nectarin |

The property of sweetness is tested by determining the minimum concentration of the substance in water which can be tasted. A solution of 5 g in 100 ml of water is prepared and tasted. This is then diluted by one-half, and tasted again. This process is continued until sweetness in the solution can no longer be detected, and the average concentration at which sweetness can be detected by a number of individuals is considered a measure of sweetness. Table 17.02 lists the relative sweetness per gram of several compounds, compared to table sugar as a standard.

TABLE 17.02   RELATIVE SWEETNESS

Nectarin	50,000
Saccharin	36,000
Sucaryl	7,100
Fructose	173
Sucrose	100
Glucose	74
Xylose	40
Maltose	32
Lactose	16

Notice that the synthetic compounds are far superior as sweetening agents, so that one teaspoon of nectarin is equivalent to 500 teaspoons of sucrose. These substances have no food value, however. Diabetics, who must reduce carbohydrate intake, can use these as sweetening agents. Unfortunately these compounds are somewhat toxic, and must be used with caution. The toxicity is approximately in the order of sweetness. Nectarin is not used widely, since it is the most toxic. It was discovered in Holland during World War II, and used there during the war in the place of sugar. Saccharin has been the most widely used of the synthetic sweetening agents. It is readily hydrolyzed, and therefore cannot be used in any food processing which requires boiling in water solution. Therefore it could not be readily used in making such diabetic foods as jellies, candy, or sterilized soft drinks. Sucaryl, however, can be used in this way, and although it is only about one-fifth as sweet as saccharin, it has wide use commercially in diabetic foods.

It is interesting to compare the sugars among themselves as sweetening agents. Since sucrose is hydrolyzed to a mixture of glucose and fructose, invert sugar must have a sweetness rating of 123. Therefore boiling sucrose in candy-making not only prevents it from crystallizing, but makes it sweeter. The natural sugar of fruits, fructose, is ten times as sweet as the natural sugar of milk.

Study Questions

1. Write structural formulas for all possible trioses. Which are optically active? What is the product of reduction of the carbonyl to alcohol group in each case?

2. What is meant by each of the following terms? Monosaccharide, dextrose, invert sugar, osazone, reducing sugar, glycoside, aldopentose, disaccharide, mutarotation, epimer.

3. How does glucose differ from mannose? From fructose? Explain why each of these sugars gives the same osazone.

4. Explain why crystalline glucose may exist in two different optical isomers, α-D-glucose and β-D-glucose. How does this account for the formation of glucosides and mutarotation?

5. In making candy, professional confectioners add a small amount of phosphoric acid to the boiling sugar solution. Amateur fudge makers usually add a small amount of vinegar. What is the advantage of acidifying the boiling sugar solution? Give two reasons why the sugar solution must be boiled. How can the professional confectioner use a polarimeter to tell when his candy is ready to harden?

6. On subjecting D(+)-erythrose to a Kiliani synthesis, two aldopentoses are obtained, A and B. Oxidation of A with nitric acid leads to a trihydroxyglutaric acid which is optically inactive. Show the reactions involved, and tell which of the two aldopentoses is ribose, and which arabinose.

7. Explain, with formulas, what is meant by a D-sugar. What is meant by α- and β-forms of a D-sugar? Why are α- and β-forms of trioses unlikely?

8. What is the biochemical importance of glyceraldehyde-3-phosphate?

9. Why is dextrose not generally used as table sugar? Why is honey sweeter than cane sugar? What is the difference between cane sugar and beet sugar? Is there any advantage to the fact that lactose is not very sweet? Why does human milk have a higher concentration of lactose than that of other mammals?

Advanced Reading References

Organic Chemistry, 3rd Ed., R. Q. Brewster and W. E. McEwen, Prentice-Hall, Inc., Englewood Cliffs, N. J., 1961, Chapter 21.

Chemistry of Organic Compounds, 2nd Ed., C. R. Noller, W. B. Saunders, Philadelphia, 1957, Chapter 17.

Organic Chemistry, 2nd Ed., L. F. Fieser and Mary Fieser, D. C. Heath and Co., Boston, 1950, Chapter 15.

"Carbohydrates," by M. L. Wolfrom, Chapter 20 in *Organic Chemistry, An Advanced Treatise,* Vol. II, 2nd Ed., ed. H. Gilman, John Wiley and Sons, Inc., New York, 1943.

new terms & concepts

Large molecules have properties different from their smaller analogs.
Synthetic and natural polymers are useful structural materials.
Low-molecular-weight monomers couple together in various ways to form
linear, or threadlike, polymers, two-dimensional sheet
polymers, or three-dimensional block polymers.
The latter two are formed by cross-linking.
The structure of polymers is related to the
molecular weight and the behavior with solvents.
Molecular weight may be related to osmotic pressure, viscosity, or
sedimentation rates in the ultra-centrifuge.
Polymers may be formed by addition or condensation.
Typical addition polymers are polyethylene, polystyrene, and Orlon.
Olefins may be polymerized in chain reactions, which are
either free-radical or ionically catalyzed.
Synthetic elastomers are formed by 1,4-polymerization of
conjugated olefins; and co-polymerization, involving two different
monomers, leads to useful polymers of many varieties.
Condensation polymers are formed by ordinary
condensation reactions which involve elimination of small
molecules between polyfunctional monomeric molecules.
Polyesters, polyamides, polyacetals,
and polyethers are all known useful substances.
Polysaccharides are polymeric glycosides, such as cellulose (wood or cotton)
or starch, and are important natural polymers.
Proteins are complex polyamides (polypeptides)
which have many important natural functions.
Protein fibers (silk or wool) are made up of linear molecules
cross-linked by hydrogen bonds.
Globular proteins are soluble substances made up of folded linear molecules.
Many important synthetic condensation polymers are known.
These include Nylon, Dacron, the glyptal resins,
and the urea-formaldehyde and phenol-formaldehyde thermosetting resins.

18

Large molecules

Certain peculiar properties of many natural substances may be ascribed to the fact that they are composed of big molecules. The very fact that these molecules are large causes them to take on unusual properties not possessed by smaller molecules of the same composition. These properties may include insolubility and low chemical activity (resistance to weather and aging), high tensile strength (in fibers) and flexibility (in rubber). These properties are desirable in structural materials, and so it is that the structural materials of nature are made up of big molecules. Wood, for example, is composed chiefly of the carbohydrate cellulose, a polymer of glucose. Cotton and linen are cellulose fibers. Starch and glycogen are soluble polyglucoses which are food substances, the reservoirs from which structural carbohydrate is drawn by the plant. Wool and silk are protein fibers, while leather and horn are massive protein, the structural material of the animal world. Protein is composed of many amino-acids in chains, the so-called polypeptides. Muscle tissue is protein. Such materials as egg albumin or blood proteins are the soluble protein polymers from which the structural materials may be made.

The natural structural and fibrous materials have been of great importance to man, and he has attempted to duplicate or improve upon them. From these efforts have grown the great plastics and synthetic elastomers industries. Although many people know how Nylon has been made "from coal and limestone" to replace silk, few realize that one of the first big developments in plastics came about in an effort to find a cheap substitute for ivory in billiard balls. We now have organic synthetic substitutes for wool, cotton, silk, leather, rubber, ivory, glass, and porcelain. Foamed plastics are used to replace feathers in pillows and mattresses; and in combination with stiffening agents, structural substitutes for wood and even metals have been obtained. Man has even been able to prepare a partial substitute for the circulating blood protein in polyvinylpyrollidone.

CHARACTERISTICS OF LARGE MOLECULES

Since large molecules of all kinds have very high molecular weight, they are nonvolatile, usually high-melting solids of very low solubility. These and other properties may be related to their structure. They are all composed of many small units (*monomers*) coupled together in various ways, forming polymers.

Linear polymers consist of chains of monomers. Each chain may be very long, and may have some branches, but is not cross-linked to other long chains. Such one-dimensional polymers occur naturally, in silk or cotton for example, and can be made in the laboratory.

Two-dimensional polymers are those composed of long chains of atoms which are cross-linked to other chains, forming a network or sheet of bonded atoms. Such a two-dimensional polymer is formed when a paint-film "dries."

Three-dimensional polymers are those in which the two-dimensional networks of monomers are cross-linked to other networks, forming a three-dimensional blocklike polymer, comparable in structure to a tablet of paper, in which all the sheets have been pasted together forming a solid block. In this case the whole mass may be considered to be a single molecule.

Behavior with solvents

Behavior of large molecules toward solvents may be a key to their structure. When a fiber, such as wool, is exposed to a hot solvent for some time, the fiber is found to swell to several times its diameter but not to change length very much. This means that the linear molecules of the fiber, lying side by side, are separated by solvent molecules. Since the tensile strength of such a fiber must depend on the attraction of molecules for each other, it is greatly reduced in the swollen fiber. If enough solvent gets into the fiber mass, it may eventually form a tacky viscous solution.

Two-dimensional polymers will also swell in solvents, in the direction of thickness, as the solvent works its way between the sheets of molecules. Sheet polymers, unless of rather low molecular weight, do not dissolve. Three-dimensional molecules will not dissolve, but may take up solvent within the network of the molecule. Little swelling can be observed, since the structure is held tightly by atomic bonds.

The way in which a sample of a polymer behaves in a solvent is an indication of whether it is linear, sheet, or block polymer.

Molecular weight of large molecules

Ordinary methods of determining molecular weight are of no value in polymer chemistry. For example, one mole of unionized solute dissolved in 1000 g of water depresses the freezing point to $-1.86°C$. Soluble starch has been found to have a molecular weight of about 50,000. Therefore, in order to depress the freezing point of water 1.86°C, it would be necessary to dissolve 50,000 g, or about 111 pounds of starch in a liter of water, which is obviously impossible. The absurdity of attempting to determine the molecular weight of an insoluble polymer, such as wool, in water is obvious.

Several physical methods have been developed which have led to reasonable average-molecular-weight values for large molecules. Since all polymers consist of molecules of large but indefinite size, the molecular weights cannot be accurate or constant, and all values found represent averages. These methods depend on solution of the polymer, and cannot be applied to insoluble polymers. The *osmotic pressure,* or the pressure developed across a semipermeable membrane between a solution of a substance unable to pass through the membrane and the pure solvent, is directly proportional to the molecular weight of the substance. The molecular weight of some of the smaller soluble polymers among the proteins and polysaccharides may be determined from the osmotic pressure of solutions. The *viscosity* of a solution of a polymeric substance is related to the molecular weight of the solute. The method is not exact, but comparisons of viscosities of solutions of polymers of a similar type can give relative molecular weights. One of the most important modern methods of molecular-weight determination depends on the *ultra-centrifuge.* Solutions of large molecules are spun at very high rates of speed, causing centrifugal forces of several hundred thousand times the force of gravity to pull the molecules toward the circumference of the spinning chamber. The rate at which the large molecules settle out of solution is proportional to the molecular weight and the shape of the molecule. Once the shape is determined by X-ray or electron-diffraction studies, the molecular weight can be calculated.

SYNTHESIS OF LARGE MOLECULES

Polymers can be classed according to the chemical reactions by which they are formed. Monomers are coupled together by two basically different methods, *addition* and *condensation*. *Addition polymers* are formed when monomer molecules chain together, one molecule adding to the next, and so on, until giant molecules are produced. Addition polymerization may be either *free-radical* or *ionic,* by virtue of the fact that a double bond may split either homolytically or heterolytically (one electron to each end of the double bond, or two electrons to one end and none to the other). Free-radical polymerization depends on catalyzing the first type, while ionic polymerization occurs

$$CH_2::CH_2 \longleftrightarrow \cdot CH_2 - CH_2 \cdot$$
homolytic

$$CH_2 : CH_2 \longleftrightarrow \overset{+}{C}H_2 - CH_2 : {}^-$$
heterolytic

when the second splitting of the *pi*-bond occurs. *Polyethylene* (Polythene) is a typical addition polymer of great industrial importance. Polyethylene film is rapidly replacing waxed paper for all sorts of food packaging (Figure 18.01). Ethylene, when heated under pressure with a peroxide catalyst, gives a solid polymer which is tough, flexible, and capable of being molded, and which is water-resistant and an electrical insulator. The molecular weight of this polymer is about 25,000, meaning that each molecule contained about 800–1000 monomeric ethylene units. It is formed by a free-radical chain reaction. The initiating reaction is formation of a free radical by the catalyst (peroxide) (Eq. 18.01).

The chain is then propagated by reaction of the radical with ethylene to produce a new radical which grows by continuous reaction (Eq. 18.02). Branching can occur during propagation when a radical chain-end strikes against itself, removing a hydrogen atom from the chain and creating a new radical, which can grow as a branch (Eq. 18.02b). The chains are terminated by coupling (Eq. 18.03) leaving linear and branched chains.

Fig. 18.01. For a close fit, items such as this icebox container and its lid made of PETROTHENE 202 must be folded at very close tolerance; that is, with an accurately pre-determined amount of shrinkage. (Courtesy of U. S. Industrial Chemicals Company, Division of National Distillers and Chemicals Corporation.)

Initiating:

18.01 $\qquad (RCOO)_2 \xrightarrow{\Delta} 2\,RCOO\cdot \longrightarrow 2\,R\cdot + 2\,CO_2$

Propagating:

18.02a $\qquad R\cdot \xrightarrow{CH_2=CH_2} R-CH_2CH_2\cdot \xrightarrow{CH_2=CH_2}$

$$RCH_2CH_2CH_2CH_2\cdot$$

linear $\qquad \xrightarrow{n\,(C_2H_4)} R(CH_2CH_2)_nCH_2CH_2\cdot$

branching

18.02b

$$R-CH-CH_2 \longrightarrow R-CH-CH_2(CH_2CH_2)_nCH_2CH_3$$

$$\underset{(H)}{|} \quad \underset{CH_2}{\overbrace{}} \qquad\qquad \underset{\cdot}{|} \quad\Big\downarrow C_2H_4$$

$$\underset{CH_2}{|}{}_n \qquad R-CH-CH_2(CH_2CH_2)_nCH_2CH_3$$

$$\cdot CH_2-CH_2 \qquad\qquad CH_2-CH_2\cdot$$

Terminating:

18.03a $2 R(CH_2CH_2)_nCH_2CH_2\cdot \longrightarrow$

linear

$$R(CH_2CH_2)_nCH_2CH_2CH_2CH_2(CH_2CH_2)_nR$$
linear polymer

branching

18.03b $R-\underset{\underset{CH_2CH_2\cdot}{|}}{CH}-CH_2(CH_2CH_2)_nCH_2CH_3 \xrightarrow{R\cdot}$

$$R-\underset{\underset{CH_2CH_2R'}{|}}{CH}-CH_2(CH_2CH_2)_nCH_2CH_3$$
branched polymer

Similar chain polymerization occurs with ionic catalysts also. Strong acids cause certain olefins to form addition polymers by reaction of carbonium ions. The chain is initiated by carbonium ion formation (Eq. 18.04) caused by addition of a proton to the heterolytically split double bond. Propagation occurs as the carbonium ion grows longer (Eq. 18.05). Chain branching may occur also by hydride transfer. Termination occurs either by reaction with a negative ion (Eq. 18.06a) or elimination of a proton (Eq. 18.06b).

Initiating:

18.04 $H^+ + \overset{\frown}{CH_2}:CHR \longrightarrow CH_3\underset{\underset{R}{|}}{CH^+}$

Propagating:

18.05 $CH_3\underset{\underset{R}{|}}{CH^+} \xrightarrow{n(C_2H_3R)} CH_3\underset{\underset{R}{|}}{CH}(CH_2\underset{\underset{R}{|}}{CH})_n{}^+$

Terminating:

18.06a $CH_3\underset{\underset{R}{|}}{CH}(CH_2\underset{\underset{R}{|}}{CH})_n{}^+ + R'^- \longrightarrow CH_3\underset{\underset{R}{|}}{CH}(CH_2\underset{\underset{R}{|}}{CH})_nR'$

18.06b $CH_3\underset{\underset{R}{|}}{CH}(CH_2\underset{\underset{R}{|}}{CH})_{n-1}-CH_2-\underset{\underset{R}{|}}{CH^+} \longrightarrow$

$$CH_3\underset{\underset{R}{|}}{CH}(CH_2\underset{\underset{R}{|}}{CH})_{n-1}CH{=}CHR + H^+$$

Recently polyethylene achieved much greater importance when a new type of catalyst was discovered which permitted polymerization at atmospheric pressure, with less-pure grades of ethylene. This low-pressure *Ziegler* process uses a trialkyl aluminum-titanum tetrachloride mixture, and produces a much more linear, less branched, polymer of better tensile strength and higher melting point.

Other vinyl polymers

Although polyethylene is probably the cheapest and most common polymeric olefin, many useful polymers may be made by this type of addition polymerization. Any suitable olefin having the structure $CH_2{=}CRR'$ may be polymerized, either ionically or by a radical process, to form polymers of the general formula

$$\left(-CH_2-\overset{\displaystyle R}{\underset{\displaystyle R'}{C}}-\right)_n$$

Some specific examples of this class may be mentioned.

Vinyl acetate, $CH_2{=}CH-OCOCH_3$, made by addition of acetic acid to acetylene (p. 67), can be polymerized to a solid plastic. *Vinyl chloride,* $CH_2{=}CHCl$, polymerizes in the same way. When dioctyl phthalate is added to soften the polymer (plastisizer), the rubberlike translucent Tygon is formed, which is used in making tubing. *Styrene,* $C_6H_5CH{=}CH_2$, forms a solid transparent material, useful as a substitute for glass in certain applications. *Methyl methacrylate,* $CH_2{=}C(CH_3)COOCH_3$, has already been mentioned (p. 151) as an important monomer. It polymerizes to a transparent solid which can be molded into sheets, and is the nearest to an organic glass of any plastic. It is used in the manufacture of safety glass under the name of *Lucite* or *Plexiglas. Acrylonitrile,* $CH_2{=}CHCN$, polymerizes readily and forms a highly insoluble polymer. By proper treatment, the polymer can be made into a fiber, called *Orlon. Orlon* fibers are used as a wool substitute.

Co-polymers

An important aspect of polymer synthesis involves the discovery that two different monomers may be mixed, and on polymerization a mixed polymer called a co-polymer may result. By choosing the proper monomers useful co-polymers are produced. These usually react so that the two monomer units alternate in the resultant polymer, but this is not always the case. *Vinyon* is a co-polymer of vinyl acetate and vinyl chloride, which contains 12 per cent of one and 88 per cent

of the other, equivalent to ten units of vinyl chloride to each vinyl
acetate molecule.

$$[-(CH_2CH)_{10}CH_2CH-]_n$$
$$\qquad\quad\; | \qquad\qquad\quad |$$
$$\qquad\quad Cl \qquad\qquad OCOCH_3$$

SYNTHETIC ELASTOMERS

Natural rubber is one of the very few addition polymers which
occur in nature. Its properties and composition were discussed in
Chapter 6. The addition polymerization of a conjugated diene is
similar to that of a simple olefin, except that each monomer unit re-
tains one double bond, and the resulting polymer is unsaturated and
elastic in nature. The establishment of the structure of rubber as a
polymer of isoprene led to early studies on polymerization of this type
of olefin.

The first success was attained by the Germans during World War I,
with methyl rubber. This was a polymer of 2,3-dimethyl-1,4-butadiene,
but it had very poor properties. The monomer was easily prepared
from acetone by reduction. A much better quality of rubber was ob-

$$
18.07 \quad 2\,CH_3COCH_3 \xrightarrow{\text{Mg}}
\begin{array}{c} CH_3\ CH_3 \\ |\quad\ | \\ CH_3-C\!-\!\!-\!C-CH_3 \\ |\quad\ | \\ O\quad O \\ \diagdown\ \diagup \\ Mg \end{array}
\xrightarrow{\text{H}^+}
\begin{array}{c} CH_3\ CH_3 \\ |\quad\ | \\ CH_3-C\!-\!\!-\!C-CH_3 \\ |\quad\ | \\ O\quad O \\ |\quad\ | \\ H\quad H \end{array}
$$

$$
\xrightarrow{-2\,H_2O}
\begin{array}{c} CH_3\ CH_3 \\ |\quad\ | \\ CH_2\!=\!C\!-\!\!-\!C\!=\!CH_2 \end{array}
\longrightarrow
\begin{array}{c} CH_3\ CH_3 \\ |\quad\ | \\ (-CH_2C\!=\!\!=\!C-CH_2-)_n \end{array}
$$

tained by the Germans in 1927, when 1,3-butadiene was polymerized
by sodium catalyst to produce *Buna rubber* (*butadiene/Na*).

American success in this field began with studies by Father Nieuw-
land, Professor of Chemistry at Notre Dame University, on the chemistry of acetylene. In cooperation with the Du Pont company, a method
was developed in 1932 for the synthesis of chloroprene, 2-chloro-1,3-
butadiene (see p. 68). Polymerization of chloroprene produced *neoprene*, a close relative of natural rubber in structure. Neoprene is more

$$(-CH_2-C=CH-CH_2-)_n$$
$$\qquad\qquad | $$
$$\qquad\qquad Cl$$

neoprene

expensive than natural rubber, but has certain improved properties, such as resistance to organic solvents and air oxidation.

At the beginning of World War II, the United States lost the sources of most of its natural rubber, in Borneo. This stimulated research in synthetics which has led to solution of many of the major problems. Today most of our rubber needs are satisfied by useful synthetics. We have found that although natural rubber is widely useful, it has been possible to synthesize polymers which are superior for specific uses in nearly every case. Many of these are co-polymers. A major advance was the introduction of emulsion polymerization. Natural latex is an emulsion, and it was found possible to prepare synthetic latex emulsions, using pure soap and gelatin with monomers. Emulsion polymerization permits accurate control of the rate of polymerization, and allows for the incorporation of modifiers.

The most important synthetic elastomer developed during the war was a co-polymer of butadiene and styrene, called *GRS* (government rubber styrene), which is used in tires. *Hycar,* or GRA, is a co-polymer of butadiene and acrylonitrile.

Cross-linking agents

Linear addition polymers may be converted to sheet or block polymers with quite different properties by the addition of cross-linking agents. Cross-linking agents contain more than one olefin unit, and during polymerization are incorporated into several chains at once, thus forming cross-links. For example, a sheet of block polymer is produced by adding divinylbenzene to polymerizing styrene (Figure 18.02).

The divinylbenzene forms an occasional cross-link between two chains of styrene polymer. A small amount of cross-linking agent tends to form sheet polymer, while a higher concentration of cross-linking agent forms three-dimensional block polymer.

CONDENSATION POLYMERS

Organic chemical bonds are ordinarily formed by the elimination of a small molecule, such as water or ammonia, between two organic molecules containing appropriate functional groups. If each organic molecule involved has two or more functional groups, a polymer may

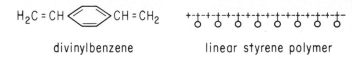

divinylbenzene   linear styrene polymer

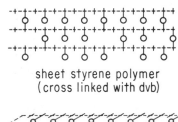

sheet styrene polymer
(cross linked with dvb)

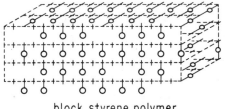

block styrene polymer
(cross linked with dvb)

Fig. 18.02.

be produced. For example, an acid and an amine react to form an amide.

$$R—COOH + H_2NR' \longrightarrow R—CONHR' + H_2O$$

An amino-acid can then be caused to react with itself to produce a polymeric molecule (Eq. 18.08). Such a polymer is known as *condensation* polymer.

$$H_2N—R—COOH \xrightarrow[-H_2O]{H_2NRCOOH} H_2NRCONHRCOOH$$

18.08

$$\xrightarrow[-n\,H_2O]{n\,(H_2NRCOOH)} H_2NRCO(NHRCO)_nNHRCOOH$$

polyamide

All condensation reactions of organic chemistry may be applied to the formation of polymers. Useful synthetic polymers have been made from polyesters, polyamides, polyethers, and polyurethanes. Monomers having three or more functional groups can function as cross-linking agents, so that all types of condensation polymers are possible. The most important natural polymers are condensation polymers. The carbohydrate polysaccharides, such as cellulose and starch, are poly-glycosides, and proteins are the so-called polypeptide, or polyamide, derivatives.

POLYSACCHARIDES

As the name indicates, polysaccharides are composed of many (poly) monosaccharide units. These compounds are more complex, and much more numerous, than either the monosaccharides or disaccharides. Their chemical reactions and properties are also quite distinct from those of the simple sugars. For example, unlike ordinary sugars, they are insoluble and are not sweet. They do not act as reducing sugars, nor do they form osazones with phenylhydrazine. The molecular weights of polysaccharides are quite high.

The sugar units in a polysaccharide molecule are joined together by α- or β-glycoside or hemi-acetal linkages, usually with the 4-hydroxy group of the cyclic sugar structure. Cross-linking can occur through the 2-hydroxy group also. In cellulose, for example, the known glucose units are united to other glucose units by *beta*-1,4-linkages. A segment of a cellulose chain is shown below. There are about 2000 to 3000 glucose units in a single molecule of cellulose.

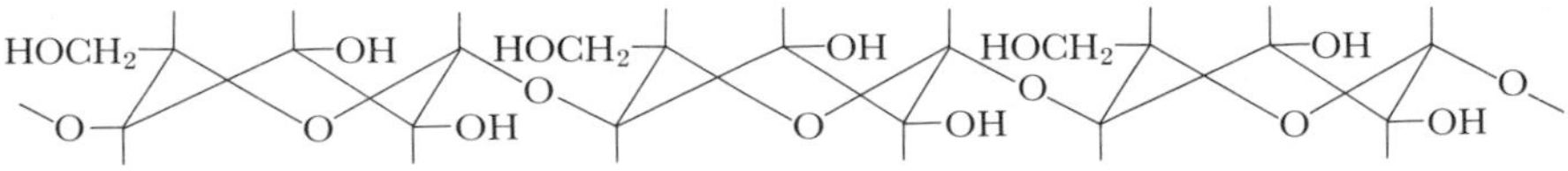

part of cellulose molecule

Cellulose represents a simple polysaccharide since all of the monosaccharide units are arranged in a chain. However, there are much more complex polysaccharides. Glycogen, for example, is composed of glucose units, but instead of the monosaccharide units being arranged in straight chains they form a branched structure (Figure 18.03).

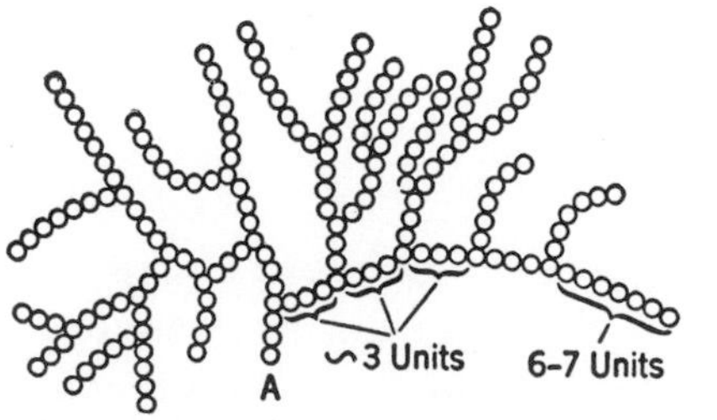

Fig. 18.03. Structure of glycogen. Each circle represents a glucose unit. A is the aldehyde end of a chain.

Polysaccharides are not generally classified by their structure, but more frequently according to the type of monosaccharide formed upon hydrolysis of the polysaccharide. Thus there are essentially three important classes of polysaccharides: the pentosans, which yield 5-carbon monosaccharides; hexosans, which yield 6-carbon monosaccharides; and the complex polysaccharides, which yield on hydrolysis more than one kind of carbohydrate or sugar derivative.

Pentosans. These compounds have the class formula $(C_5H_8O_4)_n$, where there may be from 25 to a few hundred of these 5-carbon units. These carbohydrates occur chiefly in plants, in such substances as cherry gum, corn cobs, straw, and wheat. Upon hydrolysis, the pentosans yield xylose and arabinose.

Hexosans. The general formula for this group is $(C_6H_{10}O_5)_n$. The more important members are such carbohydrates as the starches, glycogen, dextrins, and the celluloses.

Starch is one of the most important carbohydrates in this class, since it is this polysaccharide that comprises one of the most abundant of all foods. Also, it has a high caloric value, and as such provides a considerable amount of food energy. Starches occur in many plants in the leaves, stems, roots, fruits, and seeds. The most common form of starch as it is found in plants is composed of two distinct entities, *amylose* and *amylopectin.* Amylose probably consists of 200 to 300 glucose units in a chain with *alpha*-1,4-glycoside linkages. Amylopectin, on the other hand, is a branched α-glucoside molecule of about a thousand glucose units, with each branch composed of from 20 to 30 glucose units. The main chains are composed of 1,4-linkages, but the branching occurs by 1,6-α-glucoside linkages.

In both amylose and amylopectin, the reducing component of the monosaccharide is linked with other radicals so that neither amylose nor amylopectin is considered a reducing sugar. However, other characteristics can be used to identify the two hexosans, such as their solubility in water and reaction with iodine. Amylose, for example, is considerably less soluble than amylopectin and produces a blue color with iodine, while amylopectin, which is more soluble, gives a violet color. The hydrolysis of the hexosans leads to the conversion of the entire molecule into glucose, but before glucose is formed dextrins and maltose are first produced. The various steps in the degradation of the starches can be followed by the starch-iodine reaction, since the starch itself gives a pronounced blue color on reaction with iodine, and maltose gives a colorless reaction product.

Glycogen. This is an important carbohydrate since it represents the form which is more generally stored in the mammalian body. Glycogen is stored for future metabolic use in the muscles and the liver. Glycogen is readily soluble in water, gives a pronounced red color with iodine, does not act as a reducing sugar, and, like the starches, is hydrolyzed to maltose or glucose, depending upon the nature of the enzymes used to bring about the breakdown of the molecule. The enzyme amylase will break down glycogen to maltose, and acid will then convert the maltose (and some glycogen) to glucose. The number of glucose units in glycogen may frequently be as large as 200 to 250. The structure of glycogen is similar to that of amylopectin in its branched-chain molecular composition and its typical 1,4-linkage of glucose units. In glycogen, there are generally fewer glucose units in each respective chain than are normally found in amylopectin. (See Figure 18.03.)

Dextrins. These carbohydrates are intermediates in the hydrolysis of starches. They are frequently found in nature, usually in the roots and stems of plants. Since they represent a partial breakdown of the starch molecule, they may be considered to be partially digested and are therefore used in considerable quantities in invalid and infant feeding. Because of their mucilaginous nature, the dextrins are also widely used as adhesives for stamps and envelopes.

Cellulose. As its name indicates, this carbohydrate is related to the cellular portion of plant tissues. Cellulose resembles amylose except that it has a *beta*-1,4-linkage and a higher molecular weight. Although cellulose is not a large constituent of our dietary supply, it is ingested to some degree in almost every balanced diet. However, it is peculiar in being indigestible by man. Some lower forms of life, such as bacteria and termites, can digest it quite readily, and use it as a source of food. But in man, it contributes to the "roughage" of the body and is excreted in the feces in an undigested form. Cellulose does not react with iodine, it is not a reducing sugar, and upon complete hydrolysis is converted into glucose.

Inulin. This polysaccharide is found in the artichoke in large amounts. It is composed of fructose units arranged in a manner similar to that of glucose units in amylose, except that there are only about 30 fructose units in the molecule. Recently, this carbohydrate has found clinical use in several tests for determining kidney function.

In addition to the polysaccharides described above there are many more complex sugars of importance to both man and lower animals. Hemicelluloses, gums, pectins, mucopolysaccharides, and many other substances are of commercial as well as industrial value. Pectins, for example, are a class of complex polysaccharides that are responsible for the jelling properties of fruits. Gum arabic is a hemicellulose secreted by plants for protection when they are injured. Hyaluronic acid, a mixed polysaccharide, is contained in many of the synoval joints in the viscous fluids of the human body.

PROTEINS

Proteins are a group of one of the most complex of all known chemical substances and are essential for all life processes, since they are basic constituents of all animal and vegetable cellular matter. Their uniform distribution resulted in the name *protein,* which comes from the Greek word *proteios,* meaning first or primary. Proteins are important because they are necessary for cellular reconstruction or body-building purposes.

Proteins are made up entirely of substances called *amino-acids* (p. 229). The amino-acids may be regarded as the building blocks of the protein molecule, the different proteins being composed of different amino-acids. Therefore the number, as well as the size, of protein molecules is large.

The characteristic size of the protein molecule leads to a number of fundamental properties possessed by this class of organic compounds. For example, the large size of the protein molecule results in the formation of colloidal solutions, and many of the osmotic and amphoteric properties of solutions depend upon this property. Proteins are essential components of many enzymes, hormones, and vitamins. Many of the modern drugs, such as the antibiotic, tyrothricin, are protein in nature. A number of vaccines and toxins are also composed essentially of proteinous material.

Classification

Essentially three types of proteins are recognized. These are the *simple, conjugated,* and *derived* proteins. Simple proteins are those which, upon complete hydrolysis, yield only alpha-amino acids having the formula $R—CHNH_2COOH$, where R may be a hydrogen atom, an aliphatic or aromatic radical, or in some instances a heterocylic radical. (See Table 15.03.) There are several examples of simple proteins, notably the albumins, globulins, albuminoids, histones, protamines, and prolamines.

Conjugated proteins are combinations of a simple protein with an additional organic compound. Examples of conjugated proteins are the nucleoproteins, glycoproteins, phosphoproteins, lipoproteins, and chromoproteins. Nucleoproteins are combinations of nucleic acids and such simple proteins as the histones. They occur in glandular tissue such as the thymus gland. Glycoproteins are combinations of simple proteins with carbohydrates. They are usually found in saliva and other body secretions. Being slippery substances, they aid in the passage of food through the gastro-intestinal tract. The phosphoproteins are protein combinations with phosphoric acid and occur naturally in milk and eggs, while the lipoproteins are proteins united with fatty materials and occur chiefly in the tissues of the central nervous system. The chromoproteins are combinations of simple proteins with a colored product. An example of this type of protein is the hemoglobin in blood.

Derived proteins are so named because they are cleavage products or are obtained from other proteins. This group of proteins includes such subdivisions as the proteoses, peptones, and peptides.

Properties of the proteins

Many proteins can be identified if we know their solubility in water, salt solutions, acids, or bases. Generally speaking, the simple proteins are more soluble in water than the conjugated or derived proteins. For example, the albumins are soluble in water and the globulins insoluble. The histones are soluble in water but insoluble in ammonium hydroxide, while the protamines are soluble in water and ammonium hydroxide. Many proteins are precipitated by varying the concentrations of salt solutions added to them. A useful salt for such purposes is ammonium sulfate. Albumins are precipitated, for example, by full saturation of their solutions with ammonium sulfate, while globulins are precipitated by one-half saturation. Coagulation by heat is also an important distinguishing property of proteins. Both albumins and proteoses are water soluble, but albumins are coagulated by heat, while the proteoses are not.

The size of the protein molecule is of unusual interest. It is known that the size is large, the molecular weight ranging from 1000 to several billion. Pitressin, for example, has a molecular weight of about 1000, while the psittacosis virus has a molecular weight of over eight billion. Most of the more common proteins, however, range from about 10,000 to 500,000. The molecular weight of proteins is determined in a variety of ways—for example, through the use of physical methods such as membrane pore size, osmotic pressure determination, or ultra-centrifuge measurements. If the protein contains an inorganic element in its molecular composition, the determination is more accurate, since the protein must contain at least one atom of the inorganic element to each molecule of the protein.

Coagulation

Many proteins are soluble in aqueous solutions, but if heated, they become insoluble. This process of converting a soluble protein into one which is insoluble is called *coagulation*. Under certain conditions, the insoluble protein may again be dissolved. This usually requires special treatment and is generally inconvenient or impractical. An example of coagulation is the change which the white of an egg undergoes when cooked. Many agents other than heat can also coagulate proteins, notably alkali and acids. The coagulated proteins are generally more easily digested.

Denaturation

Closely resembling the phenomenon of coagulation is the process called *denaturation*. The primary process of coagulation may be *denaturation*. Thus denaturation involves an intramolecular rearrangement of the constituents of the protein molecule while coagulation is an intermolecular process. Denatured proteins are frequently soluble at certain acid strengths, but once heated, the denatured proteins become coagulated and are insoluble. It is important that certain proteins do not become denatured, since a result of this process is to produce proteins with different chemical and physical properties. For example, many antibodies and enzymes lose their biological properties when denatured; however, if the denaturation process has not progressed too far, it can be reversed and stopped, and much of the activity of the protein recovered.

Structure

Fibrous proteins, such as silk or wool, are made up of linear protein molecules which lie side by side, and are held together by inter-molecular attractions, such as hydrogen bonds between amide H and CO groups. Such a structure is shown schematically in Figure 18.04.

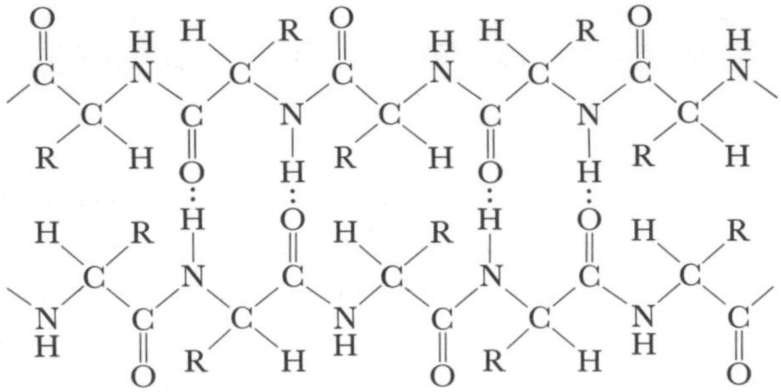

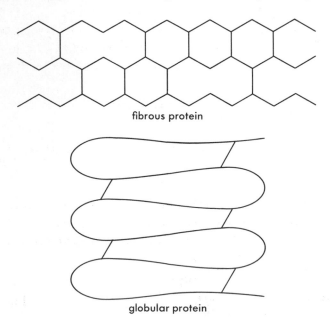

Fig. 18.04. Two polypeptide chains, showing possible hydrogen bridges.

Thousands of possible hydrogen bonds between long molecules tend to make strong fibers. The spider's silk is judged to be one of the strongest fibers. Globular proteins, such as egg albumin, are formed when polypeptide chains are coiled and cross-linked among themselves. The schematic structures of fibrous and globular proteins are shown in Figure 18.05. Conversion of a soluble globular protein, such as egg albumin, into an insoluble block polymer, such as cooked egg white, may be explained on the assumption that the bonds holding the polypeptide in a coiled structure break, and the chains are opened up. This process is denaturation. The open polypeptide chains then cross-link with other chains forming the solid coagulated protein.

fibrous protein

globular protein

Fig. 18.05. Schematic structures of proteins.

SYNTHETIC CONDENSATION POLYMERS

Nylon

Consideration of the structure of protein fibers led to the development of the synthetic polyamide, Nylon, introduced by Du Pont in 1940. This material is made by the condensation of adipic acid and hexamethylene diamine (Eq. 18.09). Both of these substances are readily available from phenol (pp. 123 and 144).

18.09
$$HOOC(CH_2)_4COOH + H_2N(CH_2)_6NH_2$$
$$\longrightarrow -OC(CH_2)_4CONH(CH_2)_6NHCO(CH_2)_4CONH(CH_2)_6$$
$$NHCO(CH_2)_4CONH(CH_2)_6NH-$$

part of Nylon molecule

The polymer melts above 260°C. Filaments are made by extruding the melted polymer through fine holes and freezing them in a stream of air. Nylon has a higher tensile strength than silk, is tougher and has better abrasion resistance. (Figure 18.06a and b.)

Dacron

Formation of esters is a simple condensation reaction. By using polyfunctional acids and alcohols, polymers may be formed. Esterification of terephthalic acid with ethylene glycol leads to a linear polyester, called Dacron (Eq. 18.10). The fiber made from this polymer

18.10
$$HOOC \langle \bigcirc \rangle COOH + HOCH_2CH_2OH \xrightarrow{-H_2O}$$
$$-CH_2CH_2OOC \langle \bigcirc \rangle COOCH_2CH_2OOC \langle \bigcirc \rangle COO$$

part of Dacron molecule

has a high tensile strength and is stable to hydrolysis. Garments made from it are crease-resistant. Recently, the condensation of carbonic acid with polyalcohols has been commercially developed to produce useful polyesters (Figure 18.06c).

Glyptal resins

The esterification of glycerol with phthalic acid produces a cross-linked polyester called a *glyptal* or *alkyd resin*. Cross-linking is brought

Fig. 18.06. (a). These tough "donuts" take much of the risk out of overwater helicopter operations. They are made of neoprene-coated nylon fabric. (Courtesy of E. I. DuPont de Nemours and Company, Wilmington, Delaware.) **(b).** This fisherman's tent is made of nylon, the first truly synthetic fiber. (Courtesy of E. I. DuPont de Nemours and Company, Wilmington, Delaware.) **(c).** Polycarbonate is so strong that objects molded of it withstand the blow of a hammer. The new plastic has exceptional dimensional stability and high temperature resistance. (Courtesy of Monsanto Chemical Company.) **(d).** This 100-foot diameter space balloon is an earth satellite that acts as a "space mirror." It is made of "Mylar" polyester film. (Courtesy of E. I. DuPont de Nemours and Company, Wilmington, Delaware.)

about by the fact that glycerol has three functional groups, permitting cross-linking ester formation (Figure 18.07). Resins of this type are used extensively in the protective-coating industry, in paints and lacquers.

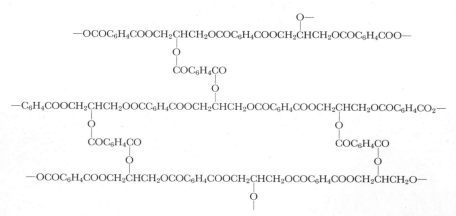

Fig. 18.07. Glyptal structure.

Polymers derived from formaldehyde

Formaldehyde reacts with compounds having an active hydrogen as a bi-functional molecule (Eq. 18.11). By condensing formaldehyde with compounds having several active hydrogen atoms per molecule, useful polymers are formed.

18.11 $\qquad$ $2\,RH + CH_2O \longrightarrow R{-}CH_2{-}R + H_2O$

Bakelite is a phenol-formaldehyde polymer. Phenol condenses with formaldehyde in the *ortho-* and *para*-positions. This allows for cross-linking, since phenol acts as a tri-functional monomer. The structure of *Bakelite* resin is shown in Figure 18.08. Bakelite molding powder is made from partially polymerized material. The powder is mixed with lubricant and plasticizer, and possibly some filler to improve strength, and then heated under pressure in a mold. This curing process results in a hard, durable Bakelite casting, such as a telephone receiver or similar structure. Plastics of this type which are partially polymerized, and then finally completely polymerized in molds, are called *thermosetting* plastics.

Urea-formaldehyde resins are important commercial materials. Urea condenses with formaldehyde to form dimethylolurea (Eq. 18.12). Further reaction produces thermosetting resins, of the general struc-

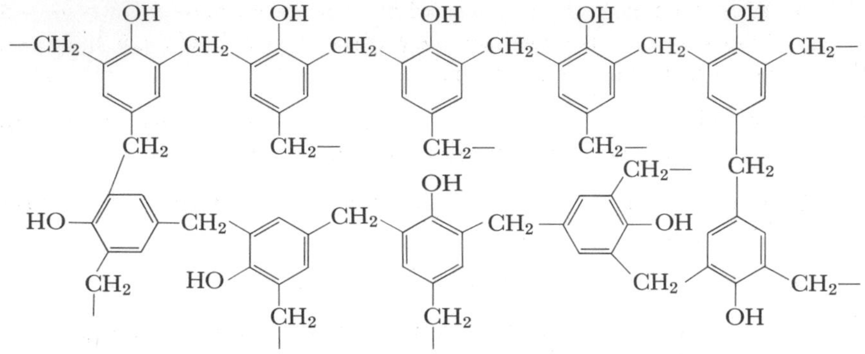

Fig. 18.08. Phenol-formaldehyde polymer structure.

ture shown in Figure 18.09. The uncured resins are water-soluble, colorless materials which are used in bonding wood, paper, or cloth. Such bonded sheets may be effectively converted into laminated

18.12
$$NH_2CONH_2 + 2\ CH_2O \longrightarrow HOCH_2NHCONHCH_2OH$$

dimethylolurea

plastics by curing under heat and pressure. Urea-formaldehyde resins are used in the manufacture of plywood, tableware, buttons, screw-caps for bottles, etc.

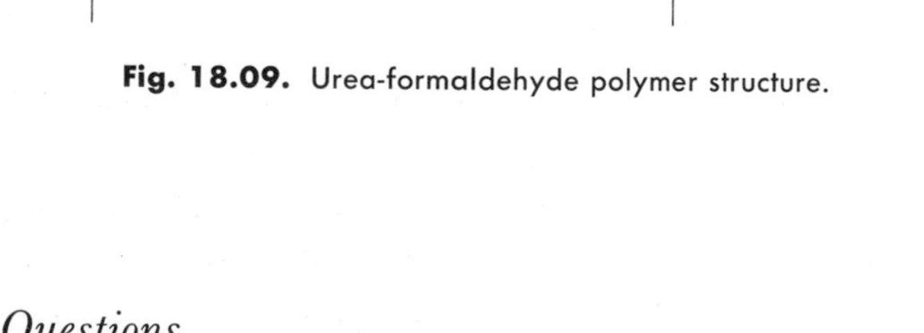

Fig. 18.09. Urea-formaldehyde polymer structure.

Study Questions

1. What is meant by the term *polymer*? What is the difference between a *linear polymer,* a *sheet polymer,* and a *block polymer*?
2. Amylose is soluble to the extent of about 50 g/100 g of water. If the mol. wt. of amylose is 50,000, what is the depression of the freezing point of this solution? ($\Delta f = 1.86$.)

3. Why does polyethylene not show the properties of unsaturated bonds, since it is made from ethylene? Show how branching can occur in polyethylene chains.

4. Explain how a strong base, such as potassium hydroxide, can catalyze the polymerization of an olefin.

5. What is meant by a co-polymer? a synthetic elastomer? a cross-linking agent?

6. How is neoprene related to natural rubber?

7. List three simple organic reactions which can be used to produce condensation polymers.

8. Why is the aldose molecule particularly suitable to polymer formation? Explain.

9. What is the difference between cellulose and starch? Humans can digest corn meal, but not cotton. Why? Why is glycogen called "animal starch"?

10. How is the structure of Nylon related to that of silk?

11. How is the coagulation of egg albumin related to curing of a thermosetting resin?

12. Show the chemical steps necessary to convert benzene (from coal tar) into Nylon.

13. "Drying oils" are triglycerides of unsaturated fatty acids, which form hard, insoluble resins on exposure to air. How can you account for this property?

Advanced Reading References

Organic Chemistry, 2nd Ed., L. F. Fieser and Mary Fieser, D. C. Heath and Co., Boston, 1950, Chapters 15, 17, 37, and 38.

Chemistry of Organic Compounds, 2nd Ed., C. R. Noller, W. G. Saunders and Company, Philadelphia, 1957, Chapters 14, 17, and 32.

Organic Chemistry, An Advanced Treatise, 2nd Ed., ed. Vols. I and II, H. Gilman, John Wiley and Sons, New York, 1943, Chapters 8, 21, and 22.

Index